ALAN R. WALD

Plant Communities

On approaching the moist tropics, forest vegetation becomes a rich assortment of complementary life forms, including evergreen trees, shrubs, herbs,
lianas, and epiphytes. Here is a perpetual-motion machine of incredible
complexity, composed of hundreds of species of plants and animals, which
evolved through millions of years until it attained a state of high efficiency
in the use of sunlight and other environmental resources.

Plant Communities

A Textbook of Plant Synecology

Rexford Daubenmire

Professor
Washington State University

HARPER & ROW, PUBLISHERS
New York, Evanston, and London

Contents

Preface

Synecology is a science centered on communities as components of ecosystems. It is aimed at understanding how these communities originate, develop, and maintain themselves and at elaborating a classification to show relationships.

Autecology, the sister science which is concerned with environmental relations of the individual organism, has contributed two important concepts to biology, namely, the constant interaction between the organism and its environment and the universal tendency for genetic adaptation to adjust local species populations to special environmental complexes. These contributions have been made with borrowed techniques, concepts, and terms, extracted from diverse sources and synthesized into a viewpoint with wide implications. But autecology still remains a viewpoint with little subject matter exclusively its own. Synecology, in contrast, deals with groups of several-to-many species living together, and this is not the primary subject matter of any other field. It is clearly a science in its own right, if only for the fact that plant groupings have attributes not easily predicted from separate studies of the constituent species. By concerning itself with large complexes of organisms plus their environment, synecology lies at the opposite extreme of the biologic spectrum from biochemistry, and it may not be remiss to point out that biochemistry is as incapable of solving complex problems at the ecosystem level as synecology is incapable of unraveling the complexity of enzyme systems.

Synecology nevertheless has strong ties with other sciences, biologic and nonbiologic. Since communities modify every other aspect of the biosphere, they are important to the pedologist, the geologist, the meteorologist, and a long list of biologic disciplines from anthropology to zoology.

Historically, the autecology and synecology of land plants have been pursued rather independently, but a good case can be made that too close adherence to one field or the other shackles any study with unnecessary and detrimental restrictions. The behavior of each organism in the community depends on the interplay between its genetic constitution and conditions imposed by the remainder of the ecosystem. Thus the autecology of a plant studied without relation to one or more of the several communities of which it may be a member has a definite aura of artificiality. It seems logical that before a student delves into the complexity of communities he should first gain an understanding of environmental factors and how they interact, of the varied ways in which these factors impinge upon life cycles, and the manifold influences that organisms in turn exert upon their environment. At least elementary knowledge of these topics is presupposed on the part of those who would use this book.

The unprecedented power man has achieved for modifying or destroying ecosystems at will, coupled with our slender knowledge of the ramifying consequences of such activity, is appalling in view of our continued dependence on the proper functioning of many ecosystems. We pollute the waters, foul the atmosphere, and degrade the land with abandon until disastrous and irreversible consequences are upon us, with most of the population either unwilling to consider the evidence or unable to comprehend its significance. As our natural resources dwindle, mistakes in their management are becoming ever more critical, and although the stock of ecological information is obviously short, considerably more is available than is being used. This is a matter about which ecologists are deeply concerned. An impressive series of books, from Paul Sears' *Deserts on the March* to Rachel Carson's *Silent Spring* and S. L. Udall's *The Quiet Crisis,* has made significant contribution toward the colossal task of developing widespread understanding that a synecologic perspective is essential to the maintenance of human populations in an environment with the amenities most of us demand. Synecology may well prove to be the most important of the sciences from the viewpoint of long-term human survival.

More than three decades ago A. G. Tansley wrote: "The study of vegetation has suffered, and still is suffering, from the wide and deep differences in training and consequent angle of approach, and from the geographic isolation of individual workers, with resulting differences in the data they have to work with." In the few decades since that was written, the geographic isolation has lessened, but one has only to compare the approaches in recent vegetation monographs by Coupland[104], Curtis[111], Daubenmire[122], and Moss[303], all working in the temperate zone of one continent, sharing a common language, and publishing in a span of 7 years, to become impressed by the applicability of the remainder of Tansley's comment even today. Vegetation science is still quite immature. Climatology and pedology, upon which it depends heavily, have themselves emerged as sciences only in the last century. Concepts, terms, and methods are still remarkably localized, and they are far too numerous to present all of them comparatively in a textbook without confusing the student. Neither have I adopted the repertory of any one school but rather have attempted to select what I consider the soundest contributions of each and integrate these into one coherent treatment. As far as my teaching and research experience go, this has proved a harmonious selection.

Since synecology makes unique contributions to science, we cannot, as in autecology, borrow appropriate and well-established terms from other sciences to express our ideas concisely and accurately. But synecologic terminology thus far has been rather notable for multiplying confusion. Rival schools in the young science have contributed distinctive vocabularies, with a remarkably consistent failure to define their terms clearly. This has resulted in a welter of terms, employed loosely, many of which are bound to fall into disuse as the field becomes more unified. It has also resulted in terminology being a favored target for critics who are ever ready to castigate other workers' use of words on the basis of vulnerable definitions of their own choosing (e.g., "climax"). Wherever in this book a special term has seemed necessary I have chosen one that seems meaningful, then either defined it or used it in a defining sense where it first appears. This practice, in conjunction with an index, makes a special glossary unnecessary, especially since an impeccable definition standing alone often raises questions that only a discussion of the subject matter can clarify. The total list of special terms used will be found to be far smaller than in most treatments of taxonomy, anatomy, cytogenetics, pedology, etc., of comparable size.

In view of the tremendous volume of synecologic literature, the list of references is indeed short. It is offered primarily to recommend sources where the English-speaking student can pursue the subjects treated in this book a little further. To make the text read more smoothly and thus favor students who will be the major users, I have used superscripts to cite the literature, knowing quite well that this is annoying to the professional who may read the book from a different point of view.

The stake included for scale in many of the photographs is one meter tall.

R. Daubenmire

Plant Communities

1 the nature of plant communities

• INTRODUCTION

Plant Communities as Components of Natural Landscapes

Even a cursory examination of natural landscapes is sufficient to show that plant species tend to be grouped in different combinations forming more or less definite communities (Fig. 1). Each of these is characterized by certain species which are inconspicuous or unrepresented in other communities, and wherever areas of equivalent environment are encountered, whether continuous or detached, essentially the same plant assemblage reappears. In other words, the individuals of each species are not scattered at random, but are distributed in a pattern over the landscape and even within a single community, as we shall see later.

The Primary Causes of Plant Communities

Communities are fundamentally the products of interaction between two phenomena: (1) differences in the environmental tolerances (or *ecologic amplitudes*) of the various taxa which comprise the flora and (2) the heterogeneity of environment. Disseminules tend to be scattered indiscriminately (to the extent that this word describes the move-

FIG. 1. A narrow belt of *Scirpus* closely follows the margin of the pond, with *Stipa comata* dominant beyond the pond influence. Elsewhere, communities dominated by *Populus tremuloides* and by *Pseudotsuga menziesii* add variety to the landscape. Vegetation mosaics such as this present a challenge to determine how the factor complexes are related to ecologic tolerances under competitive stress in such a manner as to maintain the pattern. Central British Columbia.

ments of animals and wind, which are the principal agents of dissemination), coming to rest on a wide variety of habitats. But subsequent germination and establishment are far from being equal everywhere. Those plants which require a swamp habitat* will survive only in swamps, whereas taxa with different ecologic amplitudes will grow only in other kinds of habitats. Thus the plant community is basically a consequence of rigorous habitat selection that denies opportunity to all but a relatively few of the great variety of species which can reach the habitat as disseminules. Yet from their common occupancy of a habitat it is not to be assumed that they have the same ecologic amplitudes. It is simply that their ranges of amplitude overlap in this habitat. (It will at once be recognized that competition, dissemination efficiency, and other factors may prevent a plant from growing in many places where climate and soil are suitable, but at this point only the permissive relations of physical factors are being stressed.)

A series of contrasted habitats is analogous to a series of superimposed screens which sort out special sizes of particles from originally heterogeneous material. The communities which result from such selective action are therefore products of environment insofar as they consist of those members of the local flora which possess the peculiar combinations of genes producing morphologic and physiologic characters essential for existence in their respective habitats. Several corollaries follow. (1) Each kind of community is distinguished by a group of species showing coordinate patterns of relative abundance over the landscape. (2) Any large unit of vegetation is a mosaic of plant communities the distribution of which is governed by a corresponding mosaic of habitats.[43] (3) The more heterogeneous the environment of an area, the more numerous are the kinds of plant communities it embraces. (4) Vegetation serves as a valuable criterion of degrees of similarity and difference among habitats.

The principle under discussion is well illustrated in the vegetation of the Aleutian Islands. When primitive man came into this region of relatively infertile soils, he established villages around which accumulated the refuse of the sea animals he brought home for food. Later, when the village sites were abandoned, the calcium- and phosphorus-rich middens provided a new kind of soil which certain uncommon species of the surrounding soils quickly invaded and dominated. Thus

---

* *Habitat* (= ecotope = biotope) is usually used to denote a rather specific kind of living space or *environment*, i.e., a constellation of interacting physical and biologic factors which provide at least minimal conditions for one organism to live or for a group to appear together. The scope of the term is very elastic. One may with equal justification describe the habitat of a particular clone of *Dicranum fuscescens* as being (1) the bark of *Tsuga mertensiana* tree, (2) a forested ravine, or (3) the subalpine zone of the Olympic Mountains.

a distinctive community differentiated out of the native flora in response to the appearance of a new habitat, and each of these village sites is now delimited so well by this special type of vegetation as to be easily distinguished on an aerial photograph.[21]

• BASIC PRINCIPLES OF SYNECOLOGY

Communities Are Complex Aggregations of Plants and Animals

From the time of Theophrastus to the middle of the nineteenth century, references to plant communities in the literature take almost no account of the animal life interwoven in them; but an awakening of interest in detailed field study during the past century soon brought to light the fact that communities are truly biotic. Karl Möbius is credited with being first to emphasize, in a publication in 1880, the necessity of a biotic concept of a community. He found that the oysters he studied were intimately associated with the algae they fed upon, in addition to sponges, oyster parasites, etc.

The plant constituent of a community is usually the more bulky, the more continuous, and the more regularly manifest through the year—the animal component is obscure or, if evident, the species tend to be few in numbers and to move freely from one type of community to another. Nevertheless, the animals have many important interrelations with the plants. We need only to recall the effects of earthworms and burrowing rodents in the rooting medium, insects feeding on plants or contributing to the humification of their remains, animal pollination, the grazing and trampling of large mammals, etc., to realize the many points of intersection between animal and plant life cycles.[283]

The concept of a biotic community is necessary not only because plant and animal populations are interwoven everywhere, but also because there is a certain amount of conformity in their distribution over the landscape,[242,243,365] particularly involving the relatively immobile animals. Plant distribution is controlled primarily by the physical factors of the environment. But animal distribution is often determined more by the types of food and shelter afforded by vegetation types than by the physical factors; hence their distribution tends to conform with the pattern of plant communities. However, the mobility of the larger animals complicates this relationship, with one animal commonly using different plant communities at different times of the day or year. Thus wapiti feed high in the mountains in summer, then descend to the valley floors at the approach of winter. A heron nests in the forest but flies daily to marshes to feed. Even insects may rest, feed, and lay eggs in different plant communities.[17, 131] Search for definitive animal communities that might prove coextensive with particular plant communities has been mostly unsuccessful, whether at the level of invertebrates, which has been a favorite group among European ecologists, or of highly mobile vertebrates, as emphasized in North America.

When geologic time is considered, the relation of animal to plant distribution is even weaker. For example, the midcontinental steppe of North America has changed but slowly over many thousands of years, while successive waves of different indigenous herbivore faunas have come and gone, the last of which was outstandingly dominated by *Bison bison*. And it has not been demonstrated that the change from bison to domestic cattle has produced much effect other than that associated with changes in the intensity of grazing. From these considerations it becomes clear that animal ecology is somewhat more dependent on an understanding of plant ecology than the reverse. The activities of a given animal are most significantly described in terms of the vegetation types it frequents at different times of the day, season, or year or even geologic period.

Although the spatial correlation between plant communities and animals is rather loose, there are many close relationships among the plants and animals within a given biotic community. For this reason it might seem desirable to study all the organisms simultaneously, but that is not possible. In the first place, the methods of studying soil fungi, trees, epiphytic mosses, mice, myriopods, birds, etc., are entirely different, so that one must always in practice study them separately.

Second, no biologist could possibly be competent enough in the taxonomy, life histories, and ecology of all the plants and animals of an average community to make a thorough study of them as a unit. Plankton communities, as usually investigated, would seem to constitute an exception, since the fewness of the species of algae and invertebrates, coupled with their similarities in size and dispersion through the water, makes it possible to study both at once. Yet the bacterial component of such a community is nearly always ignored! Botanists and zoologists collaborating on the *Fagus* forests of Switzerland concluded that about 10,500 taxa are represented, and North American biologists commonly refer to these *Fagus* forests as being relatively impoverished! Clearly, botanists, zoologists, and workers in other fields must labor together— the field is too wide for any single worker. The best approach is to take full cognizance of the interrelatedness of nature, but for the purpose of investigation establish the limits of isolates that are commensurate with human limitations; otherwise effort is spread so thinly that the outcome remains at the level of old-style natural history, from which ecology has directly developed. These isolates sometimes fall entirely within the plant kingdom or the animal kingdom; sometimes they overlap the two.

The Community and Its Environment Are Inseparable

Although it is generally true that habitat characteristics play the basic role in determining the kind of community, the latter certainly determines many of the characteristics of its habitat. As a community develops on a previously bare area, most of the original conditions become altered while new ones are superimposed. No progress can be made toward understanding the role of physical factors in determining community distribution unless a clear distinction is made between the primary or intrinsic characteristics of the habitat and the secondary or extrinsic characters that are superimposed as a result of biotic activity. However, the latter, in large measure vegetation influences, are very important in stabilizing a landscape mosaic. A specific example may clarify this point.

In the region of Itasca Park, Minnesota, coarse glacial till supports evergreen coniferous forests of *Picea glauca* and *Abies balsamea*, whereas interspersed patches of fine-textured calcium-rich till support forests of deciduous angiosperms characterized by *Acer saccharum* and *Tilia americana*.[253] A pattern of vegetation distribution here was long ago established by the pattern of deposition of the two kinds of glacial till. Subsequently, under the strong podsolizing influence of *Picea* and *Abies*, the coarse till easily became leached, acid, and relatively infertile. But on the calcareous material the deciduous trees, having high rates of base assimilation, maintained the fertility and pH at favorably high levels so that podsolization has not involved much loss of the originally high level of fertility. Not only have the two forests intensified the original soil differences, but they have also brought about other differences between the habitats—in the amount of precipitation interception, light regime, fauna, etc.[62] Only the initial differences in parent materials, however, may be considered intrinsic factors and used to explain the pattern of vegetation there, even though it cannot be denied that the extrinsic factors that have been superimposed may be fully as contrasted and are important in maintaining the pattern. In other situations such factors as microclimate,[263] drainage,[189] etc., serve as intrinsic factors in vegetation differentiation, with the plant cover then promoting further differentiation.

If the habitat influences the community and the community influences the habitat, it is clear that we are dealing with an interrelated complex or system that embraces not only plant and animal populations but all the aerial and edaphic characters of the area as well (Fig. 2). Thus at Itasca Park, *Picea-Abies* + coarse soil + associated animals + the microclimate of an evergreen forest all make up one natural unit, while

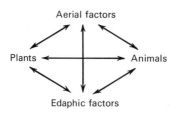

FIG. 2. Diagrammatic representation of the interrelationships among components of ecosystems. The concept may be applied to communities as small as a decaying blade of grass with its complement of fungi, protozoa, etc., or as large as the earth with its atmosphere and all known biologic organisms, and to units that appear stable as well as to others that are evidently in the process of changing. It may be used in connection with a specific kind of landscape unit or to express the abstract concept of relatedness.

Acer-Tilia + fine-textured soil + associated animals + the microclimate of a deciduous forest make up another.

Although the indissoluble bond between an organism and its physical environment was recognized by Hippocrates as an autecologic concept, it was not until 1894 that V. V. Dokuchayev developed the idea as a synecologic concept. It has become widely recognized as a major improvement over the older idea of the biotic community, and terms such as *ecosystem, biogeocoenosis,* and *holocoen* have been offered to designate it. [142,157,395,413] Since oyster bed communities have definite limits regarding the nature of the substrate, depth of water, temperature, salinity, etc., it is remarkable in retrospect that Möbius stopped short of emphasizing the physical environment as an integral part of his unit.

From a botanical point of view, the interdependence of ecosystem components can be expressed in mathematical form, such as:

$$\text{vegetation} = f\,(\text{soil} + \text{climate} + \text{animals} + \text{flora})$$

But such an equation is insoluble because quantitative values cannot be assigned the terms and because the variables, except for macroclimate and parent rock, are interdependent.[289] In fact ecosystems are so fantastically complex that we can never hope to fully describe and understand any but a few of the simplest of them.

Since the ecosystem represents a dynamic interlocking equilibrium, it is not always easy to predict in advance all the ultimate consequences of a specific type of interference. Man must disturb ecosystems, but he should recognize that there are limits to safety in so doing, for disturbance becomes dangerous when induced conditions exceed the range of fluctuating natural conditions to which the organisms have been inured. As in the case of a watch or an engine, only a limited amount of manipulation can be accommodated before a disastrous chain reaction is started. The civilized world is beset with examples of ecosystems that have deteriorated as a consequence of exploitative or even casual activities of man. Expensive corrective action has been necessary in consequence of either burning communities excessively or giving them complete protection from fire; moving species beyond their natural limits where they became pests (e.g., mongoose, chestnut blight, *Salsola pestifer*); simplifying communities to the point of pure stands of one economic species; removing one species that played a critical role (e.g., cougar); or drastic alteration of soil,[279] to name a few modes of interference. An appreciation of this principle is one of the most important contributions synecology can make to man's intellectual repertory.

The ecosystem concept has also been very important in another way, for its widespread acceptance by ecologists has been a powerful force tending to unify what is undoubtedly one of the most complex and diversified fields of science.

Ecologically Diverse Groups of Organisms Are Superimposed on the Same Area

Examination of an area that appears to have homogeneous vegetation usually reveals that the species differ widely in their size or gross morphology, yet most of them can be grouped into a few categories on this basis. Two concepts concerning these groupings will be discussed.

Layers are subdivisions of a piece of vegetation based on plant height. In the latter part of the nineteenth century it became customary in describing European forests to recognize a tree layer, a shrub layer, and herb (i.e., "field") layer, and a bryophyte-lichen (i.e., "bottom" or "ground") layer. In the wet tropics it is often possible to divide the trees among several superimposed layers, and on steppes there are commonly two herb layers (Fig. 3).

The reality of such units cannot be disputed, but at the same time the layer is a relatively crude descriptive unit. It does not put into separate categories trees and the lianas of equal height which they support. It does not allow one to refer separately to a group of obligative heliophytic herbs that may mingle temporarily with a group of facultative heliophytic herbs that persist after a forest is logged. And it is clear that a given layer exhibits great ecologic diversity from one habitat to another. The term has practical value in describing the gross morphology of a particular unit of vegetation, but it lacks fundamental significance because stature bears limited relation to the ecologic requirements of plants.

During the second decade of the present century,[144] *synusiae* were suggested as another way of grouping plants belonging to one complex community. In this concept, morphology is used differently, allowing bulbous herbs, annual herbs, and perennial herbaceous grasses, for example, to be distinguished. A distinct advantage over the layer con-

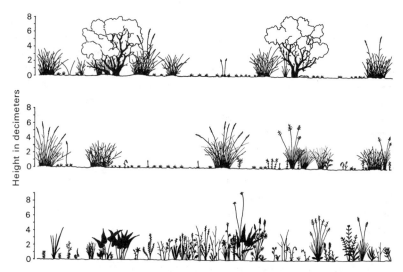

FIG. 3. Profile drawing, to scale, of all vascular plants whose shoot bases impinged on strips 2 cm wide × 400 cm long. Top illustrates a three-layered community, the middle another type of community with two-layered structure. There is no clear stratification in the bottom community.

cept is apparent in the fact that there may be recognized a synusia of woody lianas as well as a synusia of supporting trees. Also, it permits distinguishing epiphytes from the trees that support them, and herbs from shrubs of the same height, etc. Still, synusiae often do not serve in describing the general appearance of vegetation as well as the layer concept.

Zoologists, in dealing with the principle under discussion, have commonly used the term *niche,* defining this either as a way of life or a particular microhabitat. The term is equally appropriate for the plant constituents of a biotic community.

Although there is no universally satisfactory way to divide the plants in a complex community into groups based on morphology, no one would question the existence of groups with distinctive environmental requirements. These commonly take up water at different levels in the soil, they differ in light requirements, they may depend on different agents of pollination or dissemination, and they often make their heaviest demands on the habitat at different seasons (Fig. 4). Superficially these groups inhabit the same general environment, but actually they live in well-defined sectors of it, the demarcation being temporal, or spatial, or both. To mix all these groups, as in a single alphabetic list, is to obscure a great amount of fundamental ecologic diversity within the community as a whole.

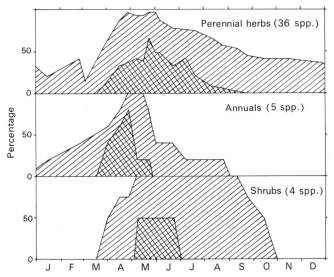

FIG. 4. Annual cycle of vegetative activity (parallel shading) and flowering activity (cross-hatched) in a climax steppe community near Pullman, Washington. The climate is one with cold moist winters centered on January and warm dry summers centered on July. Important differences in activity among the three main life forms would have been obscured if the data for all species had been merged.

This ecologic diversity within the large community is of great biologic importance. Plants differing in stature or season of development are at least partly complementary in their use of environmental resources, whereas competition is at maximum among individuals of the same ecotype.[39] Thus the differentiation of vegetation into units with diverse ecologies favors a more complete utilization of environmental resources (see Frontispiece), whereas in a field containing one cultivated species every plant is making the same demands on the same parts of the habitat at the same season. Aside from the competitive problem, when man supplants a complex natural ecosystem, with its many checks and balances and varied requirements and tolerances, with a simple ecosystem such as a wheat field, dry matter production varies more widely from year to year since everything depends on the favorableness of weather to the one kind of organism, and there must be a constant struggle to keep down fungus and insect pests that have no natural controls. And in order to maintain such a monoculture at a satisfactory level of productivity, there must be a constantly high input of energy

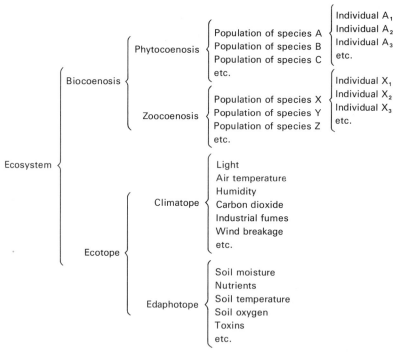

FIG. 5. Components of the ecosystem. The biocoenosis, population (any group of interbreeding organisms), and individual are commonly referred to as "levels of organization" of living matter, and the idea can be continued downward as organ, tissue, cell, organelle, molecule, etc.

(cultivation, planting, fertilizing, disease control, harvesting), coupled with skill. Agronomic practice could probably be improved substantially in many places by taking advantage of this basic synecologic principle. Thus, if it were not for the difficulties of mechanical harvesting, alternating rows of different types of crops would enhance productivity considerably.

Some special terminology can be conveniently introduced at this point. When referring to all the layers or synusiae that are superimposed on a particular habitat, the term *phytocoenosis* is appropriate. A phytocoenosis plus its accompanying *zoocoenosis* comprise a *biocoenosis*. The physical environment of a biocoenosis is its *ecotope* or habitat. The ecotope with its biocoenosis make up an ecosystem (Fig. 5).

The word *community* may be used for any assemblage of organisms, large or small, i.e., for a biocoenosis or any constituent part composed of two or more species. Like the term ecosystem, it can be used in an abstract or a concrete sense.

All Organisms in a Community
Are Ecologically Interrelated

Although each plant has a large measure of functional and structural individualism, it must always respond to an environment that is conditioned by others, and the nature of the conditioning varies with the species. It has been shown experimentally that for species A the optimum intensity for certain environmental variables differs according to whether it is grown in pure culture, or mixed with B, or mixed with C, etc.

The supply of water, nutrients, and solar energy is almost never adequate to permit the maximum development of every individual plant in the community. To this disadvantage of crowded conditions must be added the influence of toxic materials produced by some plants that harm their associates. On the other hand, there are delicate plants for which these consequences of proximity to neighbors are less injurious than exposure to sun, wind, and grazers, so that they prosper only in dense communities, or in thorny thickets. Soil microbes are deeply involved here, too—some fix nitrogen and are very beneficial to higher plants, whereas others immobilize certain nutrients to create deficiencies for the higher plants. Thus a conclusion is warranted that in nature there are strong restrictions on the individualistic behavior of plants, unless they are widely spaced. In fact, the structure and function of each plant is so strongly conditioned by the biologic as well as the physical attributes of the ecosystem in which it gets established that autecologic information obtained outside the relevant ecosystem is in part an artifact.

Interrelationships among associated plants differ greatly in degree as well as in kind. A vascular plant and its mycorrhizal fungus represent a close and frequently obligative partnership. At the other extreme, the plants of one synusia may appear to be completely lacking relationships with those of another, as between an epiphytic synusia on a tree trunk and an herbaceous synusia rooted in the soil beneath. Even here, however, there is an indirect relationship vertically through the tree synusia, which may intercept approximately a third of the total precipitation, and thus provide the epiphyte with water and solutes which the ground-inhabiting plants would otherwise have received. No one relationship extends through the community, but chains of influences of infinite degree and kind link each organism with all others. The community is truly a "system."

Competition for environmental resources, shelter, nutrient enrichment of soil through foliage drip, toxic secretions, and nitrogen-fixation are influences that operate vertically *among different layers* in the same phytocoenosis. At the same time in a horizontal direction these forces plus root grafting, cross-pollination requirements, transmission of parasites, and maintenance of readily available sources of mycorrhizal fungi operate laterally *within each layer*. Although synusiae or layers merit separate consideration because of their sharp differences in life-form, phenology, microenvironmental requirements and influences, there are so many interrelationships among the subdivisions of one phytocoenosis that they can scarcely be considered other than as components of a larger entity.[182] When such morphologic components are isolated, they lose some of their character, if they can survive at all, which emphasizes their interrelatedness.

While we have been concerned above with only the interrelationships among plants, there are of course corresponding interrelationships between the plants and animals of a biocoenosis. Since the solar energy necessary to establish and maintain ecosystems is captured and made available only by means of chlorophyll, green plants (and the few chemosynthetic bacteria) are collectively referred to as the *producers* of the biocoenosis. Animals, along with parasitic plants (fungi, bacteria, *Striga, Orobanche,* etc.), all of which get their energy directly from plants, or from herbivores, are classed as *consumers*.

Still other organisms, such as saprophytic bacteria, fungi, protozoa, flies, vultures, crayfish, and suckers, which are responsible for the decay of excretions and the dead bodies of producers and consumers, are referred to as *decomposers* (Fig. 6). These organisms complete the release of stored energy and make nutrients once again available to producers. Thus, starting with the initial food synthesis in plants, nutritional dependence fans out through the remainder of the biocoenosis in many diverse sequences (food chains) that are interconnected by alternative pathways at each level, resulting in a multidimensional web.

When a unit of plant tissue is used by a consumer, only about 10 percent is converted into its own substance, the remainder being lost as excretions or used up in respiration. Secondary consumers (e.g., carnivores), primary decomposers (e.g., millipedes), and secondary decomposers (e.g., bacteria) in turn are scarcely more efficient in converting foodstuffs into their own tissue than are primary consumers. With so much energy being lost at each step, less and less living tissue can be supported by the geometrically dwindling supply, and after four or five transformations (with highly variable time elapsing between each of them), there is insufficient energy left to support another step. The sum of the leakages is of course balanced by green plants capturing new supplies from solar radiation. Every organism in the biocoenosis is involved in these processes, so that we may think of them collectively as representing the metabolism of the community. In short, it can be said

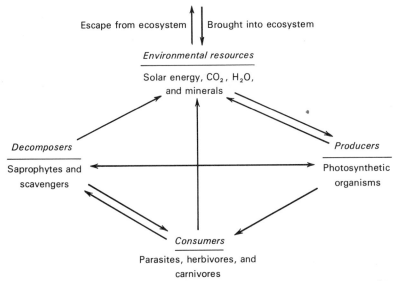

FIG. 6. Trophic-dynamic interrelations in the ecosystem. Only three trophic levels (producer, consumer, decomposer) are diagrammed, whereas in actuality there are usually more: producers sustaining herbivores (first-order consumers), with a sequence of carnivores (second-order, third-order, etc., consumers), then several orders of decomposers. Neither is it indicated that the environmental resources are subject to repeated cycling within an ecosystem.

that the components of an ecosystem are related by a continuous cycling of matter and flow of energy that involves all species as well as all components of their physical environment.

Interrelatedness does not stop at the horizontal boundaries of a particular ecosystem. For example, consider what is involved when a toad forsakes a pond where it developed as a tadpole and becomes part of a terrestrial ecosystem, or when birds congregate at the end of day to roost in a particular group of trees, or when a brook carries leaves, nutrients, and heat from an upland ecosystem into a pond.

The Organisms in a Community Are Not of Equal Sociologic Importance

To the taxonomist a forest consists of a certain number of taxa, and either he gives all of them equal consideration in his list or gives more emphasis to the rarest. The synecologist, in contrast, is less concerned with the list than with the striking differences in the functional significance of each taxon in the ecosystem and is prone therefore to emphasize the larger and more common organisms at the expense of the smaller and rarer, although these latter are by no means ignored. When the ecosystem is viewed as a complex and dynamic system, the presence or absence of a considerable number of species may be relatively inconsequential, whereas at the other extreme one or a few may determine most of the character of the ecosystem. These categories of plants may be referred to as *subordinates* and *dominants*, respectively.

It is useful to think of dominants as those species whose removal would bring about the greatest readjustments in the edaphic, aerial, and biotic character of their ecosystems.* They are often the tallest plants, for tall plants tend to control light and other habitat factors so that, directly or indirectly, they influence the shorter organisms more than the latter can affect the former. In a forest the trees are dominant because of their size, regardless of whether or not they are outnumbered by undergrowth plants. For example, *Populus tremuloides* may be the sole dominant of a community in which there are hundreds of subordinate taxa, several of the latter being much more abundant per unit land area than the *Populus*. But where there is little difference in size, dominance is determined primarily by numbers of individuals, as meadow grasses dominating forbs that are about the same height but less abundant. Numerical strength rises to the point of outweighing stature in some savannas, for the herbaceous cover is essentially uninfluenced by the scattered woody plants, whereas the amount of water available to the larger plants and the survival of their seedlings are strongly affected by the presence of the herbs.

Often a single species is clearly the dominant of an ecosystem, but where the flora is rich in species capable of filling the dominant niche in community structure, dominance becomes an attribute of a group of species.

Since dominant plants exert the greatest influence on microclimate, soil profile, and animal associates, since they tend to be subject to the fullest impact of the macroclimate, and since they are commonly the chief means of capturing solar energy for the ecosystem, they are the key to the character of an ecosystem. For example, following the destruction of all *Picea engelmanni* in a forest where this tree was dominant, records showed that nearly all other kinds of plants and animals in the area changed in abundance, some increasing and others decreasing.[476] Subordinates may be defined as those species which if removed singly would not occasion much rearrangement within their ecosystem. Collectively, subordinates are by no means ineffectual however, for when a forest is young the trees may keep their roots in deep horizons until

---

* Foresters use the word *dominant* in a structural rather than a functional sense, applying it to those individual trees that project sufficiently above the general forest canopy for their foliage to be more than half free of shade.

shade increases and eliminates the herb layer, after which new tree roots develop in the more fertile A horizon, allowing more rapid growth.[134, 274]

Among subordinates, two categories may be distinguished. One group, the *dependent subordinates,* is so very dependent on the conditions maintained by the dominants that the removal of the latter would spell their extinction on the habitat. Epiphytes, parasites, obligative mycorrhizal fungi, and obligative sciophytes provide well-known examples. Obviously these organisms cannot enter a habitat until after the dominants become established there. A less predictable example of dependency was illustrated in England where plantations of *Pinus sylvestris* developed an undergrowth dominated by *Pteridium,* with contiguous plantations of *Quercus* favoring *Endymion, Holcus,* and *Oxalis* beneath.[327]

Another category of subordinates includes those species which can perpetuate themselves in the habitat regardless of the presence or absence of the dominants. These, the *tolerant subordinates,* tolerate but do not require the conditions imposed on the habitat by the dominants. To illustrate, in the northern Rocky Mountains a ground cover of *Xerophyllum tenax* and *Vaccinium membranaceum* thrives under the canopy of an *Abies lasiocarpa* forest. Following a fire, the lower plants, which can sprout readily from underground organs, continue to flourish until the next generation of trees is established from seed.[122] Tolerant subordinates need not await the establishment of dominants on a new habitat. The *Xerophyllum-Vaccinium* layer becomes established on rubble well in advance of the first invasion of *Abies* there.[130] Thus it can be said that tolerants, together with dominants, have relatively more dependence on the intrinsic physical attributes of environment, whereas the success of dependents hinges more on the extrinsic conditions imposed by the dominants.

Taking the earth's surface as a whole, the total animal biomass (live weight) is equal to only about 0.1 percent of the total plant biomass. It is not surprising therefore that over most of the land surface animals belong to the subordinate class. Plants control animals by the types of food and shelter they provide. Although everywhere plant life must furnish the energy-containing compounds which support all kinds of animal life, animals normally use vegetation without effecting any great change in its structure or composition.

There are, however, a number of communities in which animals other than man have a high measure of dominance. Domestic livestock determines much of the character of ecosystems on nonagricultural land, and man-induced imbalances have often allowed deer, elk, goats, or rabbits to devastate vegetation. In these cases, however, one can hardly say that animal dominance exceeds that of plants, for if the plants were removed all animals would perish. In aquatic ecosystems animals such as carp or corals frequently play an equivalent role,[6] and colonial shore-birds may limit vegetation locally to algae and fungi.[176] The carp and shorebirds can dominate only because their sources of energy lie in habitats where they are definitely not dominant. It is not uncommon for an organism to be a dominant in one community and a subordinate in another.

The Community Has Boundaries in Space

The concept of community necessarily presumes a degree of biologic homogeneity in structure and species composition that is associated with area having boundaries. As two communities come into contact they intergrade, and the zone of intergradation, whether narrow or wide, is called an *ecotone*.

Three types of ecotones between contiguous communities may be recognized. (1) The transition may be abrupt as a result of an abrupt discontinuity in environmental conditions (Fig. 7). (2) The transition may be abrupt as a result of plant interactions, especially competition, even though the extrinsic factors exhibit a continuous gradient (Figs. 8, 9). (3) The ecotone may be a zone of gradual blending of two

FIG. 7. *Cerocarpus montanus* scrub on thin, stony soil stops abruptly at the edge of deep, fine-textured soil which supports steppe vegetation. Colorado.

FIG. 8. Shallow saline basin near Whitehorse, Yukon Territory, with *Salicornia rubra* on the dried salt crust, surrounded by a zone of *Puccinellia*, then *Salix*. *Picea-Populus* forest in background is on nonsaline soil. Vegetation here is organized similar to a "stepped ramp" across a uniform environmental gradient.

vegetation types that reflects a gradual blending of two distinct factor complexes (Fig. 10).

The ecologic significance of the first type of ecotone is so obvious that discussion of it is unnecessary.

About a pond the relation between the soil and water surfaces changes gradually in progressing from deep water toward the surrounding upland, whereas the vegetation exhibits steplike discontinuities along the same gradient. The series of vegetation belts is analogous to a stepped ramp, the ecotones corresponding to the risers with the belts of low vegetation gradient corresponding to sloping treads. While sharp differences in the physical environment may be demonstrated on either side of the ecotones, these are all secondary factors wholly attributable to community influences. Observations on recently deglaciated areas (compare Figs. 47, 48, 49) show that when ponds are first formed the vegetation belts are not sharply defined as they become later when peat accumulation and other vegetation influences have accentuated boundaries and unified the composition of each belt. Within a sector of the gradual ecologic gradient one or a few plant species assume dominance,

FIG. 9. The right side of this smoothly surfaced palm trunk faces into moist onshore winds along a tropical coast. A discrete community of low-growing cryptogams occupies the dry surface and a rich and heterogenous community occupies the rain-exposed surface, with a clearly defined belt dominated by a light-colored species between. These communities exhibit little gradient across their width, but clear discontinuities occur where they meet, despite the gradualness of the environmental gradient.

excluding or nearly excluding others which could grow there if these dominants were removed. Such a community exhibits ecologic amplitude since it occupies a sector of the gradient rather than a point. This phenomenon of a dominant having a range of ecologic amplitude with rather sharp limits was strikingly demonstrated by the results of liberating harmful irradiation from a point source in a forest. After 6 months five clearly defined concentric zones of vegetation had been produced, although the original forest had been homogeneous and the intensity of irradiation had decreased at a uniform rate from the source.[473]

Ecotones of the third type are actually more abrupt than the environmental gradient would seem to warrant.[408] For example, in Fig. 10 there is a conspicuous vegetation transition a few hundred meters in breadth, the forest below and the alpine vegetation above exhibiting relatively

FIG. 10. Gradual ecotone on a gradual environmental gradient at upper timberline in Montana.

little gradient. Yet on this slope wind velocity, and the related intrinsic factors that help make it critical, probably do not increase more steeply within the limits of the ecotone than on either side of it. It seems more likely that the ecotone reflects an approach toward the limit of tolerance of trees along a scale of gradually decreasing temperature and increasing wind, with dependent subordinates accompanying the trees upslope only as far as their protection extends, whereas wind-tolerant but shade-intolerant plants from above diminish downslope as tree cover becomes more and more continuous.

In both the second and third types of ecotones we have discussed, the superior competitors on one side of an ecotone extend as far as their adaptability allows population maintenance, beyond which inferior competitors, dominants of the contiguous community, take over. Interspecific competition between potential dominants at ecotones is quite different from the intraspecific competition among individuals back from the zone of contact.

Another example of ecotones probably more abrupt than the environmental gradient is illustrated by species distribution about a knob, as shown in Table 1. The table shows that (1) two ecologic groups are present, one restricted to the relatively dry microclimate of the south-westerly slope, (2) the members of one community are not invariably present in plots where the presence of normal associates suggests that the environment is suitable, (3) the groupings are significant even if not sharply delimited, (4) life-forms bear a degree of correlation with microclimate.

The word ecotone is sometimes used in a different sense than above,

Table 1   **Distribution of herbs and shrubs on one contour following completely around a thinly forested knob in western Montana**

Compass Direction:	NW			W	SW		SE		NE			Life-form
Azimuth of Plot:	330	320	295	270	230	205	105	93	78	86	15	
Group A												
Anemone piperi	X	X	X	X		X	X	X	X	X	X	H
Astragalus virginiana mortoni			X									H
Bromus vulgaris	X											H
Clintonia uniflora	X											H
Coptis occidentalis		X	X					X	X			Ch
Cornus canadensis		X										Ch
Hieraceum albiflorum		X	X					X	X	X	X	H
Linnaea borealis americana	X		X									Ch
Lonicera utahensis											X	N
Pachistima myrsinites	X	X	X	X	X		X		X	X		N
Pyrola secunda	X								X			Ch
Rosa gymnocarpa	X	X	X	X			X		X	X		N
Rubus parviflorus		X	X	X					X	X	X	N
Vaccinium membranaceum	X	X	X				X		X		X	N
Viola glabella			X	X					X			H
Xerophyllum tenax			X									H
Totals	8	8	11	5	1	1	4	3	9	5	5	
Group B												
Achillea lanulosa						X						H
Apocynum pumilum				X								H
Arenarea macrophylla					X	X						H
Calochortus apiculatus				X		X	X					G
Collinsia parviflora				X	X	X						Th
Cryptantha sp.					X							Th
Epilobium paniculatum				X	X	X						Th
Microsteris gracile					X	X						Th
Montia parviflora						X						Th
Phacelia heterophylla					X							Ch
Polygonum majus						X						Th
Symphoricarpos albus				X	X	X						N
Totals				5	7	9	1					

NOTE: Occurrence indicated on plots with 2-m radii, spaced at 50-m intervals. Abbreviations stand for categories in Raunkiaer's life-form classification, which are defined on p. 64.

to designate the transitional area between two vegetation units in which the latter interdigitate rather than merge by degrees (Fig. 11). In crossing such a transitional area, the relative coverage of peninsular or islandlike areas of one community decreases, with the other community becoming a matrix with fewer and fewer interruptions. Such *mosaic*

FIG. 11. Interfingering type of ecotone illustrated by *Quercus* and *Pinus cembroides* dominating the thin, stony soil of eroding mountain slopes, and *Artemisia tridentata*–dominated vegetation on deep, fine-textured material that has accumulated on the basal plain. Mesa Verde, Colorado.

ecotones (in contrast with *simple* ecotones) are common where climate causes one type of vegetation to give way spatially to another. Small variations in soil or microclimate repeatedly shift the environmental balance from favoring one community to favoring the other. In a very broad perspective the two vegetation types may be described as "blending," but any attention to details reveals that islands and peninsulas of the vegetation types remain true to type despite the greatly increased opportunities for the rare establishment of species in habitats that are almost inimical to them.[224]

The position of an ecotone may be fixed rather permanently if it is set by a relatively immutable environmental discontinuity, such as the margin of a dune that rests on a loamy plain, or the sharp crest of an east-west ridge at high latitude. But where ecotones are set by climate or depth to a water table, they can shift in a direction and at a rate which depends directly on the character of change in the controlling factor complex.[197, 211] Only ecotones of the latter category may properly be called tension zones. Perfect adjustment of vegetation to ecotones of this category is so slow in comparison with the rate of climatic fluctuations that relics in varying stages of decadence are commonly found on both sides of the ecotone, and the transitional belt would narrow if climate remained static.

At an ecotone there is maximum opportunity for disseminules to alight on the side opposite the one on which they are produced in abun-dance. Even though the probability of their survival there is very low, the continuing shower of reproductive structures results in occasional successes in the habitat where suitable microsites are rare. This remote probability of success of course diminishes with increasing distance beyond the ecotone, even if only as a result of an attenuated supply of disseminules. Thus at an ecotone there is maximum opportunity for the mixing of two communities, so that in a small area a continuum results, whereas the same communities examined farther from their edges ex-hibit less contamination. The fact of this continuum is less remarkable than the ability of the two types to retain their individuality as well as they do in the face of continuing reciprocal invasion pressure.

Ecotones have special advantages for highly mobile animals in the form of special mixtures of food plants, or contrasting vegetation types which satisfy alternating needs.[358]

Because at an ecotone there is commonly a shift of dominance in conspicuous species, the impression is fostered that the floras are different on the two sides. Occasionally this is almost wholly true, but at the vast majority of ecotones a high percentage of the taxa are shared by both communities.

In areas with great environmental heterogeneity the vegetation may consist almost wholly of ecotones, environmental gradients too fre-quently changing their direction to allow space for a homogeneous community to develop. In such places one must search for the rare places which support small units of vegetation showing little gradient. If these are repeated over the mosaic, they can be considered basic types and used as convenient reference points in describing the status of any point in the large expanse of mixture. Intergradation among classification units is always a problem in the natural sciences, whether one studies rocks, cloud forms, mice, soil profiles, or plant communities. It is interesting to note the clear insight into this problem that was expressed by Anton Kerner, who wrote (as translated) in 1863: "Only when one has studied the vegetation long and intimately . . . one per-ceives there also the orderliness which enables us to discover unity in diversity. . . . As in working with the microscope one must learn by long training to interpret the visible picture correctly, so it is in the consideration of natural vegetation. Only after a time do the green riddles of the plant communities before us, which at first seem like a mixture without law and order, resolve themselves into a harmonious whole."[91]

The Community Has Boundaries in Time

The geologic record shows that every part of the land surface has from time to time been denuded of its vegetation. New bare areas are continually being formed by submergence, emergence, deglaciation, landslide, vulcanism, cultivation, fire, etc., and on these may be observed the origin and development of new communities. On all but extremely dry or extremely cold land surfaces the first scattered plants to appear are followed by others at successive intervals in the course of time, and the habitat changes from one freely exposed to sun and wind to one so protected from the elements as to offer very different conditions for plant growth. These environmental changes are definitely related to the changes in plant populations, for no two of the sequential communities have the same influence in modifying the soil and atmosphere, and in attracting animal life. Often a given community must await the attainment of special conditions produced by an earlier one before it can make its appearance.[440]

These changes, commonly referred to as *succession*, are not without end, for eventually the habitat ceases to undergo measurable change in a constant direction and when this happens the last community to gain control of the area retains its supremacy.

The first plants to invade a new bare area are usually so scattered they have no interrelationships, and only intrinsic habitat factors determine survival. But subsequently, population pressure develops, and mutual interference stops the reproduction of those species having inferior capacities to endure crowded conditions. Extrinsic as well as intrinsic factors now become critical. Eventually all organisms other than those capable of living and reproducing under crowded conditions have been eliminated, and those that remain have become adjusted to each other. The community which thus gains essentially permanent occupancy of the habitat, the *climax* community, perpetuates itself there indefinitely unless it is disturbed by outside forces. So long as the total biota and climate remain constant, this climax community can usually redevelop following destruction.

In some situations the rate of succession is rapid enough that one can see striking differences in the composition of the vegetation within a few years, but in other places decades, if not centuries, must pass for the same degree of change to be brought about.

A major objective in any science is to predict and control. Since vegetation is dynamic, it is only through careful study of successional processes that man gains an ability to predict natural trends and to develop feasible objectives in modifying them, both of which are essential for success in managing vegetation.

• THE ASSOCIATION CONCEPT

One cannot work with vegetation long before realizing that there are "kinds" or "types" of communities which reappear wherever equivalent environmental conditions occur. To communicate intelligently, if for no other reason, it becomes necessary to define and name such units.

Classification involves the establishment of abstract collective names, each representing a series of closely similar concrete units, then grouping such series into successively larger and more heterogeneous groups that reflect successively lower degrees of similarity. The starting point in this procedure, as it applies to synecology, is defining the limits of the smallest units of the landscape so that all which are closely similar can be referred to by the same name, and this is the problem to which attention will now be directed. Higher units of synecologic classification will be considered later.

Kinds of Variation in Vegetation

A unit of vegetation can be recognized as such only if it appears homogeneous. But homogeneity in vegetation is a relative matter, for even where soil and microclimate seem perfectly uniform, unequal dissemination and opportunities for establishment result in no two places having identical species composition. Sometimes the vegetative spread of one species results in large pure clones (e.g., *Antennaria, Celastrus scandens, Serenoa repens*) dotted conspicuously over an area of otherwise uniform plant cover. Variations of these types, however, are of a different order, and of relatively minor ecologic importance, in comparison with vegetation differentiation that is a consequence of intrinsic differences in soil or microclimate.

As a rule the erratic distribution of a single species may be suspected of having no fundamental significance, but where two or more exhibit similar patterns one may suspect intrinsic differences in environment even where none is apparent. Even here another interpretation is possible. If certain annuals occur only in the shade of shrubs in the desert, such microenvironmental islands have limited significance because intrinsic habitat factors are not involved. As each shrub dies and is eventually replaced by another in a slightly different location, the shrub + annual groups shift positions through time over an environment which may be intrinsically very homogeneous. In synecologic classification the intention is to distinguish such fluctuating and accidental variations from other variations that are relatively permanent in the parent materials, microclimate or drainage, using only the latter category as a basis for distinguishing kinds of ecosystems.

With the above points in mind, we may define a homogeneous piece of vegetation as one in which variations are attributable to chance, rather than to intrinsic habitat factors.

The discussion above shows that from the very start vegetation classification is more difficult than species taxonomy. Whereas the species taxonomist usually has no doubt as to what constitutes an individual (but not in species forming clones by rhizomes, runners, or root suckers), the synecologist must always decide just what constitutes separate units before he can start to classify them.

The Plant Association

The term association appears to have been first used for categories of vegetation by Alexander von Humboldt early in the nineteenth century, and in the subsequent century and a half it has been defined in many ways. At the Third International Botanical Congress held in Brussels in 1910 the term association was officially adopted as the name to be applied to the fundamental categories of vegetation classification. Although the following definition was proposed at this meeting without gaining acceptance, it still expresses average opinion as to the meaning of the term. A plant association is a kind of "plant community of definite composition, presenting a uniform physiognomy* and growing in uniform habitat conditions" (translation). It was further specified that the term should apply to the entire phytocoenosis rather than to component layers or synusiae, and this too has generally been accepted. Such a definition, however, is subject to a much wider latitude of interpretation than might seem possible at first. "Definite" and "uniform" are relative terms meaning different things to different people. As in most natural sciences, this definition of the basic units is but a rough guide, and the limits of units must be set in large part by man's logic and convenience.[70] No single definition of the association could possibly be made that would be applicable throughout the earth's vegetation, just as no definition of species can be applied throughout the plant kingdom.

As implied above, many ecologists have used the term association for the basic category of vegetation, but their interpretations of its inclusiveness have varied tremendously. For example, F. E. Clements included in a single association all climax forests in approximately the northeastern quarter of the United States, including communities with no species in common. At the other extreme, T. Lippmaa used the term association for entities no more comprehensive than one layer of a phytocoenosis. The viewpoint which will be elaborated below is conservative in that it lies within these two extremes.

Each piece of vegetation that is essentially homogeneous in all layers and differs from contiguous vegetation types by either quantitative or qualitative characters is a *stand*. All climax stands in which the dominants of corresponding layers are essentially the same, to the extent that

---

* Physiognomy refers to the gross appearance of a kind of vegetation, ignoring its taxonomic composition.

any differences in composition are due to chance dissemination or to a transitory historic factor rather than to a fundamental dissimilarity in habitat potentialities, comprise one *association*. It is recognized that no two of the stands grouped into one association are ever identical, and that the soil, climate, and animals may differ from one stand to another so long as their ecologic sums produce plant groupings with a high degree of similarity. The stand is a concrete and objective reality. The association, on the other hand, is a subjective concept based on those characters at least potentially common to all the separate stands which represent it, and which serve to separate the group from all other stands. It is abstract in the sense that all stands are never studied, and we must assume that the range and mean characters in those that have been studied represent the entire group.

A problem is posed by all vegetation types that precede climaxes. Where plant succession is very slow, reasonably distinct and homogeneous stages may be defined, and ecologists have designated them as *associes* if not associations. But where succession proceeds rapidly, or where an agent such as fire partly destroys a climax so that invaders are mingled with survivors, temporary vegetation is not easily divided into units that have much significance. It seems better to look upon the situation as an ecosystem temporarily thrown into imbalance, laying emphasis on the potentialities of the area rather than upon an ephemeral condition. The intrinsic characters of soil and climate usually remain unaltered during successive cycles of destruction and regeneration of climaxes, so that if temporary and climax communities are given equal weight, one cannot relate biocoenoses very closely with soil and climate. Therefore, in synecology as in pedology or species taxonomy, many believe that the immature units are best related in classification according to the mature forms they represent. The reason is precisely parallel to that of the botanist who might file a specimen of moss protonema with the species of moss it represents rather than with algae, even though an objective enumeration of characters would show that it more closely resembles the algae. The successional status of each community must be established early in the study of a vegetational mosaic if the ecologic potentialities are considered important and the classification is to reflect these potentialities.

An important advantage of centering classification on the most stable types that can be found is that it draws together different successional communities represented by an infinite variety of subtly intergrading stages, but all leading to the same few stable types. This results in a far more simplified classification than is possible when all variants of the earth's vegetation are considered of equal significance.

The association concept is useful only to the extent that biologists can agree on the amount of variation among stands which can reason-

ably be included in one association. As information accumulates, classifications evolve that are objective in the sense that workers with different
backgrounds of training and experience agree on significant discontinuities.[114, 290] Conspicuous differences among workers as to terminology, methods of approach, and tendencies for lumping or splitting
have obscured this far more significant point.

Since the association serves the same purpose in synecology as the
species does in taxonomy, it has long been compared with the species.[181]
Neither is susceptible to rigorous definition, yet both are equally indispensable in their respective branches of biology.

For many years serious students of vegetation maintained that vegetation types ought to be defined in terms of vegetational characters
alone, but such a narrow viewpoint originated before the ecosystem
concept had wide adoption. If the latter has any merit, a study of
environment should be of considerable assistance in distinguishing
variation that is accidental from that which has an ecologic basis, and
should therefore be useful in deciding the most significant groupings
of stands. Small vegetational differences must be given relatively great
weight if regularly associated with sharp environmental differences,
whereas wide variation in floristic composition may be rather meaningless if not correlated with intrinsic characters of the environment. Since
the basic units we are classifying are really ecosystem types, the list of
defining characters for synecologic units may well include all such
edaphic, aerial, and zoologic attributes as may be useful, in addition to
the botanical characters.

The number of associations recognized in a vegetation mosaic is
always influenced by the judgment of the synecologist, who must take
into account the fact that the smaller the units he recognizes the more
precisely these can be related to environment, yet the smaller the units
the more unwieldy the classification. The practical use to which a
classification might be put in some form of land management may be
important enough to favor recognition of rather small units in some
places and favor lumping minor variations elsewhere. Most synecologists would not favor so narrow a view as H. Osvald adopted when he
recognized 164 vegetation types in a peat area of approximately 40
square miles in Sweden, yet most of those who might object would
probably have settled on such coarse divisions that a number of fundamental vegetation-environment relationships discovered by Osvald would
have been missed. Of the alternatives, it is probably better to err on the
side of splitting, since subsequent lumping does not require reinvestiga-
tion, as would be true if splitting were found necessary.

The term association may be applied to any distinctive type of climax
vegetation, whether large or small, simple or complex. Some workers,
however, consider it desirable to recognize broadly defined associations,

these being subdivided into *subassociations* or *phases* in which the presence or absence of a few botanical characters is regularly associated with some minor spatial variation in environment.

It is often convenient to give names to structural components of one association, since one of these may be recognizable in a different environment as a component of a different association. Thus on the southerly slopes of high ridges of the Bitterroot Mountains a tree stratum consisting of *Abies lasiocarpa* with a low shrub undergrowth of *Xerophyllum tenax* + *Vaccinium membranaceum* may be found. On northerly slopes, where the microclimate is cooler and wetter, and the soils even more depleted of calcium, these same two layers occur, but with a tall shrub layer consisting chiefly of *Menziesia ferruginea* inserted between. Thus one must recognize a *Menziesia* component and a *Xerophyllum-Vaccinium* component (two unions) beneath the trees on the north slope, with only one of these two unions beneath the *Abies* (which constitutes the third union) on south slopes. Three unions here comprise the salient structural features of two associations. In the climatically distinctive Cascade Mountains the same *Xerophyllum-Vaccinium* union reappears beneath a different kind of stable tree union.

A *union* is thus one of several major subdivisions of one association that reappears in other associations. It is composed of one abundant species (e.g., *Abies lasiocarpa*), or of several that it is convenient to group on the basis of similarity in life-form, phenology, stature, or somewhat coextensive distribution in a local vegetation mosaic. The union includes only a fraction of the total floristic list—just those species or species combinations that are useful in vegetation classification.

Nomenclature of Associations

To develop the synecology of a region involves analyses of stands at many places, determination of reasonable limits for ecosystem types, then giving names to the associations that characterize each of them.

An association might be designated by some word or word combination taken from a modern language, e.g., muskeg, pocosin, shinnery, encinal, or subalpine forest. But such colloquialisms are meaningless to most botanists, and inevitably cause confusion. Even such a widely used term as rain forest has been applied to forests dominated by (1) evergreen broad-leaved trees growing in wet tropical climates, (2) *Tsuga heterophylla* in the temperate climate of the Olympic Peninsula, and (3) *Abies lasiocarpa* growing in the very cold climates of glacial cirques just below alpine timberline in Colorado. Names may be arbitrary, but they need not be obscure or ambiguous.

There seems little hope for any method of naming plant associations that will meet with widespread approval unless it reflects as much as possible the names of species that differentiate them. If the plant association can be characterized by a unique combination of species (each of which may also participate individually in other associations), then a critical name might well indicate this combination. Naming is most meaningful when based on the conspicuous dominants of the different layers, but often distinctive communities have similar dominants, so that minor species must be used in defining associations or subassociations. The fewer the words that will suffice, the more acceptable the name. But even a very long name cannot embrace all the distinguishing criteria of the stands being classed together.

Vernacular names of indicator plants may be strung together, e.g., subalpine fir-beargrass association. But vernacular names used as scientific terms have the same disadvantage in vegetation science as in species taxonomy—they are not international in application. Many kinds of plants are referred to as "beargrass" in different parts of the English-speaking world, and the subalpine firs are different taxa in Wyoming, Switzerland, and India. Thus to avoid confusion, the international latinized names of the plants should always be used, e.g., *Abies lasiocarpa-Xerophyllum tenax* association.

Another form of internationalization was initiated by J. F. Schouw as early as 1822 when he suggested names formed by adding the suffix *-etum* (meaning "community of") to the stem of the generic name, e.g., *Abietum, Stipetum,* or *Rhizophoretum.* In 1903 A. K. Cajander pointed out that this system could be made far more useful by appending the specific epithet of the characteristic species, in the genitive case, thus making the association name more explicit,[301] e.g., *Abietum lasiocarpae.* Where there are two characteristic genera, the first name is given an *-eto* ending and the two are hyphenated, e.g., *Abieto-Fagetum,* meaning a "community of *Fagus* characterized by the inclusion of *Abies* as well."

The next step that can be taken to make the association name more specific is to add the name of a second diagnostic species, and for these modifiers capitalization is dropped and the suffix *-etosum* (meaning "with") is used. Thus the name of the association used as an illustration earlier might be written *Abietum lasiocarpae xerophylletosum.*

Some workers have coined names which refer to the character of the habitat in part (e.g., *Xerobrometum* or *Thujeto-Blechnetum gleyosolicum* or using *Rudereto-* as a prefix) or to a geographic region (e.g., *Aceretum saccharophori laurentianum*), and others have used the species name apart from its genus (e.g., *Curvuletum,* referring to *Carex curvula*). The last practice is objectionable in that it reduces the name to a symbol that has meaning to very few workers.[25]

When an animal is conspicuous in a biocoenosis, a case has been made for naming the biocoenosis in part after the animal, e.g., *Bison-*

Bouteloua association. Most synecologists, however, do not favor this practice since an animal conspicuous enough to be a useful community indicator wanders so widely that it is equally at home in a number of vegetation types without being regularly present in any one of them.

Regardless of the nomenclatural system followed, after the most appropriate name combination of organisms has been selected, a few stands are inevitably found that seem to belong to the same ecosystem type, yet lack one or even both of the plants that are usually distinctive. But are there not some plants classed in the genus *Trifolium* that regularly have more than three leaflets, and dicots that have just one cotyledon? It must be kept in mind that the object of study is not simply two or three indicator species but rather an entire ecosystem, that ecosystems differ by a series of characters spread among their biologic and physical components, and that no one character of the series can always be relied on, even though that character may usually be quite diagnostic. The name can be little more than a symbol, and the problem is to make it as meaningful, as distinctive, and as brief as possible. A balance must be struck between a short and ambiguous name and one that is very long but completely diagnostic. Neither extreme is desirable.

Significance of the Association Concept

The association was defined above as a type of climax phytocoenosis. But owing to the frequency of disturbance of the landscape by fire, cultivation, logging, livestock grazing, geologic processes, etc., very little of the earth's surface supports climax vegetation. Most landscapes instead comprise a great number of small stands representing different successional stages, due to different types and intensities of disturbance that took place at different times in the past. Upon careful study, however, all the stands in one landscape mosaic are usually found to be components of a few successional sequences leading to still fewer climax types. Since each climax can normally regenerate itself repeatedly following destruction, and since its potential share of the landscape remains fixed, field ecology is simplified by focusing attention on the *area* belonging to each association, which for the most part is actually occupied by different successional communities representing it. All the area (sum of discrete units) that now supports, or within recent time has supported, and presumably is still capable of supporting, one plant association will be called a *habitat type* (syn.: homoece, equivalent environment).

If the ecosystem concept is well founded, the pattern of vegetation types should correlate with patterns in climate, soil, and fauna (although by no means do all features of these components change at each ecotone). In theory any of the four basic components might be used to classify the landscape into habitat types, but this is not practical. A conspicuous animal generally occurs in several ecosystems, without being evenly distributed over any of them, as is true of plant dominants in the different layers. Then, throughout its geographic range, a single habitat type is demonstrably variable as to both climate and soil. It has the potentiality of supporting what may reasonably be considered a single plant association only because, through factor compensation, the ecologic sum of all variations in climate and soil remains essentially the same throughout. If every detail of climatic and edaphic variation throughout a landscape were known, man would still lack the ability to integrate all this information and divide the landscape into areas of essentially equivalent vegetative potentialities, at least with the precision that plant communities do this as they progress toward climax. Thus plant associations serve as the best guide to habitat types, and without using vegetation, the potentialities of every acre of ground could be estimated only by some method less directly related to biologic potential, and hence less satisfactory. This indicator value of vegetation finds many applications.

Correlation of information. If the place where a specimen was collected, or some observation was made, is characterized as to habitat type and successional status, a great many attributes of the locality are indicated. Such information provides a framework for correlating biologic and pedologic phenomena in both time and space. Association intergrades are most succinctly characterized by reference to the relevant communities that represent the pure types, just as the notation *Picea engelmanni* $\times$ *glauca* conveys a great amount of information about the distribution, appearance, taxonomic relations, and autecology of a tree.

Key to subtle genetic variation. It is a matter of common knowledge that a species exhibits different behavior in different places. Growth rate, susceptibility to disease, longevity, method of reproduction, competitive abilities, etc., are among the characters that vary. Whether these variations represent ecotypes or ecophenes, the habitat type is the best indicator of the extent of each type of variance. Much economic use can be made of this concept in collecting seed for forest or range rehabilitation, since, in general, seed produced by plants native to one habitat type are more successful in that habitat type than elsewhere.

Collecting herbarium specimens deliberately to represent the full range of habitat types is a good way of ensuring that herbarium material encompasses the range of a species' genetic variability.

Planning experiments. In planning field experiments it is often difficult to assemble valid replicates, and this is essential to the critical evaluation of results. Species lists alone are not adequate indicators of habitat equivalence, for areas with different potentialities may support nonclimax vegetation essentially identical as to appearance and floras, and conversely, areas with different physiognomy and species lists may have closely similar potentialities.[122] The soundest procedure is to make sure that all replicates fall in the same habitat type.

Extension of experimental results. An experiment usually involves an area so small as to be geographically no more than a point, and if we had no means of judging where the same result could be obtained, the experiment would have to be repeated many times to determine the extent of its applicability over the earth's surface. If, on the other hand, the response of vegetation to burning, fertilization, grazing, or other type of treatment is determined at one place on a known habitat type, one can have reasonable assurance that similar results will follow on other parts of the same habitat type. Thus the degree to which the results of experimentation can be extrapolated depends on the degree to which the study site is representative of some specific habitat type (Fig. 12). Ecotones, or habitats of limited extent, must be avoided when selecting sites to conduct experiments if the results are to be extrapolated.

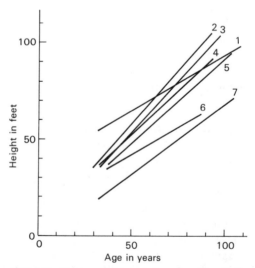

FIG. 12. Regression analyses showing variation in mean rates of growth of *Pinus ponderosa* when growing in seven habitat types in eastern Washington and northern Idaho. (Daubenmire, 1961)

Guide to wildland management. When the potentialities of a series of habitat types have been determined, each can be managed in complementary fashion to utilize the landscape as a whole most efficiently. Different habitat types are not equally favorable to natural forest regeneration, nor will they all produce the highest quality trees in the shortest time.[127, 183, 452] Disease hazard for a species varies significantly from one habitat type to another, and this information is useful in planning control measures or planting alternative species.[127, 244, 392, 416] It has been shown that the factors responsible for vegetation differentiation are also involved in determining the concentration of radioactive fallout, so that habitat types where plants, and in turn animal tissue and milk, are likely to be seriously contaminated can get special consideration in land-use planning.[366, 384]

The value of vegetation indicators on uncultivated lands varies in direct proportion to the heterogeneity of environment, for optimal management demands recognition of all the habitat types in an area, and management of each according to its unique potentialities. For example, rumen analyses of mule deer showed that food preferences differed according to the plant community in which the animal was collected. In managing mule deer it is therefore important to consider separately the species proportions and area of each vegetation type, rather than trying to manage the entire landscape mosaic as a unit, assuming one palatability rating for each kind of plant, and uniform usage of the plants throughout.[10]

Although the forester, in planting and harvesting trees, can take advantage of the special potentialities of even small elements of a habitat mosaic, this practice is limited where animals are free to make their own choices of communities and species. For if some of the units are too small to fence and manage separately, they may be overutilized while others remain virtually unused, although the judicious location of salt, water, plantings, burned openings, logged areas, etc., still provide some measure of control.

2 analysis and description of plant communities

• DESCRIPTIVE CONCEPTS

Introduction

The objects of any science may be described and classified in a number of ways, each based on a different characteristic. Species, for example, have been classified according to floral morphology, somatic anatomy, chromosome number, chemical composition, life-form, longevity, nutrient requirements, geographic distribution, etc. Since each type of classification tends to cut across groupings established by the others, the more types that are considered the more facts are brought out, and the more complete becomes our understanding of species relationships. In like manner communities have a number of characters which must be studied for adequacy of description and understanding. Information derived from any one technique brings out but a single facet of a community's character.

The data of science must be expressed quantitatively and with as much precision as the nature of the subject matter allows. Thus the need for quantitative techniques for expressing the different attributes of communities has long been recognized. These permit making descriptions that facilitate precise comparisons in space (plant geography) or time (succession), detecting and analyzing the consequences of experimental treatments of vegetation, studying the impact of climate on plant evolution, etc. It is the purpose of Chapter 2 to outline the principal techniques and indicate their values and limitations.

Importance of Taxonomy

At the beginning of any serious study of a plant community it is important not only to learn precisely which species are present, but to be able to recognize them at different stages of development. The time is not long past when the field biologist felt well satisfied with his work after presenting a mere list of the dominants, identifying these as they came into flower. It is now widely acknowledged as poor policy to learn only a few of the dominants and neglect the remaining flora. Subordinate and even rare plants often have much value for indicating special conditions, present and past, and they sometimes foretell the future. *All* species have some indicator significance, whether it is known at present or not.

One must often commence study without knowing all the plants. But to work with no more than collection numbers often results in failure to recognize subtle taxonomic distinctions which always merit careful attention. Working at the level of the ecotype would be theoretically ideal, but it is usually impossible owing to their lack of morphologic distinctiveness, so our nearest approach is to pay close attention to subspecies and varieties. In short, the highest level of taxonomic accuracy is required for fundamental synecology. The synecology of a particular area can never rise above the quality of the taxonomic treatment available for that area, nor the taxonomic competence of the synecologist.

Of all the plants a synecologist must record in his study areas, only a small fraction will be in flower or fruit at the time his records are taken, and since thousands of individuals of what appear to be the same taxon must be tallied in sample plots, even pressed vouchers have limited value as proof of identity. However, a set of preserved specimens collected at taxonomically critical stages of development is desirable to indicate which plants the worker thought he was recording, and perhaps later to clear up problems of nomenclature.

Analytic Concepts

Density. In synecology the word density is usually taken to mean the number of individuals of a species per unit area or volume.

Rough estimates of density (distinguished as *abundance*) are sometimes used in reconnaissance work where the objective is to get enough information at many places in short time in order to plan detailed work. For this purpose each entry in the taxonomic list for a stand may be annotated with a number representing one of five or more[304] abundance classes: (1) very rare, (2) rare, (3) occasional, (4) abundant, or (5) very abundant. However, evaluations of this type are subject to so much variation in interpretation that abundance ratings have very little standing as a research technique.

By definition, density requires actual counts of individuals in a definite space. But as applied to plant communities, this technique has two serious limitations.

First, the majority of plant communities contain species which reproduce vegetatively (i.e., rhizomatous species, prostrate plants that root along the stem, trees that send up sucker shoots from shallow roots, caespitose grasses in which large plants become dismembered, etc.) so that it often is impossible to ascertain just what constitutes a single individual. The problem cannot be evaded simply by counting each stem or tuft that rises from a rhizome, unless we do likewise for the shoots of other plants which rise vertically from horizontal branches elevated above the ground, and for the clustered tillers of a caespitose grass. Thus density is generally not satisfactory as a basis for comparing species in a phytocoenosis.

Second, the size of the mature individuals of one plant species (unlike animals) may vary a thousandfold under different growing conditions, so that a statement that there are two individuals of a given species per meter imparts very little biologic information.

For intraspecific comparisons, however, density is a valuable statistic. Where the nature of a perennial makes it possible to keep separate density records for different age classes, density provides the key to an understanding of population dynamics, and population variation through time and space lies at the core of synecology.

In populations of annuals, density may vary considerably from year to year owing to weather influences on the setting of seed, conditions necessary for germination, fungal destruction of seeds and seedlings, etc. In fact, in arid regions certain annuals may not appear at all in unfavorable years (Table 2). Since annuals do not reproduce vegetatively,

Table 2   **Year-to-year variation in frequency (percent occurrence in 40 permanent plots, each 2 X 5 dm) of annuals in an undisturbed stand of shrub-steppe in Washington**

Species	Frequency, %						
	1958	1959	1960	1961	1962	1963	1964
Festuca pacifica	92	100	32	88	58	90	80
Festuca octoflora	92	85	40	88	30	98	47
Bromus tectorum	45	90	55	62	18	50	52
Descurainia pinnata	18	20		25		18	2
Lappula redowskii	8	12		12			
Cryptantha flaccida	12	10	4				
Draba verna	2					12	
Lagophylla ramosissima	4						
Linanthus pharnaceoides		2					
Gilia minutiflora		2					

NOTE: Annual precipitation is about 180 mm per year. These annuals are all tiny subordinates, but they comprise half the vascular flora.

density can be used to good advantage in studying their ecology, providing the density is not so excessive as to make counting impractical.

Dominance.   In addition to those limitations of density data which have been pointed out above, it is important to note that they would be very misleading if presented for the whole phytoconeosis, since thousands of small subordinates can occur in a plot that supports only a few large dominants. Clearly, in complex communities there is need for a type of analysis that takes plant dimensions into account.

Any evaluation that expresses the size or bulk of the shoots of each species in relation to space may be referred to as a *dominance* analysis. In such an analytic procedure every species has a dominance rating with respect to its occupancy of space, even though most of them are subordinates. By stressing size or bulk, emphasis is directed toward the degree of influence that different kinds of plants are exerting on other components of the ecosystem, and this is a highly important matter. Also, within a group of plants of similar size, a relatively high dominance rating seems certain indication of a species well adapted to the physical factors of the habitat. However, the reverse is not necessarily true since low dominance may indicate no more than strong competition from other species equally at home on the site.

With most of the techniques used to measure dominance, the values not only show variation from place to place, but with herbs and deciduous woody plants the rating differs according to the seasonal stage of development. Since comparisons are valid only if they represent equivalent stages of development, and the logical basis is maximal seasonal development, it is often necessary to revisit a stand at different seasons, each time making records of just those species that are near their prime. Also, among herbs the maximal size of shoot attained varies from year to year depending on the nature of the weather at the time the shoots develop, so that results for a given year are only approximations of the values that would be obtained by averaging repeated determinations in successive seasons.[171, 473]

There are five principal methods of measuring dominance, each of which is more useful in certain types of plant communities than others.

Coverage.   There are three principal definitions of coverage, each providing data not necessarily correlated with the others.

Determination of the *leaf area index* (total blade surface/unit land surface), abbreviated as LAI, is a very useful criterion of the degree to which a crop or natural community is utilizing the available light energy. It has been shown that in a developing monoculture, or in a mixture of species with comparable shoot morphology, the LAI becomes stable after reaching a value usually between 4 and 11, the value varying with the shape and angle of the blades. But where different life forms are mixed, the LAI may be much larger. This concept appears not to have been used in complex natural communities, owing to the labor involved in working with a mixture of plant types.

Secondly, coverage may be evaluated as the sum of shadows that would be cast by leaves and stems, taking each species separately, and expressing the result as a percentage of the land surface. With the sun at zenith, as is assumed, this should yield a lower value than the LAI since intraspecific leaf overlap is ignored. Many synecologists have used this approach. However, a plant with vertical foliage, as many species of *Eucalyptus*, would get a low *foliar cover* rating in comparison with species of *Acer*, although both canopies might have the same LAI, produce the same dry matter, be of equal height and breadth, with roots extending through the same volume of soil. Microphyllous and aphyllous species would also get ratings much smaller than they would seem to deserve.

In the third interpretation, coverage is taken as an expression of the percentage of the ground included in a vertical projection of imaginary polygons drawn about the total natural spread of foliage of the individuals of a species.[125] Since dominance is asserted as much by the roots as by the shoot system, and underground parts tend to be at least as extensive as the latter, there is little point in subtracting from the gross *canopy coverage* small discontinuities that reflect no more than accidents in the positions of foliage sprays, orientation of leaf blades, or peculiarities of phyllotaxy. The aim is to estimate the two-dimensional area that is directly influenced by the individuals of each species. This canopy coverage percentage should be higher than foliar coverage for the same community as a result of ignoring sunflecks between leaves and gaps between foliage sprays, but lower than the LAI which counts intraspecific leaf overlap. The next few paragraphs refer primarily to canopy coverage, although the principles to be discussed can be applied to foliar coverage as well.

Usually some system of estimation is used in gathering coverage data, and if this is properly done it gives results as accurate as vegetational heterogeneity warrants. Some investigators estimate coverage in each of several small plots to the nearest tenth, the values for the series then being averaged.[345] Others prefer a series of unequal classes[428] such as those in Table 3.

Table 3 **Values for a coverage estimation technique**

Coverage Class	Range of Coverage, %	Midpoint of Coverage Class, %
1	0–5	2.5
2	5–25	15
3	25–50	37.5
4	50–75	62.5
5	75–95	85
6	95–100	97.5

SOURCE: Daubenmire, 1959.

One may apply this method simply by estimating the value for each species in a single large plot (e.g., 10 × 10 m), and such estimates are satisfactory for the purpose of characterizing stands and grouping them into associations.[205] But if one wishes a more accurate estimate of coverage so that a relatively precise quantitative correlation can be made between vegetation composition and environmental measurements at a number of locations, or if he wishes to evaluate the same stand repeatedly to detect successional trends, a more precise application of the method is necessary. To accomplish this, a series of small plots may be scattered over the stand and a separate coverage estimate made of each species in each plot. The advantage of a relatively coarse scale in this

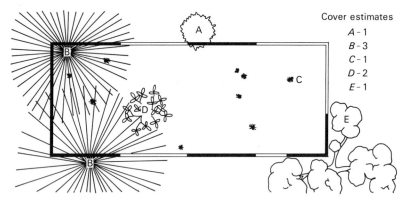

FIG. 13. Diagram illustrating a method for estimating canopy coverage. The painted pattern on the 20 × 50 cm frame provides areas for visual comparison equal to 5, 25, 50, 75, and 95 percent of the frame. The biologic soundness of using a vertical projection of a polygon drawn about the extremities of the plant canopy is illustrated by *E*, which, by accident of foliage arrangement, has no leaves directly above the plot. Such a plant probably exerts at least as much influence on the 20 × 50 cm portion of an ecosystem as does *A*.

operation is that there is little chance for personal error in class assignments, yet when the results from a considerable number of small plots are averaged, rather fine differences can be brought out. Only the class number is recorded in the field. Then later, in averaging records for a series of plots, the midpoint in the range of each coverage class (i.e., 15 percent for Class 2) must be used, rather than averaging the class numbers. Class 1 is made small so as not to overestimate poorly represented species, for there tend to be many plants with small representation, and few with large. Class 6 is necessarily small since the midpoint of even this small range would give a plant which covered all of every plot, an average of only 97.5 percent.

Coverage is determined separately for each species overlapping the plot regardless of where the individuals are rooted and regardless of superimposed canopies of different species, but ignoring intraspecific overlap (Fig. 13). Since the canopies of different species are commonly interlaced, and those of different stature are commonly superimposed over the same area, the sums of coverages for a stand commonly exceed 100 percent. Where it is desirable to know the percentage of bare ground or the coverage of separate layers, special estimates of these can be made when tallying the species individually.

With dominance (as with density) the absolute percentages (or numbers) are more meaningful than the relative ratings of the taxa. It is more important to know that species A has 12 percent coverage in a stand than that it provides 75 percent of the total plant cover. Only the absolute values give an insight into the capacity of the environment to support vegetation. If they are stated, the relative values can always be calculated if needed.

The canopy coverage method just described is sufficiently accurate to repeat year after year on the same area and follow the course of succession, but such a study would not show *how* the net changes are brought about. For this purpose the positions and sizes of each plant or clone must be entered on a detailed map.

For low-growing vegetation permanent records of individual plant coverage can be made by: (1) gridding the plot with string or moving a rod crosswise down the length of a narrow plot,[338] then sketching freehand the outline of the plants on paper ruled to correspond with the grid or strip; by (2) using an especially constructed pantograph in the field to reproduce the outlines of plants growing beside a drafting board;[332] by (3) looking through clear plastic laid on glass, and drawing the outlines of plants on the plastic, with a tripod maintaining both the eye and the plastic at standard levels;[49] by (4) focusing a large camera vertically on a plot, then drawing the outlines of the plants on a piece of translucent paper laid on clear glass that has been substituted for the regular ground glass;[375] or by (5) taking a vertical photograph of the plot from an especially tall support[97] or from a small tethered balloon.[148]

Although the pantograph method would seem highly accurate, a surprising amount of human error may enter the results.[206] Methods (3) and (4) are difficult to apply to several-layered vegetation unless one person moves aside foliage of the taller plants while another sketches the lower ones. A serious disadvantage of (5) is that many plants are very difficult to identify from a photograph, even if the community is so open that there are no overlapping canopies and the lighting is so perfect that there are no confusing shadows.

Having obtained maps or photographs by any of these methods, coverage percentages can be determined by using a planimeter, or by cutting out and weighing separately those parts of the map representing each species, or by superimposing a transparent grid with dots. These dots (or circles with dot-sized openings) are regularly spaced so that the frequency of hits in relation to the total dots can be assumed proportional to coverage. The dots are divided by grid lines to facilitate counting large areas, and those dots falling on a plant margin are given half value. Direct comparisons of successive maps are facilitated if these are made on transparent materials such as tracing paper or plastic so they can be superimposed for study.[152]

There is little reward for making detailed maps unless repeated observations are to be made of the areas, and to do this the plots must be marked permanently so they can be relocated. Any posts or stakes used for this purpose must be inconspicuous if left at the edges of the plots, for animals tend to investigate such objects and trample the area excessively. It is a good practice to use conspicuous markers (e.g., steel fence posts, or paint marks on a boulder) as reference points from which the plots can be relocated using a tape and compass to find spikes, only the heads of which are left showing above ground.

Different techniques must be used for overhead canopies. Foliar coverage may be estimated directly by making a series of illumination readings at fixed intervals along a tape stretched near the ground, then expressing the average as a percentage of the total illumination as determined in an unobstructed area before and after.[174] Such a technique can be used only on an absolutely clear or a uniformly overcast day, with all measurements made near noon. The greatest drawback to the method is that most overstories are taxonomically complex, and the method does not permit distinction among taxa.

A technique which permits the study of species separately involves the use of a box fitted like a periscope (Fig. 14) with a mirror inside so that a reflection of the canopy above the observer can be evaluated, species by species, against a grid drawn on the top glass.[170] Alternatively, a suspended periscope with crosshairs can be used to judge presence or absence of canopy above 200 or so points over the stand.[382]

A number of serious limitations restrict the value of data obtained by any of the above methods.[7] If the canopy has much thickness, the apparent coverage of a unit of foliage varies with its height above the observer, and the coverage of the lowest layer is not only exaggerated but it prevents the evaluation of all layers above it. It is impractical to record the stratum to which each of the staggered canopies belongs, and this is as important as the coverage value itself.

Aerial photographs, always useful in preparing maps of gross vegetational patterns, have limited value for complex vegetation since overstory species often cannot be distinguished, and the understory layers are impossible to evaluate. The technique is thus most useful in the study of low vegetation such as tundra, steppe, and desert.

Coverage, since its introduction into North American synecology by H. L. Shantz in 1906, has come to be considered a highly significant concept. It serves as a criterion of relative dominance, of potential productivity, of the influence of plants on precipitation interception and soil temperature, and of the value of vegetation to animals. It is applicable to almost all phytocoenoses, owing to the universal importance of light coming from above. Not the least of its virtues is that it permits comparison on a common basis of all plants from mosses to trees, since the different-sized plots that must be used for different-sized plants have no influence on the data. Finally, evaluations precise enough for research purposes do not require excessive field time, unless detailed maps are needed.

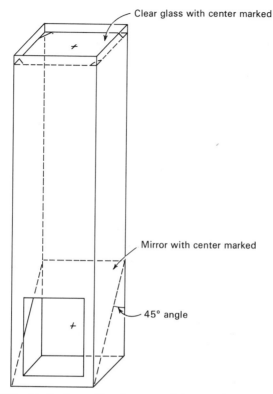

FIG. 14. Periscopelike device useful in evaluating the kind and amount of canopy coverage above the observer.

The chief limitation of coverage lies in omission of the vertical dimension, and while attempts have been made to weight coverage data with a height factor,[161] height is far more difficult to account for than might be suspected.[213] The height problem can be lessened by grouping species according to layers when the data are tabulated.

Basal area. Basal area refers to a comparison of species as to the aggregate cross-sectional area of the individual plants taken at or near the ground surface, per unit of land area. Usually the circumferences of woody stems or diameters of bunch grasses are measured, the cross-sectional areas obtained from standard tables, and these added up for each taxon. Sometimes an average of east-west and north-south diameters is used as an approximation of mean diameter. Calipers may be used for woody plants up to about 5 dm in diameter, but these are less accurate than especially calibrated "diameter tapes" that show diameter when drawn about the circumference. Grasses are commonly measured at a height of 1 cm or less, but trees are usually measured at "breast height," 1.3 m (or 4.5 feet).

Among herbaceous plants the theoretical advantage of the basal area method is that the stage of growth, weather, and herbivory should affect basal area less than dominance methods involving spread of foliage. However, the basal area of a grass may exhibit a surprising amount of annual fluctuation that is correlated with weather,[9, 71, 276] and this tends to nullify the major advantage claimed for the method.

A disadvantage of the method is that the height chosen for measurement has a strong influence on the results obtained. This is so important that the relative dominance among the species in a community varies considerably, depending on the arbitrary level chosen for measurement (Table 4). In cold and temperate climates the custom of measuring

Table 4 **Variations in relative dominance of two grasses resulting from differences in methods of analysis**

Methods of Recording Dominance	Percentage of Total Vegetation	
	Aristida longiseta	*Schedonnardus paniculatus*
Basal area at ground surface	33	3.7
Basal area at height of 1 inch	39	2.4
Max. spread of foliage above 1-inch level	18	0.6

SOURCE: Hanson and Love, 1930.

trees at breast height avoids most of the effects of variation due to different amounts of swelling of the tree base, but in tropical rain forest the highly variable heights of buttresses makes basal area impractical there.

A meaningful basal area value is also difficult to obtain for rosette plants, or those that spread to form mats.

Among herbaceous plants the method is invalid where a comparison is desired between caespitose grasses and single-stemmed forbs (Fig. 15), and grasses cannot be compared if some are rhizomatous and others caespitose. Even among caespitose grasses an appraisal of basal area is often frustrating and far from objective owing to the fragmentation of individuals into highly irregular tufts of varying sizes as the plant ages.

For trees, basal area has been more widely used than coverage simply because it is so much more easily measured, and because stem form is relatively uniform in cold and temperate climates. However, determinations of basal area and canopy coverage can lead to opposite conclusions as to relative dominance, for the basal area of a tree continues to increase until death, whereas the canopy, especially of shade-intolerant pioneers, declines over many years late in their lives.

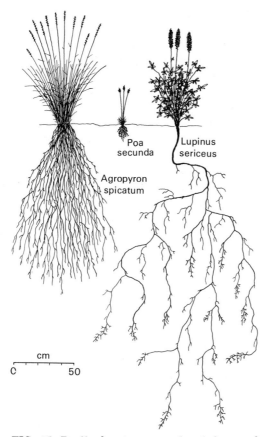

FIG. 15. Profile drawings, to scale, of shoot and root systems of three plants that grow in the same stand. Relative dominance based on canopy coverage, on dry weight of shoots, and on basal area would differ greatly. In selecting among bases for comparison one must decide which is the most meaningful. (Root systems redrawn from Weaver, 1917)

Variation in plant form is sometimes disconcerting when making coverage determinations, but it creates so many problems for basal area that the method is unsatisfactory as a basis for evaluating dominance throughout a phytocoenosis. Its major use is in special studies of limited scope.

Line interception.[228] Line interception is a special technique for obtaining coverage (or basal area), rather than a different concept. After a line has been stretched just above low-growing vegetation, an observer can follow along it and record the lengths of those segments of the line which cross individual plants. The sums of the measurements for each species, in relation to the total length of line studied, are then used as the basis for computing coverage percentages, the data being the exact equivalent of coverage as determined by two-dimensional plots, if in both cases coverage is based on an imaginary polygon drawn about the periphery of the undisturbed canopy.

The advantages of line interception must all be qualified. Owing to the irregular fragmentation of old individuals of caespitose grasses, line interception at the usual basal area height is a good means of determining basal area for such grasses, but then extending the method to other plant forms does not provide data valid for interspecific comparisons. While two stakes permit replacement of a line for repeated observations, several to many lines must be tallied to obtain coverage data as reliable as those obtained by relatively few two-dimensional plots arranged along one line. It is not easy to use the method for species that send up an abundance of slender shoots from subterranean rhizomes or roots, and it is not easy to determine which small plants are crossed by a line if the line cannot be placed close to the ground, so that small plants are commonly accorded arbitrary values and a uniform treatment of taxa is sacrificed.

Line interception is convenient only for canopies entirely below eye level, yet it can be used for overhead canopies. One can walk along the line while looking into a periscope from which hangs a plumb bob. When the edge of a canopy crosses the center of the viewing area, the position of the plumb bob allows accurate location of this point on the line that is being followed. More simple, yet apparently satisfactory methods of estimating line interception of overhead canopies have also been described.[7]

In addition to its use in evaluating species within one stand, line interception can be applied on a gross scale to study changes in the proportions of communities in a mosaic over a period of years. The study area is permanently marked off with parallel lines and the amount of community intercept is recorded from time to time, the data serving as a substitute for the more tedious method of making complete vegetation maps, yet serving well to show changes in the proportions of alternating communities.[210]

Volume.   In plankton communities volume is commonly obtained by multiplying the average size of the individual of a species by the numbers of individuals found in a given quantity of water. Application of this three-dimensional method to terrestrial vegetation has been very limited, however.

By measuring the heights and diameters of shoot systems, then calculating volumes by assuming a cylindrical form, dominance among the vascular plants of very open vegetation could be compared very effectively. In denser vegetation canopy coverage values might be weighted by a height factor, as pointed out earlier. This is an especially valuable technique for inventorying the amount of scattered shrubs available for forage.

For fleshy fungi, records have been kept of the numbers of sporophores per unit area, then this figure multiplied by the average volume of some representative specimens as determined by displacement in water. Such a technique may be useful in other connections, but it is not easily defended as a criterion of dominance, for mushrooms do not compete with each other or exert their major influence upon the environment by means of their fructifications. A much more meaningful criterion of dominance would be the volume of substrate occupied by the mycelium, and at present there is no easy means of making such a measurement, although radioactive tracers seem to offer possibilities.

Productivity. *Primary productivity* refers to the weight of dry matter produced in a given period by all the green plants growing in a given space. *Gross primary production* is the amount actually produced, but all we can measure is *net primary production,* a lower value owing to respiratory use by the plants while they are producing. Ideally, net primary production should include roots[54] as well as shoots, since from a low percentage to 85 percent of the dry weight of a green plant may be underground, but in practice attention is usually restricted to shoots (stems + leaves + flowers + fruits + seeds). When primary productivity is used as a measure of dominance, attention is focused on the yearly production of the different associated species. Its use in this connection implies that species producing the most dry matter are exerting the most influence on the ecosystem, with dominants channeling a greater share of environmental resources into their own bodies and largely determining the amount, character, and timing of litter cast.

The dry weight of herbs is commonly determined by laying out a plot, clipping all shoot material to the ground surface at one or more dates that allow an evaluation of each species at approximately the time it attains maximum dry weight, and discarding dead stalks left from the preceding year's growth. In the study of woody plants only the current season's elongation is removed, and, as with herbs, this is done when growth is completed.[360] Fresh weight of living plant tissue is of limited value owing to wide differences in degree of hydration throughout the day and season. Therefore the clipped material is usually air-dried quickly to minimize respiration loss, then desiccated to constant weight at $70°C$ so that dominance can be expressed as grams of ovendry material per square meter. Sometimes this value is then converted to carbon content or calorie content.[185]

The technique described above is applicable only to vegetation having a season of activity alternating with a season of dormancy. Where environment permits rapid and continuous overturn of matter, productivity must be measured by determining CO_2 use or O_2 release by whole shoots.

The use of productivity as a measure of dominance has an advantage in that it allows differentiation among species having equal coverage or basal area but different amounts of shoot tissue as a result of variation in height or denseness of foliage.

A serious limitation of the method is the limited accuracy, since it does not account for materials transported below ground, respiration loss, wood laid down on old stems, withering and loss of leaves or reproductive structures during the growing season prior to clipping, or losses due to consumption by insects, birds, mammals, fungi, etc., that the green plants are obviously supporting,[55] and which are offset to an unknown extent by the uptake and accumulation of salts.

Second, clipping is highly injurious to most plants, and in shrubs it greatly alters the ratio of new to old wood, these effects preventing subsequent use of the plots. Again, it is difficult but important to maintain a constant height of clipping for herbs. Most of the weight of the plant is near the ground, so that slight variations in height of clipping greatly influence the data. Some bunches of grass may be pedestalled as a result of loss of the surrounding topsoil, or frost lifting, or of soil accumulation among the tiller bases, so that care must be taken to establish a uniform technique at the beginning of study.

A final limitation is that plant texture (hard-leaved versus succulent) may strongly affect comparisons on a dry weight basis, in which case volume or coverage may yield more significant data.

In some vegetation types it is practical to use a mechanical clipper to denude a plot, mix the materials thoroughly in the laboratory, and separate a subsample for meticulous analysis. But this technique complicates separation of last year's straw from the current year's production, and since mechanical clippers do not cut plants at the soil surface, the productivity of low-growing species is underestimated.

Where a survey of grasslands must be so extensive that considerable accuracy on individual plots can be sacrificed to favor speed in covering a large area, estimation of weight by species in sample plots has been tried. Crews are trained in estimation, then every tenth plot or so is clipped and weighed, the results being used to correct the direction and degree of error in each person's estimates.[419, 463] Since weight is more closely related to forage yield than any other analysis, a fair amount of error can be tolerated in a rangeland inventory that provides weight data, yet even with maximum care the weight estimates of trained observers may vary 40 percent and group means may differ 10 percent

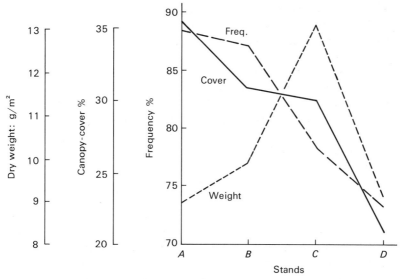

FIG. 16. Relationships among dry weight of shoots, canopy coverage, and frequency of *Poa secunda* at four locations along the eastern flank of the Cascade Mountains. Frequency is based on any inclusion of basal area in systematically distributed circular plots 1 dm² in area. Ovendry weights represent 5–7 m² areas from which plants were clipped immediately after the other measurements were made.

from the correct value.[397] The method cannot be considered a research technique.

A hope that has long been attractive is that a useful degree of correlation might be found between an attribute difficult to measure (e.g., dry weight) and another easy of evaluation (e.g., coverage), with obvious implications for economy of field time. However, success has been limited. Different attributes of vegetation do not vary together, each having different factors influencing its variability; hence close interrelationships are hardly to be expected[143, 149, 254, 357] (Fig. 16). The inaccuracies of most shortcut methods appear to fully cancel their advantages.[463]

Frequency.   A limitation of either density or dominance evaluations is that a species may be very well represented but occur only at places scattered over the stand, whereas the statistics suggest moderate representation throughout. Frequency, on the other hand, provides information about the uniformity of distribution without necessarily indicating how many or how much. It is defined as the percentage of occurrence of a species in a series of samples of uniform size contained in a single stand, the numbers and sizes of plants in each sample being ignored.

While two-dimensional plots are usually employed, segments of a line, or dimensionless points, may be used as observational units. In any case the percentage value obtained is primarily an expression of the probability of encountering a species from place to place.

Four bases of inclusion have been used. C. Raunkiaer, who originally developed the technique, included a plant in his plots only if one or more of its perennating buds fell within the boundaries of the plot (*life-form frequency*). Many have counted only those plants having the center of the stem or clump within the plot (*rooted frequency*). Others consider any plant with canopy coverage in the plot as included (*coverage frequency*). Finally, *basal frequency* counts any basal area as included. All of these variants yield different species ratings, and the morphology of the plant affects all except rooted frequency.

At first relatively large plots were used in frequency analyses, but then some advantages of small plots were discovered, and smaller and smaller sizes were tried. Since frequency as usually measured with two-dimensional plots is strongly influenced by both density and dispersion of individuals, if plot size is reduced until two individuals of the same species are rarely included in the same plot, the influence of dispersion is minimized and the frequency ratings of the species closely parallel their ratings on the basis of density (if plant center is the basis of recording) or coverage (if coverage is the basis of inclusion). In fact, when Raunkiaer developed the frequency method he looked on it primarily as a measure of the relative amounts of different species, rather than a criterion of ubiquity. As early as 1909 he discovered that $\frac{1}{100}$ m^2 plots gave frequency ratings that approximate density ratings more closely than do larger plots.[354] Later investigators, interested more in amount than in ubiquity, have used small plots extensively as measures of coverage or basal area.

For pasture evaluation in Holland, plugs $\frac{1}{400}$ m^2 (25 cm^2) are cut out of the sward and taken to the laboratory for analysis.[432] In North America, some investigators have used circular plots $\frac{3}{4}$ inch in diameter, as seen through a wire loop extending horizontally from the end of a vertical rod, which is used as a handle and held against a tape at fixed intervals.[236] A similar but much more convenient variant is to peer successively through a battery of tubes, or pairs of superimposed rings, which are kept at a constant height at each setting, and record presence or absence in the area that is visible.

Still smaller sampling units are represented by the tip of a rod, 0–5 mm in diameter, which is dropped successively through a row of holes in a bar that is suspended temporarily above vegetation.[401] This application is called *point frequency*, which is most appropriate if the tip of the rod is pointed, i.e., dimensionless. The unique advantage of the method is that litter and other features of the ground surface can be recorded where the rod strikes, and often such information is desirable. But usually point frequency is used to evaluate dominance among species.

In point frequency one can record only the first hit (which over-emphasizes tall plants), or all contacts of the descending rod (placing tall and short plants on a par), or only those hits made within a centimeter of the ground (which overemphasizes prostrate plants), or one can simply list all taxa hit during one drop of the rod. Field records can then be tallied counting species contacted at all pin drops without ignoring drops that make no contacts (the frequency method in its original form) or as percentages based on just those points where at least one plant was hit (giving percentage composition but not giving any clue as to ubiquity of distribution).

Point frequency has proved to have many limitations. There are so many possible ways of recording data and computing values that most studies are individualistic and therefore not comparable. In no sense does point frequency evaluate spheres of influence as does canopy coverage, for a rod descending between closely spaced leaves might as well have fallen on an area totally devoid of vegetation. On account of this ease with which vertical rods may pass through a canopy without making contact, point-frequency values give increasing values as leaves grow through summer, then decreasing values as foliage starts to wither —a problem much more acute than in methods where discontinuities in the canopy are ignored. Also, the greater the diameter of a blunt rod, the more contacts and the higher the estimate, this effect varying disproportionately among species because vertical gaps between the leaves of forbs are smaller than the gaps between graminoid leaves.[465] Only by sharpening the rod and confining attention to the tip can the effects of its diameter and of plant form be eliminated; then the data reflect foliar cover directly.

Even with pointed rods, plants with horizontal leaves are evaluated to the maximum warranted by their LAI, whereas those with vertical leaves are greatly underestimated, and erectness differs not only with the species but with the hour and season. Thus the apparent order of importance among species varies according to the shape of leaf, angle of leaf, and stage of seasonal development, with errors sometimes rising to 300 percent. This strong bias in favor of horizontal blades can be neutralized in large measure by tilting the bar so that the rods descend at an angle of about 32° from vertical; but then since leaves may not face all compass directions equally, the compass direction of the bar must be rotated evenly among the settings used to evaluate one stand.[464]

Still other problems must be pointed out. When used to compare all vascular plants in a stand, the method of tallying all hits is not valid if the community contains caespitose graminoids, since it is impossible to count the numerous hits that are made in the center of the bunch, which of course must not be parted. If there is any wind (and wind is highly characteristic of open grasslands where the technique would be most useful) the foliage is in constant agitation so that reproducible results are difficult to obtain. Hence the method is seldom used except in swards where the foliage is less than about 15 cm tall.

About 400 points are a bare minimum to sample adequately the most common species, and with vegetation that is open or is taxonomically complex, or where one wishes to get a fair appraisal of nearly all the species in the community, many thousands of points are required.[457] Thus, although points can be observed and recorded quickly, the numbers required cancel this advantage. Furthermore, so small a percentage of the land surface is actually sampled that many uncommon plants are completely missed, and these cannot safely be ignored even in applied ecology. Finally, there can be a surprising difference in the data recorded by different observers, even for identical locations of point-frequency rods.[152]

The most important use of point frequency is in range or pasture management where by frequent reassessment of basal area with this technique (i.e., counting only hits at the ground level), one can easily determine whether the amount of a key species of caespitose grass is maintaining itself or declining. This check can be made regardless of the degree to which current grazing has removed foliage.

Let us return to a consideration of frequency involving relatively large observational units. Among data obtained by sample plots, a frequency value of 100 percent signifies that plot size exceeds the maximal size of gaps between individuals of the species. It should be apparent that plot size can be increased to the point that even thinly scattered species get ratings of 100 percent. Therefore, frequency is not simply a character of the species, but a character of the species plus the sampling technique. Not unless frequency is determined with a sharpened rod is the effect of size of the observational unit removed.

Rarely would two species be expected to have exactly equal probabilities of occurrence over a stand. Therefore, plots may be considered too large for the type of community studied if more than one, or at least a very few taxa, have frequencies of 100 percent, for so large a plot fails to show differences that smaller plots would probably reveal. On the other hand, the smaller the plot the greater the number of relatively rare species that is missed. Therefore, a case can be made for keeping plot size as large as possible without throwing more than one, or at most a few, species in an undifferentiated 100 percent class.

Raunkiaer, using circular plots of 0.1 m², divided frequencies into five equal classes (1–20 percent, 21–40, etc.), then calculated the percentage of species in a stand which fell into each of these classes (Fig. 17). He

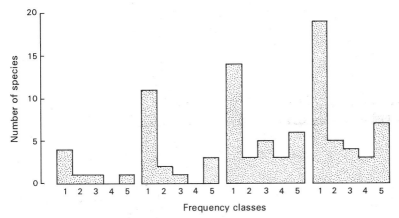

FIG. 17. Frequency class distribution in four stands of steppe vegetation with varied species diversity. Frequencies were based on canopy coverage in forty plots, 20 × 50 cm each, in each stand.

found that usually more than half of the species fall into the 1–20 percent class, from which the conclusion may be drawn that most species are present in very small numbers or are far from evenly dispersed. The second largest class included species with 81–100 percent frequencies. These are plants which are either very uniformly dispersed or have very high densities. The curve that can be made by plotting frequency distributions as five classes is thus J-shaped, and this phenomenon has proved remarkably consistent for natural communities of wide variety. So long as the 81–100 percent class (Class 5) is larger than Class 4, the phenomenon has often been looked on as evidence that practically all plots fell within a homogeneous stand.[345] However, the fundamental significance of the J-shaped curve is questionable.[286] First, a single species may overwhelm all others to the extent that it becomes the sole representative of Class 5 and the curve cannot turn up at the end. The uniformity of distribution and completeness of dominance of this species would seem a good indication of homogeneity, despite the lack of a J-shaped curve. Second, if plot size is progressively enlarged, the size of Class 5 increases until practically all taxa are included, whereas reduction in size pulls all taxa into Class 1. Finally, the J-shaped curve has been obtained from plots scattered over a landscape irrespective of vegetation types.

Sociability.[196, 256] Whereas frequency expresses the relation of individuals to different parts of space, *sociability* (or *dispersion*) expresses the relation of individuals to each other. The term sociability will be used here in deference to its long and widespread use in synecology, despite its anthropomorphic connotation.

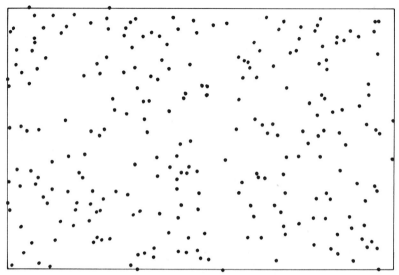

FIG. 18. Random distribution in space as illustrated by the positions of the first raindrops on a flat surface at the start of a shower.

In a random pattern, the location of each unit has not been influenced by the location of any other unit. There is a slight tendency toward grouping at many places, with poorer representation in the remaining space (Fig. 18). Such a distribution pattern is uncommon in natural communities, except where a new and uniform habitat has been laid bare. Here the first plants to colonize are distributed in accord with the random manner in which their disseminules find lodgement, providing environmental variation is low in relation to ecologic amplitude of the plant, and providing uneven microrelief does not cause seeds to collect in depressions.

Usually the plants representing a species tend to be more definitely grouped (resulting in a *contagious* distribution), this resulting from (1) the clustering of offspring about their parents, which is particularly evident where dissemination is relatively inefficient, or reproduction is largely vegetative, or (2) differential lodgement of disseminules, or differential germination and survival, resulting from variations in microenvironment,[237, 333] or (3) the influence of one species (e.g., a nitrogen-fixer, or a plant with an elevated canopy that casts a pool of shade) in creating islands of environment especially favorable (Figs. 19, 20) for other plants or for their own offspring,[451] or (4) the influence of one species which through the production of shade, toxins, etc., prevents other species from growing in certain areas, or (5) many seedlings growing where an old plant has recently died, leaving an opening.

FIG. 19. Expansion by layering of *Abies lasiocarpa* which seeded under *Pinus albicaulis* after the latter had become established in the forest-tundra ecotone. Montana.

FIG. 20. *Phlox longifolia* showing positive association with *Agropyron spicatum* in consequence of its near elimination by jackrabbits wherever its foliage is easily seen and available.

In contrast to random or contagious distributions, plants may show less tendency toward grouping than in a random pattern—a *regular* distribution. Thus in open communities of arid lands, or in dense pure stands of trees, the individuals may be rather uniformly spaced as a result of (1) competitive elimination, (2) toxins produced by older plants that prevent establishment of their seedlings within their own spheres of influence, or (3) damping-off fungi that thin a stand of seedlings to the point that distance between individuals limits the activity of the fungus.[208]

The sociability of a species may vary from one association to another. Also, in the same stand, different age classes of the same species commonly differ in their sociability.[94] For example, tree seedlings in a forest may be strongly clustered, reflecting the importance of variation in light (or other factors) which permits groups of seedlings to get started at scattered places. Older individuals, however, may show little if any clustering, because most openings in the canopy are too small to permit more than one out of a small cluster of seedlings to mature, and the locations of these openings may be determined by chance.[113] Distribution patterns may also be compound, with the individuals collected together in groups having random or regular patterns within, whereas the groups are scattered at random.[372] It seems generally true that contagion weakens progressively as succession advances.

Distribution patterns exhibited by different species seem of infinite variety, and as yet little progress has been made in classifying types of sociability. The simplest classification would be trifurcate—recognizing random scattering, then patterns in which the individuals are more uniformly or less uniformly distributed. The awkward feature of such a logical system arises from the fact that by far the majority of plant species fall in the contagious class,* among which different degrees of contagiousness are undifferentiated.

An alternative that has been widely used is to rate the species in a stand subjectively according to the following scale of sociability classes:

So 1—growing singly
So 2—slightly grouped
So 3—in small patches
So 4—in large patches
So 5—in essentially continuous population

Since these ratings are assigned the plants simply by inspection of the stand, and suitable limits for the groups are matters of opinion, there is considerable room for variation in interpretation of the definitions

* It is chiefly for this reason that density, dominance, and frequency ratings bear no necessary relation to each other, as would be true if dispersion were random.

among investigators. The technique would seem to have limited value except at the reconnaissance level. A more objective method is clearly desirable.

If in a stand, one species has a low rating according to its rooted frequency, but occurs near the top of a list based on density, it must be represented by many individuals aggregated in clumps.[119] Therefore an index of sociability[456] can be calculated for each species as:

$$\frac{\text{average density per plot}}{\text{frequency for the same plot size, expressed as a decimal}}$$

The higher this index the greater the degree of sociability. In Table 5

Table 5 **Index of sociability as derived from density and frequency of shrubs in a forest dominated by Acer saccharum and Tilia americana**

Species	Average Density per Plot	Frequency, %	Index of Sociability
Parthenocissus vitacea	23.52	68	34.6
Celastrus scandens	21.76	16	136.0
Sambucus pubens	4.48	48	9.3
Menispermum canadense	4.48	12	36.6
Ribes cynosbati	3.20	32	10.0
Zanthoxylum americanum	2.56	4	64.0
Rhus radicans	0.96	4	24.0
Vitis vulpina	0.48	12	4.0
Rubus occidentalis	0.48	4	12.0

NOTE: There are 25 plots, 2 × 8 m each. Frequency is converted to a decimal, then divided into density.
SOURCE: Daubenmire, 1936.

it will be noted that *Celastrus,* with low frequency and high density, has a high index of sociability which reflects effective vegetative reproduction following the rare establishment of a seedling. On the other hand *Vitis,* although bird-disseminated like *Celastrus,* becomes established almost as often but there is no vegetative reproduction, with a result that isolated individuals occur scattered over the forest and the index is low. This method allows fine quantitative distinctions, but it depends on counting individuals, which is not easy with many species, and depends on frequency, the value of which varies according to plot size. While the method is thus worthless for general use throughout a phytocoenosis, it still could be very useful in comparing the behavior of one species in different ecosystems, providing the sampling procedure is kept uniform. Coverage/frequency might be more generally useful.

A number of biometric methods of evaluating dispersion have been proposed.[196] The relative merits of any method must be judged by the extent to which it provides information on the sizes of the aggregates, their numbers per unit area, their dynamism, and their ecology. Our fundamental problem in sociability is to understand propagation effectivity, senescence, attractions and repulsions, these being the net effects of balances among processes that allow patterns to originate, then maintain themselves or decline.

The discussion thus far has concerned the spatial relations among individuals representing a single species. But as indicated earlier, there is another aspect of sociability where one species has a favorable or unfavorable effect on the establishment of another.[409, 451] Such relationships might be demonstrated, or discovered, as follows.[188, 391]

If species A occurs in 50 percent of all plots in a stand, and species B in 50 percent of them, then on purely mathematical grounds one would expect the two to occur together in 25 percent of all plots. But should the value exceed 25 percent considerably, a tendency toward correlated distribution is indicated, and vice versa. Again, if the plots containing A are segregated from all others, some of the other species may prove to be wholly in one group of plots or the other.

The results of such an analysis are significant only when a large number of plots is taken into account, and when great care is exercised in their interpretation. Species A may show negative correlation with B only because individuals of A are larger (in relation to plot size) and occupy an area so thoroughly as to leave no room for B. Species B and C may show positive correlation only as a result of being crowded into the same interspaces between plants of A. Therefore, if the size of plot does not much exceed that of the largest plant under study, some of the relationships may be purely mechanical.

Much interest is being directed to sociability at the present time, especially in regions where none but disturbed vegetation is available for study and contagious patterns are especially conspicuous.

Life-forms.[2]   Classification of plants according to *growth-form*, i.e., according to the size, morphology, and duration of the vegetative body, irrespective of taxonomic relations, early came into use simply as a means of describing vegetation, as when one states that chaparral is dominated by broad-leaved evergreen shrubs. But after Darwin's evolution concept was expounded, some botanists were prompted to emphasize only those growth-forms that could be interpreted as adaptations. These came to be known as *life-forms*, and their use was developed as a means of quantitatively relating vegetation structure to climate.

Such a concept must recognize that not only are some structural features unrelated to climate (e.g., excurrent versus deliquescent branching habit, thorniness, smoothness of bark, stilt roots, soft-wooded versus hard-wooded stems, etc.), but that many adaptations of climatic significance cannot be taken into account because they are not reflected in morphology (e.g., frost hardiness, drought tolerance). Yet the nature of the vegetative shoot seems more closely related to climate than is any other evident character of plants, and a great many studies have convincingly demonstrated its usefulness in this connection. This relationship may be interpreted as the net result of evolution and competitive advantage operating on a variety of growth forms over a long period under closely similar climatic conditions.

Annuals have the simplest method of withstanding unfavorable climate by enduring it as seeds. So long as the embryonic plant remains in the seed coat, it retains a high degree of immunity to climatic vicissitudes, but it has often been demonstrated that this immunity is rapidly lost as germination gets under way.

Perennial herbs are fairly tolerant of climatic extremes after their aerial parts die down at the onset of a cold or dry season, for subterranean organs have the advantage of a well-tempered environment within the soil.

Among deciduous woody plants, the aerial stems must endure the vicissitudes of the most critical season, and in evergreen plants even the leaves are exposed to the entire annual cycle of weather. The taller such plants the more vulnerable they are.

The essential soundness of this adaptational interpretation of plant morphology is attested by the well-documented facts that (1) of the weeds that have spread from the tropics into temperate latitudes, practically all are annuals, (2) among herbs, a severe freeze may kill plants with overwintering buds near the surface, whereas more deeply placed buds escape damage, (3) species normally woody, or at least perennial, may become herbs if not annuals at the cold or dry limits of their ranges, (4) tall plants become relatively dwarfed in dry or cold climates, (5) evergreens are often injured by weather extremes that do no harm to deciduous plants, and (6) some species are evergreen in moist climates but regularly deciduous in dry climates.

Geographic evidence also supports the interpretation in that there is a significant degree of uniformity in the life-forms of plants within a given climatic type wherever it reappears over the face of the globe, and the prevailing structural types are related to climate in a manner agreeing with the above interpretations. In addition, the abundance of lianas and vascular epiphytes always increases with approach toward the wet, frost-free climates.[229, 319]

Finally, paleobotany has demonstrated that the tree life-form dominated most of the earth's surface in early Cenozoic times when climates were relatively warm and moist nearly everywhere, with shrubs, perennial herbs, and annuals appearing and becoming dominant at successively later periods when cold and dry regions developed.

The most useful life-form classification is one developed by C. Raunkiaer between 1903 and 1907. His emphasis was on the degree of protection afforded the renewal buds of shoot apices by their position in relation to the soil surface during the season of minimal plant activity. Although many details of his classification cannot be defended on physiologic grounds and have been dropped by most users of the system, the following major categories have gained universal acceptance:

Therophytes   annuals in which the renewal bud is protected by a seed coat

Geophytes   renewal buds well covered by soil, as in most cormous, bulbous, tuberous, and many rhizomatous plants

Hemicryptophytes   renewal buds barely embedded in the surface of the soil so that their protection from climatic extremes depends on litter or snow cover

Chamaephytes   prostrate plants or low shrubs with buds a little above the soil, but not over 25 cm above

Phanerophytes   taller shrubs and trees, subdivided into:

> *Nanophanerophytes*   0.25–2 m tall
> *Microphanerophytes*   2–8 m tall
> *Mesophanerophytes*   8–30 m tall
> *Megaphanerophytes*   over 30 m tall

Epiphytes   including vascular types only

Raunkiaer also proposed a *stem-succulent* category which some workers have accepted. Others have expanded the category to include *leaf-succulents,* while still others have abolished the succulent class and divided such plants among other groups according to their height, as intended in the above version of the classification. Also, his hydrophyte-helophyte group (aquatics and emergents, respectively) has dubious value in any classification intended to reflect climatic hazards. Some hydrophytes are therophytes, others hemicryptophytes or chamaephytes in relation to the pond bottom, and the perennating buds of all enjoy equal protection under water, which is superior to the protection afforded by drained soil. This group might be lumped with geophytes or, better yet, be ignored entirely, as was done above.

In using this classification Raunkiaer determined the percentage of species representing each of the categories in a given flora. The resultant series of percentages is appropriately called a *life-form spectrum.* Raunkiaer devised a *normal spectrum* based on 1000 species systematically chosen from the earth's entire flora, this being intended to serve as a base for evaluating the kind and degree of specialization in each regional flora. It was demonstrated that areas with similar climates had spectra that are correspondingly similar (Table 6).

Several generalizations may be drawn from Table 6. In all climates

Table 6 *Compilation of representative analyses of floras according to Raunkiaer's life-form classification*

Natural Vegetation		Geographic Region	Epi.	Phanerophytes				Cham.	Hemi.	Geo.	Ther.	Succ.
				Meg.	Mes.	Mic.	Nan.					
Tundra	Arctic	Iceland					2	13	54	10	11	
		St. Lawr. Is., Alaska						23	61	11	1	
		Spitsbergen					1	22	60	13	2	
	Alpine	Alps					3	22	64	7	4	
		Olympic Mountains, Washington						21	69	9		
		San Francisco Peak, Arizona						10	83	2	4	
Temperate mesophytic forest	Evergreen	Sitka, Alaska			3	3	5	7	60	10	5	
		Olympic Mountains, Washington			15			3	43	25	14	
	Deciduous	Denmark			1	3	3	3	50	11	18	
		Connecticut			5	6	4	2	49	13	12	
		Mississippi			9	5	4	3	49	12	13	
Tropical mesophytic forest (rain forest)		Seychelle Islands	3		10	23	24	6	12	3	16	1
		Queensland, Australia			96			2		2		
		Virgin Islands	1		5	23	30	12	9	3	14	2
Monsoon forest		Matheran, India			34			23	10	5	15	
		Tuticorim, India			3	20		28	8	3	37	
		M'war, India	3		29	20		20	3	3	13	
Chaparral		Argentario, Italy			2	4	6	6	29	9	42	
		Crete				4	5	13	27	10	38	
		Madeira Islands				1	14	7	24		51	
Steppe		Danube Valley					7	5	55	10	23	
		Toole, Utah					2	23	46	3	14	
		Akron, Colorado						19	58	8	15	
Desert		Tucson, Arizona			18			11	24		47	
		Central Sahara					9	13	15	5	56	
		Trans-Caspian Asia					10	7	27	9	41	
"Normal spectrum": average for world			3		8	18	15	9	26	4	13	2

NOTE: Since hydrophyte-heliophyte percentages in the original publications are omitted here, the percentages do not all add up to 100. Some sources probably did not recognize succulents as a distinctive category.

having much freezing weather, hemicryptophytes appear to be the most successful life-form, making up 43 percent or more of the floras. Phanerophytes make up 57 percent or more of floras only in wet tropical forests, with the percentage dropping to 49 percent or lower even in the closely related monsoonal forest. Therophytes are well represented only in climates with a dry season.

Although Raunkiaer applied his life-form classification to the study of only macroclimates, limited tests in temperate mesophytic forest regions have shown that life-form spectra for the microclimates of north-facing and south-facing slopes tend to differ as between moist and dry macroclimates.[296]

While the solid values of life-form analyses cannot be denied, the concept has several shortcomings. First, the low phanerophyte percentages for west central Europe, as compared with southeastern North America and east central Asia, suggest climatic differences greater than really exist. Rather than reflecting modern climatic limitations, the poor phanerophyte flora of Europe is a consequence of more rigorous conditions during the Ice Age which severely purged a flora that had formerly been rich in tree species.

Second, most life-forms are represented in most climates, which shows that life-form makes but a limited contribution to climatic adaptability. Third, contiguous communities may have sharply different life-form spectra, with no evidence of corresponding difference in microclimates, and all this nonclimatic element of variation is submerged in one average when the spectrum of a large area is calculated. Each association in a vegetation mosaic may have its own distinctive spectrum (Table 7). Fourth, although Raunkiaer's system achieved its success by

Table 7   **Life-form analyses of two steppe associations**

Association	Nan.	Cham.	Hemi.	Geo.	Ther.
Festuca idahoensis–Symphoricarpos albus	2	4	34	42	18
Agropyron spicatum–Poa secunda		4	15	30	52

NOTE: Both associations are characterized by deep, well-drained loess and gently sloping topography and have climates that are closely similar except for the amount of precipitation. Median annual precipitation where the upper stand occurs is about 500 mm, with the lower stand representing 370 mm.

uniform emphasis on one aspect of life-form, other morphologic features (especially the percentage of evergreen species, and abundance of vegetative propagation) are also related to climate and thereby tend to be unduly ignored.

Finally, Raunkiaer noted that in a classification which is floristic rather than vegetational in perspective, abundant species contribute no more than rare ones to the percentages, and in this sense the spectrum does not completely reflect the relative success of life-form types. This led him to weight life-form with frequency, e.g., the frequency values for all species of geophytes were added, then the geophyte sum expressed as a percentage of all such sums for all life-forms in the vegetation, etc. Others have weighted life-forms with some measure of dominance, such as coverage.[296] But the results of such weightings still leave much to be desired, for the same product can now be obtained from many different combinations of single values. For example, twenty species of geophytes, each with 1 percent frequency, yield the same percentage as one geophyte with 20 percent frequency, and this difference in community composition is too important to be hidden.

There has been some interest in developing special life-form classifications for mosses.[36, 201, 227, 390]

Leaf Size and Margination. The leaf, as well as the plant as a whole, has its own measure of morphologic variation that can be related to climate independently of life-form.

Large leaf blades are most frequently encountered in warm, wet climates of the tropics, whereas small blades characterize vegetation of very dry or cold regions. Even the species of parasitic Loranthaceae in the tropics show reduction in leaf size in progressing from wet to dry climates.[447]

The ecologic significance of leaf size which might be inferred from these facts finds solid support in experimental ecology in that the size attained by an expanding blade is greatly influenced by the availability of warmth and moisture.

Leaf size becomes amenable to statistical expression and correlation with climate if species are classified according to the area of the surface presented by a typical leaf (or its ecologic equivalent, a leaflet), and the percentage of the flora falling into each of a series of classes is calculated. Raunkiaer's delimitation of leaf size classes, proposed for this purpose, is as follows:

Leptophylls—smaller than 25 mm^2
Nanophylls—25–225 mm^2
Microphylls—225–2025 mm^2
Mesophylls—2,025–18,225 mm^2
Macrophylls—18,225–164,025 mm^2
Megaphylls—larger than 164,025 mm^2

Many leaf blades can be categorized rapidly by comparison with Fig. 21. Lobed leaves, however, must often be measured by use of a planimeter or by weighing paper patterns of specimens that are carefully selected as representative.

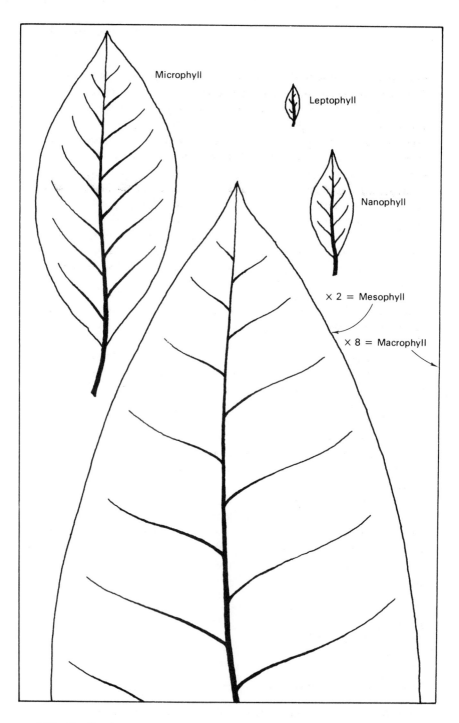

FIG. 21. Graphic representation of the maximum sizes of leaf size classes. Only half of the area of a mesophyll is indicated, and only one-eighth of a macrophyll. Still larger leaves are megaphylls.

Although leaf size analysis was originally intended to be used in comparing whole floras to evaluate degrees of climatic similarity of the regions involved, its value might be increased, as for life-forms, by dropping from consideration abnormally wet and abnormally dry habitats (Table 8).

Table 8 **Leaf size analyses of two steppe associations**

Association	Lep.	Nan.	Mic.	Mes.
Festuca idahoensis–Symphoricarpos albus	16	40	34	10
Agropyron spicatum–Poa secunda	48	41	11	

NOTE: These are the same steppe associations as those of Table 7.

Another character of leaves that is correlated with climate is the percentage of entire-leaved species among the dicot trees in a flora. The value is very high in tropical rain forests (90 percent in the Amazon lowlands), and very low in mesophytic forests of temperate latitudes (10 percent in east-central North America), or at high altitudes in the tropics.[18,379] Paleobotanists have used this relationship as an index by which to align floras in time and space sequences representing intergradations between moist temperate and moist tropical conditions in past geologic ages.

Entire leaves prevail also among microphyllous plants of desertic climates, but for lack of fossilization, and the pronounced microphylly in such environments, this phenomenon creates no problem in paleontologic interpretations. Oddly enough, the leaf margins of herbaceous plants show no broad geographic relationships to climate, as do those of shrubs, and especially those of trees, but again the situation is innocuous for paleobotany since herbaceous plants are rarely represented in fossil floras.

Whereas life-form and leaf size may be interpreted as adaptational, and the interpretation buttressed by experimental evidence, leaf margin correlations with environment, striking as they are, present an enigma since there is no hint of adaptational relationship.

Still other characters of leaves, e.g., thickness, venation, arrangement of stomata, etc., may prove to have significance with respect to climate when more fully studied.[155]

Dissemination types.[118] The prevailing agent of dissemination often differs from one vegetation type to another, and since this characteristic is so clearly related to other components of the ecosystem, it is a significant phase of vegetation analysis. As with life-form and leaf size, the technique is one of establishing categories having similar ecologic significance, then preparing a spectrum showing the percentage of species falling into each category.

It would be ideal to have the categories reflect the actual *agent* normally responsible for dissemination, but to do this accurately for even one community would require meticulous study of each component species over a long period. An alternative would be to base categories on the *morphology* of the reproductive part, and draw inferences as to the most probable agents involved (Table 9). There are bound to be

Table 9   **Classification of dissemination types of terrestrial plants, arranged somewhat in order of decreasing efficiency**

Classification According to Agent	Classification According to Morphology	Examples
Anemochore	Plumose	*Salix, Taraxacum*
	Minute	*Orchis, Pteridium*
	Winged	*Pinus, Tilia*
	Tumbleweed	*Salsola, Physalis*
	Catapult	*Iris, Papaver*
Zoochore	Fleshy	*Juniperus, Rubus*
	Nutlike	*Pinus, Quercus*
	Adhesive	*Adenocaulon, Arctium*
Hydrochore	Buoyant	*Nuphar, Elodea, Eichhornia*
	Splash-cup	*Marchantia, Nidularia*
Autochore	Expulsive	*Impatiens, Viola*
	Stoloniferous	*Ammophila, Fragaria*
Nonadapted		*Convolvulus arvensis*

errors in such interpretations, for there are known examples of function being unrelated to form in the way man's logic would suggest: the bur of *Xanthium* is disseminated chiefly by running water; the comose achene of *Artemisia tridentata* is readily disseminated on the fur of animals, etc. However, it would appear that despite some errors, a spectrum involving interpretations of morphology would probably give a rather significant evaluation of the dispersal ecology of the community since the proportion of errors should not be great.

A problem of a different type arises when a species has more than one effective means of dissemination. To discover which agent is usually the more effective would be a formidable assignment, so it has been suggested that where a plant has two effective means of dispersal (e.g., stolons and berries in *Fragaria*), each should contribute half a unit to the respective categories when the community spectrum is being constructed.

Dissemination types may be tallied separately for the different layers or synusiae of one phytocoenosis. The value of this practice is suggested by the fact that categories adapted to long-distance dissemination by wind are mostly confined to the tallest stratum.[250]

The fact is well established although not quantitatively documented that low, open communities characterizing early successional sequences of humid regions have more mobile disseminules than do climaxes.

• • •

In a manner parallel with life-form, leaf type, and dispersal analyses, classifications of the plants in a community might profitably be made on the basis of pollinating mechanisms, flower color,[447] or underground organs.[72, 73, 442]

Productivity. One may determine the annual dry matter production of the different species of green plants in a community and consider the results as evaluations of relative dominance, as discussed earlier. Also, the individual values can be summed for all the species and the result considered a measure of the net effectivity of the environment for dry-matter production. Total production, varying from about 0–7000 $gm/m^2/year$, is at maximum in environments that are continually warm, moist, and well supplied with nutrients, and where the plant community is evergreen and shades the ground thoroughly. Since production serves as a very important biologic yardstick for evaluating the relative favorableness of a habitat, it is a most significant attribute of an ecosystem. Rather than use ovendry weights of the plant organs, one can go a step farther and determine the caloric content of the harvested material, then calculate the efficiency of use of the total incoming supply of solar energy, providing this is likewise measured.

Successive determinations of the weight of the standing crop are sometimes made at weekly or semimonthly intervals to show the seasonal distribution of photosynthetic activity of the phytocoenosis as a whole.

Turnover is a term useful in these studies to denote the time elapsing between the production and complete decay of an organism. Rate of increase in weight of consumers and decomposers represents *secondary productivity*. Turnover and secondary production are additional functional attributes of an ecosystem that deserve characterization.

Phenology. Periodicity refers to the changing phases of activity of an organism that are repeated each cycle of the seasons, such as the development of new foliage, pollination, root growth, seed dissemination, etc. The nature of these activities is determined by genetic constitution, but the activity is set in motion by changes in light, heat, and moisture supplies. The study of biologic periodicity in relation to the seasonal sequence of climatic factors is called *phenology*.

Since the phasic development of each species in the community must have at least minimal conformity with the climatic rhythms of the habitat, group phenology provides a convincing clue to the relative importance of moisture and temperature at different seasons.

To express the phenology of an association requires tabulation for each species of the dates of various events, such as the beginning and end of the period when foliage is photosynthetically active, the period of flowering (using pollination as the criterion), etc. From this tabulation one can construct curves showing the percentage of species in leaf, in flower, or dormant, as these vary through the year. Graphs showing climatic trends may then be compared. Different synusiae or layers of one association may show remarkably distinctive periods of develop-ment, and therefore deserve separate sets of curves (Fig. 4). As with life-form analyses, it has been suggested that the basic data weighted with dominance ratings might be even more meaningful.

Vitality and vigor.   Studies of *vitality*, i.e., the reproductive success of a plant, can provide much information on its autecology and succes-sional status. Using the following classification, one can compare either the same species in different places or different species in the same stand:

Vi 1   plants which germinate, but die soon without reproducing
Vi 2   plants which linger after germination, but cannot reproduce
Vi 3   plants reproducing, but only vegetatively
Vi 4   plants reproducing sexually, but rather feebly by this method
Vi 5   plants reproducing very well sexually

Classes 1 and 2 represent species whose occurrence in the community is made possible only by the occurrence of other habitats within dissemi-nation range where their vitality class is either 4 or 5. Weed seedlings from roadsides often appear in stabilized vegetation where they die so young as to pass unnoticed for the most part. They illustrate Vi 1. Some trees at alpine timberline maintain their populations only by means of disseminules brought up from the forest below by occasional strong updrafts (Vi 2). Class 3 may include some successful dominants, such as *Parthenocissus* in the undergrowth of *Acer-Tilia* forests in central Minnesota, yet any species that lacks the ability to produce seeds is somewhat at a disadvantage, at least in an evolutionary sense. It is common for plants of forest undergrowth to have vitality wavering be-tween classes 3 and 4 until the tree layer is removed by cutting or burning; then these plants flower and fruit abundantly until a new canopy develops. Obligate sciophytes, however, may decline in vitality, if they do not perish, during that phase of the cycle when the facultative sciophytes are flowering so abundantly.

Closely related to vitality is the concept of *vigor*, which refers to the relative size and health of the individual without reference to its repro-ductive success. They are distinctive concepts since vitality and vigor may vary independently. Neither bears any necessary relation to domi-nance or density.

Since the expansion of cells in the vegetative body is sensitive to the general level of favorableness of environment for a plant, simply the average height of individuals in different habitats provides a graduated scale of vigor. Thus the rate of height growth of trees, or the height they maintain rather constantly after maturity, has long been used by foresters as a measure of the productivity of the land for a given kind of tree, and the height growth of *Pteridium* fronds is likewise useful in some regions as a measure of environmental potentiality.[258] In other connections foliage color, diameters of clones, size of leaves, etc., may be useful criteria of vigor, hence a standard system for expressing vigor is not practical.

A serious limitation to the vigor concept, and to some extent to vitality also, is the tendency toward ecotypic specialization in different habitat types, and possibly even at different stages of succession.[127] Thus, without a great amount of careful experimentation one never knows the extent to which vigor and vitality ratings are an expression of genetic variability as opposed to more direct environmental influences. Only comparisons within one habitat type and at roughly equivalent successional stages can be accepted without much question.

The vitality and vigor of one species commonly vary independently on the same habitat at different stages of succession, and herein lies the practical value of the concepts. In managed vegetation periodic re-classifications of plants as to vitality and vigor may reveal incipient successional tendencies, for trends toward decline or increase become evident in these attributes before other analytic techniques may reveal them. In this way the net effects of management practices may be assessed and corrective measures taken while it is still feasible to do so, or at least plans can be made to accommodate the predicted change. Rare species may respond more readily in this way than the dominants.

The remarkable flexibility of plants (but not of animals) regarding their ability to reduce size and thereby maintain high population density under adverse conditions must be a distinct advantage in allowing the perpetuation of a wide range of biotypes.

Techniques of Summarizing Analytic Data

Punched cards and computers are of great value in the analysis, storage, and retrieval of stand data,[30, 151] but there are so many attributes of ecosystems deserving study that the problem of condensing the information in a form suitable for communication is a formidable one. Direct fusion of certain analyses is one of the possibilities that has been tried.

One attempt in this direction has been to allow 100 points for the density of all individuals in the stand, these being divided among the species in proportion to actual population counts, with the same procedure followed for dominance and frequency. The relative density, dominance, and frequency ratings are then summed separately for each species and referred to as their "importance values," the grand sum of which for the stand is always 300.

But the question may be raised of whether density, and especially frequency, have any necessary bearing on the "importance" of species as components of an ecosystem. In the steppe vegetation of eastern Washington the relative importance of *Agropyron spicatum* and *Draba verna* may be 100:0.01 on a productivity basis, but on a density basis the relation is reverse. *Agropyron* exerts overwhelming control over the remainder of the biocoenosis, yet *Draba* has by far the greater population density and is far more uniformly present over the stand, and so would have a much higher "importance value" by the above summation method. These reversals of ratings should be emphasized, not obscured (Table 10).

Table 10   **Ratings of grasses in the native steppe near Ravia, Oklahoma, according to different types of analyses**

Species	Relative Productivity	Relative Density	Relative Frequency	Sums ("Importance Values")
Sorghastrum nutans	46.5	26.0	23.3	95.8
Andropogon scoparius	17.4	13.7	12.5	43.6
Andropogon gerardi	9.3	2.8	4.2	16.3
Panicum virgatum	5.5	2.5	3.7	11.7
Sporobolus asper	3.9	5.0	5.8	14.7
Manisuris cylindrica	3.7	6.3	7.9	17.9
Aristida oligantha	1.1	13.9	11.7	26.7

NOTE: Note that *Andropogon gerardi* produces almost 9 times as much dry matter per year as *Aristida*, with correspondingly greater use of environmental resources, yet it appears scarcely more than half as "important" as the latter.
SOURCE: Penfound, 1963.

Note also that while density and dominance are absolute characters of the stand, frequency has a somewhat questionable status since size and shape of sample plots affect this statistic, and by fusing all three analyses, density and dominance tend to be degraded. Even density is an arbitrary value for certain species and for this reason should not be fused with other data. Then from the standpoint of animals in the ecosystem, a plant may be much more important if highly aggregated, but the resultant low frequency value of the species would detract from its "importance value." The "importance value" of a species can be the sum of any of hundreds of different combinations of density, domi-

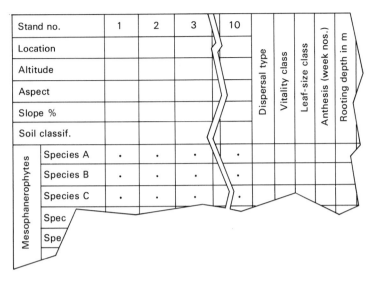

FIG. 22. Synecologic data for one association can be rather concisely summarized on a form such as this. The environmental data that are pertinent depend on the particular situation. For example, salinity or depth to water table might be critical. Coverage percentage would be entered to the left of the dot, with frequency or sociability to the right. If presence in the stand but outside the sampling system is indicated simply by a plus in the appropriate box, both constancy and presence (see later discussions) can be derived from the tabulation. Within one life-form group, the species might be listed according to height, so that the tabulation will suggest stratification. Tabulations of this type (association tables), representing areas over which a high degree of homogeneity can be demonstrated, provide concrete evidence of the validity of an association.

nance, and frequency ratings, and these parameters do not have equal significance.

As an alternative to such a fusion of data, others have generally preferred straightforward tabulation, which not only is more informative (albeit more space-requiring) but, as is more important in science, permits the reader to see if conclusions are justified and if there may not be alternative conclusions of equal or superior validity. There is a large area of agreement among these synecologists that coverage data are worth presenting in full as the most significant single parameter of terrestrial plant communities, and that some evaluation of the distribution of individuals over the stand (as frequency or sociability) can also be presented in detail without overcomplicating the tabulation. Then it is generally conceded that the range of variation among stands with respect to these attributes is important enough to be indicated.

To a tabulation of coverage and frequency (or sociability) for all the stands studied, additional columns can be used to show the average character of life-form, leaf size, vitality, vigor, etc., for each species that is encountered in the series of stands (Fig. 22). Significant environmental features of each of the stands can also be included, so that quantitative correlations between vegetation and environment can be documented. By such a tabulation a tremendous quantity of basic information can be organized and made available for study or reorganization.

Synthetic Concepts

Synthetic concepts are concerned with the grouping of stands into associations and involve the use of analyses discussed in the preceding section. During the study of a vegetation mosaic, tentative groupings suggest themselves to a worker. The validity of these groupings needs to be tested and the characters that are most useful in distinguishing among them determined.

Constancy and presence. Constancy may be defined as the percentage of occurrence of a species in samples of a uniform size scattered over the geographic range of an association. Like frequency, it is a measure of ubiquity, but ubiquity among a *series* of stands representing one association, rather than among plots within a *single* stand. Constancy may be based on the list of species that have been encountered in a group of small plots that have been analyzed in each of a number of stands, or upon a single large plot in each stand. Whatever the area used, it should be the same in all stands considered, for otherwise the statistics are not reproducible.

Constancy may be expressed as a percentage, or the species may be listed simply as belonging to one of five constancy classes: 1–20 percent, 21–40 percent, etc. Plants in the highest class are commonly called *constants.*

Although there is considerable variation in the structure and composition of any ecosystem type from place to place where it is represented, it can be recognized as a unit only if there is a framework of common characters that distinguishes it from all others. Constancy provides a measure of the degree to which taxonomy contributes to this list of common characters, revealing a group of species that can grow together only under a particular range of environmental conditions. Although zootic, edaphic, and aerial components of the ecosystem should also be taken into account in establishing the limits of ecosystem types, usually a combination of plant species may be found that serves as a convenient group of indicators. The defining combination of constants commonly includes members of the subordinate strata as well as the dominant stratum. In practice, stands are selected according to apparent similarities in physiognomy and dominance in the different layers; then after many stands have been analyzed, the lists are scrutinized for a species combination that serves as a specific criterion of the association.

Since all species are individualistic with regard to habitat tolerances and requirements, relatively few can be expected to fall into the pattern of the group showing high constancy that distinguishes an association. Furthermore, all members of an indicator group are not invariably present, and an occasional stand may warrant inclusion even when all the usual indicator plants are absent, providing other aspects of the ecosystem suggest such a placement. One must either accept the idea that ecologically equivalent species may replace each other in various stands over the range of an association, with perhaps an occasional coincidence of absences, or else exclude chance as a factor governing plant distribution. While a species growing at a point is proof that the environment of that place is favorable to it, the absence of a species from a point proves nothing.

Too rigid dependence on constancy data alone for defining an ecosystem type is also questionable since the size of the sample used in each stand governs the number of species with high constancy ratings. The larger the sample in each stand the less important this factor, so that one should make sure the sample is adequate (see later discussion), and always those species which are present but do not fall in the sampling system should be listed.

Several mathematical tests have been proposed for application to plot records within one stand, or to constancy data, with the purpose of testing for degrees of homogeneity of stand or association.[115, 431] Most of these coefficients of degrees of similarity seem to imply that (1) every plant occurs wherever the environment is suitable for it, (2) floristic lists alone are sufficient for judging degrees of similarity and difference among ecosystem types, (3) all species, dominants as well as accidentals, have equal indicator value, and (4) biologic classifications can be rigorously objective. But even when coefficients of similarity are altered to reflect dominance as well as presence, the results of lengthy computation often do no more than verify vegetation discontinuities that are evident to a trained synecologist by careful inspection.[269, 352]

Still another difficulty with purely mechanical processing of plot data results from the fact that two ecotypes in different species are often more closely related to each other ecologically than they are to other ecotypes in their respective species. Thus two communities sharing a number of species may not be so closely related ecologically as their taxonomic lists suggest. Clearly, the abiotic components of ecosystems need to be given some weight, and plant lists should not be relied upon entirely.

A different type of test that has been proposed for evaluating the propriety of grouping a particular series of stands into the same association is founded on the opinion that in constancy, as well as in frequency, Class 1 should be the largest, with Class 5 the second largest, if the series is to be considered homogeneous. But since the size of sample affects the relative sizes of constancy classes, this concept is open to the same question as frequency.

In conclusion, it seems doubtful that any rigid procedure for evaluating constancy data can prove satisfactory if we accept either the principle that all species do not have equal indicator significance or the principle that chance can operate to prevent the occurrence of indicators in some of the environments suitable for them, so that abiotic features of the ecosystem must be depended on for proper classification. It has proved impossible to mechanize species taxonomy, and community taxonomy would seem even less tractable in this regard.

• • •

Where land use has been so intensive that the stands of natural vegetation remaining for study are fragmentary and a really adequate sample is rarely found, workers sometimes use all of each stand regardless of wide differences in size. Even in some undisturbed situations, such as the plant life of temporary pools, the stands may all be small by nature, so that a uniform sample size is not practical. In either case the statistics based on a series of stands of dissimilar size are referred to as *presence* rather than constancy, so as to maintain a distinction between values that are as reproducible as the character of the vegetation permits and values that fall distinctly short of such a desirable status.

Fidelity. A species occurring regularly in every stand of an association may also have high constancy in others; therefore all plants of high constancy are not necessarily useful in defining vegetation types. It is thus essential to determine the extent to which the species of one association are also represented in others, a characteristic referred to as *fidelity*, faithfulness, or exclusiveness.

A subjective scale that has been widely used in expressing degrees of restriction to a given association is as follows:

F 1   rare in the association, common in at least one other ("strangers")

F 2   not showing special affinities for the association ("companion species")

F 3   better represented in this association than in others, but common elsewhere ("preferentials")

F 4   rather uncommon in other associations in comparison with this ("selectives")

F 5   completely, or almost completely, confined to this association ("exclusives")

Many plants fall into fidelity Classes 1–3, few into Class 4, and extremely few into Class 5, reflecting the fact that most species are members of two or more associations.

Constancy and fidelity tend to be inversely related, with "exclusives" nearly always being so low in constancy as to be rather useless as criteria for recognizing the limits of the ecosystem to which they are confined. Thus for the taxonomic characterization of an association one must depend on a group of species that (1) have high constancy, and (2) occur *as a group* only within a distinctive range of environment. Individually the members of this group may have low fidelity so long as they *as a group* show discontinuities at all ecotones formed with other associations. Such a group of course has synecologic meaning only if it defines areas of potential biologic homogeneity that are consistently different from other areas in certain physical conditions.

Since every species has a distinctive ecologic amplitude, and nearly all are found in two or more associations, it follows that the range of ecologic conditions indicated by a particular association is much narrower than the combined ranges of the species contained in it. The principle has long been recognized that *communities* are much more useful as indicators of specific environmental conditions than are species taken *singly*, and the rather recent discovery of the ubiquity of ecotypic specialization underscores the importance of this principle.

• SAMPLING TECHNIQUES[58]

Purpose and Perspective in Sampling

If one studied all of every stand representing a given association, he could then make exact statements as to the kinds, amounts, and conditions of species included. He could, for example, state the average number of individuals per hectare. Such figures for density, coverage, etc., are *parameters* of the association. But it is almost never feasible to study all of one association. Instead we study bits (or *samples*) of it, and assume that the averages (or *statistics*) so obtained are usefully close estimates of the true parameters. The accuracy of the estimates, in terms of the true parameters, depends on the quantity and quality of the samples.

One of the most fundamental requirements for a valid statistic is that the stand which is sampled must be homogeneous, for a fraction of an area cannot be relied upon to represent the entire area unless the latter is homogeneous. But as we saw earlier, in synecology absolute homogeneity is unobtainable, so that our problem is one of eliminating as much heterogeneity as possible, especially variability attributable to differences in intrinsic habitat factors and history of disturbance.

First of all, no sample may overlap even part of an ecotone. By staying well beyond the ecotones of a stand, the exact position of the sample to be studied is of little consequence, but where even part of an ecotone is included, the exact position of the sample has a strong influence on the resultant average, so that the average is representative of no more than the sample itself. Second, if the ecosystem concept has any merit, differences in soil types, direction and degree of slope, and position between top and bottom of a slope all have an influence on vegetation composition whether it is readily apparent or not. Therefore, the sample should never overlap two soil types, and should embrace a minimum variation in topography. Since heterogeneity in environment, and consequently in vegetation, increases with the amount of area considered, the most compact sample that can yield a close approximation of parameters is ideal for the purpose of critically evaluating the relation between a specific set of environmental conditions and a specific aggregation of plants. Only to the extent that one can be reasonably certain that soil, topography, and vegetation history remain uniform does he dare space plots widely with the purpose of including as much as possible of nonenvironmentally induced variation in the sample average. Where a series of stands is studied to document an association, and a single set of averages is used to represent each stand, any significant heterogeneity in areas accepted as stands rapidly obscures the differences between associations.

In practical land management where it is desirable to know only the volume of lumber in a timber tract, or pounds of forage in a pasture, etc., it is feasible to completely ignore communities and sample an artificially bounded segment of the landscape as a unit. The desired data can be obtained accurately, but they serve only one purpose. They apply to only the area sampled and become worthless after the resource has been harvested or otherwise disturbed even in part, or after natural succession has had time to change the vegetation composition. One cannot synthesize associations from samples taken at random over a landscape. Widespread associations are needlessly oversampled, uncommon types are undersampled, and many samples fall astride ecotones so that the "association" lists include incongruous combinations (Fig. 23).

Instead of a resource inventory, the ecologist is interested in statistics that can be used for extrapolation to areas not sampled, and he wants to relate community structure and composition to environment as closely as possible. To accomplish this the vegetation mosaic must be

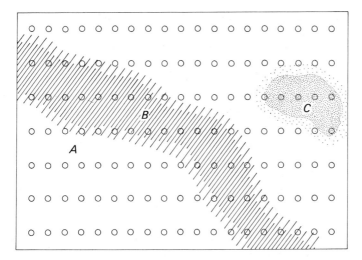

FIG. 23. Diagram representing a fenced tract composed of three vegetation types (A, B, C), with their ecotones, that has been sampled for purposes of inventory, the 133 circles representing plots. Assuming that the
texture of the vegetation allows a good approximation of parameters with
40 plots per community, the situation from a synecologic viewpoint can be
summarized:

Plots Actually Studied			Theoretical Needs	Excess or Deficiency
Homogeneous	A	88	40	+48
	B	22	40	−18
	C	5	40	−35
Ecotonal		18	0	
Total		133	120	

Although more work has already been done than would have been necessary to obtain synecologically useful data for all three community types, 53
more plots are still needed.

stratified into units of maximum homogeneity, and these units studied
independently.

The Multiple Plot Method

When quantitative studies of plant communities first began, one or a
few large plots were used to estimate the character of a stand, and some
workers, especially those of southern Europe, still favor a single large
plot, e.g., 10×10 m in temperate zone forests, estimating coverage and

sociability as their main analytic technique. In defense of this method, it may be said that such a sampling unit is laid out with maximum rapidity, and since no unused space is included, the total area considered can be small. This maximizes the precision with which a particular piece of vegetation can be related to a specific soil profile located at the center of the plot. But there are important advantages to using a series of small plots (technically "subsamples") rather than a single larger plot, as is common practice in northwestern Europe, then averaging the data to express the character of the stand as a whole.

First, the use of a single large plot precludes any quantitative evaluation of variability within the area enclosed, and this is a very important attribute of vegetation. Studying a series of small plots permits an evaluation of frequency or sociability, as well as checking variations in density or coverage from plot to plot. The data from a series of plots may show trends from one extremity of the series to the other, revealing an unacceptable amount of heterogeneity that was overlooked when the sampling pattern was laid out.

Second, estimates of coverage in a large plot can be accurate only if a very crude series of coverage classes is employed, and there is no means of refinement to enhance correlations between biologic and physical attributes of an ecosystem. If, however, the same crude coverage scale is used in many small plots, and the results averaged, one can obtain statistics as precise as vegetational heterogeneity warrants. The precision thus obtained is entirely adequate to reflect subtle ecologic relations, or portray small annual changes in plant cover resulting from weather variations or from successional trends.

Third, with small plots, data can be tested to evaluate the adequacy of sampling (see subsequent discussion).

Fourth, small plots, if scattered, can be staked permanently and evaluated repeatedly without damaging by trampling the areas actually studied.

In view of these advantages, many workers prefer to sample each stand by use of a number of small plots which collectively provide an estimate of the parameters of the community. There is less unanimity, however, on the best method of locating the plots within the stand. The principal procedures for doing this are as follows:

1 Many European synecologists carefully select the location for each plot that is to be studied in detail, each one representing the investigator's best judgment of a typical part of the stand (Fig. 24). Many investigators in North America are actually following this practice when they select places "at random" for sampling. This technique is open to the criticism that different investigators studying the same stand could easily obtain different statistics. Anyone who first appraises a character

FIG. 24. Alpine tundra with ptarmigan feeding on *Carex* fruits. Here where there is an intricate mosaic of *Carex*-dominated and lichen-dominated communities, the positions of each sample plot would have to be located subjectively to provide rational statistics representing community types.

of a stand, then studies that stand by means of sample plots that are objectively distributed, discovers that human judgment is subject to bias accruing perhaps from the order in which impressions are first received against a highly individualistic background of experience. For this reason there is much in favor of some alternative technique that virtually eliminates personal choice as to the exact position of each plot, and since all the following methods accomplish this, their relative merits must rest on other grounds.

2 Some investigators prepare a crude map of the outline of an acceptably uniform stand, distribute the plots evenly over the map, then locate the actual plot boundaries in the field by surveyor's method. This technique is excellent for stands that have highly irregular shapes.

3 A line may be stretched and plots located along it at fixed intervals, skipping spaces approximately equal to the plot diameter, if the size of the stand permits. Spacing plots has the advantage of including more floristic variability in the series, and of more quickly attaining average values representing highly aggregated species; yet one must make certain that the spaced series falls entirely within a homogeneous unit. The line may be as long as convenient, but if the land has much slope it should follow a contour so as to minimize the risk of crossing soil type boundaries. A tape, or multiple-strand wire with dots of solder marking intervals, or a cord with spaced knots are all satisfactory for this purpose. This technique is especially valuable in that it allows easy relocation of plots where they are to be studied repeatedly in order to follow vegetational changes. Methods (2) and (3) exemplify *systematic* sampling.

4 Rather than preparing a map or using lines, early investigators often tossed a plot frame, ball, or other object backward over the head, repeating this as a means of locating each sample plot. But this technique is faulty in that firm-textured plants tend to catch a frame or deflect a ball, thus introducing bias. Completely *randomized* sampling, which was the objective, may better be accomplished by erecting coordinate axes along two sides of the stand that divide it into suitable plot sizes, then using a table of random numbers to determine which plots are to be studied and which rejected. A variant is to completely randomize starting points for small clusters of systematically spaced plots.

5 All the stand may be divided into blocks, each block subdivided into plots, then one plot in each block studied after adopting a method of choosing that gives equal probability of it falling anywhere within the block. This is *restricted randomization*, or random-within-block. Like (4), every plant in the stand has equal chance of being studied, but here there is a means of ensuring a more even distribution of plots throughout the stand.

Many mathematicians, following R. A. Fisher, believe that either complete or restricted randomization is necessary where biometric techniques are to be employed to estimate the adequacy of sampling, but

FIG. 25. Animals grazing back and forth on steep slopes often create a systematic pattern less evident than the terracettes shown here.

others, following W. S. Gosset ("Student"), hold that systematic sampling is usually unbiased, gives greater accuracy from the same number of plots,[232, 260, 325, 381, 389] and that biometric techniques are validly applied although they tend to overestimate the amount of error in the statistic.[86, 308, 380]

Randomized and systematized sampling methods are equally objective. The only disadvantage in systematic sampling seems to be the likelihood of error should vegetation show some spatial periodicity (e.g., wave-cut terraces about a receding shoreline, furrows in an abandoned field, or parallel paths formed by animals grazing along a slope [Fig. 25]) and the sampling interval might happen to be a multiple of the basic period. But such phenomena are rare in natural vegetation, and, if suspected, a line of systematic plots can be oriented at a slight angle to the possible pattern so as to provide averages for the vegetation pattern as a whole if this is desired.

The inefficiency of randomized sampling accrues from the fact that most species in the plant community are markedly aggregated. If a sampling system is superimposed which likewise has grouped units, and this is not completely avoided even with restricted randomization, some species will be grossly overrated when a cluster of plots happens to coincide with a family group, whereas for intervening areas the values for the species are very low. Many plots are required to average out such vagaries in the records, with a result that systematic sampling usually proves more efficient.

There are also mechanical aspects to the inefficiency of randomization. Much more time is required to determine the plot locations, and it complicates the problem of laying out plots so that they may be relocated for another analysis at a later date to determine vegetational changes.

Finally, if one is interested in determining the average structure or composition of a stand using systematic sampling, it is desirable to ignore those plots that happen to fall astride a path or an ant nest, or are occupied by the base of a tree, etc. The path, the nest, and the tree base all support distinctive communities with distinctive floras and parameters, and it is improper to average them along with plots falling in the intervening matrix vegetation. Randomization theory does not permit using so much judgment, although some workers who practice randomization deviate by deciding in advance some arbitrary procedure to follow when, in their subjective judgment, a plot should be rejected.

All methods of vegetation analysis can be shown to involve far more human judgment than is apparent, when they are checked by a second person, but there is no reason why good judgment should be ignored. In a zealous effort to avoid subjectivity it is easy to commit the worse sin of violating common sense.

Plotless Sampling

The use of sample plots in vegetation dates back at least to 1848,[312] and their increasing use has made synecology a quantitative if not exact science. In the middle of the present century, methods of quantitative sampling without the use of plots were developed. These methods are based on the principle that density can be easily calculated from the average distance between individuals, and from density estimates by size classes, basal area of trees or canopy coverage of shrubs can be derived. The technique, originated by W. Bitterlich, has proved highly valuable for forest inventory, but it is not generally useful in synecology. It is applicable to only a fragment of the phytocoenosis (e.g., trees over 1 inch in diameter, or shrubs of a given size and spacing),[461] so that the ultimate synthesis of data derived in part from sample plots and in part from plotless samples is awkward at best; it has been used without realization of the bias for aggregated species;[76, 187] so much area is required in a stand that a homogeneous area meeting the size requirement is rarely found; and when the method is simplified in an effort to make it widely useful, the theoretical implications become highly complex.[95] Admittedly, the large-sized plots needed to study large plants take appreciable time to lay out, yet the small plots needed for seedlings and other small plants must still be laid out even if the plotless technique is used for the large plants. By using the sides of the large plots as parts of the boundaries of smaller plots, as in "nesting" small plots in their corners, or distributing them at fixed intervals along their sides (Fig. 26), the time difference between plot and plotless methods is in favor of plots, if the vascular flora as a whole is to be studied.

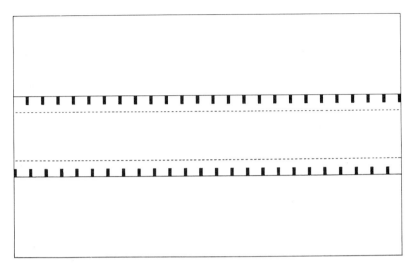

FIG. 26. A system of nested plots that has proved satisfactory in sampling coniferous forests in western North America. All trees >1 m tall are counted and recorded by D.B.H. (in decimeters) classes to determine population structure (see Table 18), using all three of the contiguous macroplots, each 5 × 25 m. Trees < 1 m tall are counted in two strips 1 m wide along the sides of the central macroplot. Coverage of shrubs, herbs, and macroscopic cryptogams is tallied in plots 20 × 50 cm at meter intervals along the sides of the central macroplot. Other species, too rare to be encountered in the sampling system, are also listed. If the total area is homogeneous, a soil profile study made at the center should be reasonably representative of the entire set of data.

Shape of Plot

The shape of the sample plots first used in North American vegetation studies (by F. E. Clements and co-workers) was square, and the term *quadrat* was appropriately coined for the unit. Later, circular, triangular, oblong, linear, and dimensionless observational units were used by other workers. These cannot properly be called quadrats.

Dozens of investigators working independently and using statistical techniques have compared the efficiencies of plots of different shapes, and nearly all have agreed that, areas being equal, elongate plots are superior to isodiametric shapes since fewer plots need to be studied to obtain averages highly representative of the whole stand. One investigator, for example, showed that plots 16 times as long as wide were more efficient than the less elongate shapes he tested.[81] This tendency toward the use of long, narrow plots reaches its culmination in studies where segments of a line are the observational units. Linear plots were indeed used by North American synecologists more than half a century ago, but they were then referred to as "line" or "belt transects" and employed only to analyze gradients across ecotones.

An explanation of the superiority of the elongate plot is not difficult. Since the individuals representing each species tend to be grouped into isodiametric clusters, an elongate plot has a high probability of intercepting parts of several clusters at once without falling entirely within one. On the other hand, an isodiametric plot may fall entirely within a cluster, or entirely within the space between clusters, and the individual plot records are so varied that many of them must be used to get an average that will not change significantly with a study of more. The chief disadvantage of elongate plots is that they have more margin in proportion to area, and the human tendency is to include too many marginal plants in the plot when tallying density or basal area.

Point-frequency analyses are usually subject to the same disadvantage as isodiametric plots. Most workers have used a row of ten points spaced at about 5 cm so that all ten can be recorded without the observer changing places. Such a compact unit frequently allows most of the ten points to make the same kind of distinctive contacts. Consequently, it has been found more efficient from a mathematical standpoint to increase the distance between points, but the advantages thus gained are offset in large part by the necessity for the observer to change places more frequently.[255]

In all these problems the texture of the patterns of aggregation needs individual consideration in order for a sampling system to be devised that will provide a reasonably reliable estimate with a minimum of field time.

Size of Plot

Appropriate plot size depends in part on the size of the plants to be studied. Areas as small as 25 cm² may be best for the tiny mosses and lichens of arid regions and for low herbaceous swards; 0.1 m² is often satisfactory for larger mosses, herbs, and shrubs up to a meter or so in height; and plots 4–100 m² are useful for larger plants.

As pointed out earlier, size of plot has an important influence on the values of constancy, frequency, and any index of sociability which depends in part on frequency, so that such data can be used comparatively only when there has been an exact duplication of plot technique. Fortunately, plot size has no influence on dominance or density so that the data for different layers can be obtained by use of different-sized plots and still be directly comparable.

Where dominance is to be estimated, plot size should be small enough in relation to vegetation complexity for the entire plot to be viewed without much shifting of the eyes, if personal error is to be kept at a minimum. If density is to be determined and some of the species are numerous in relation to plot size, it may be expedient to subdivide a plot roughly with cord or sticks, making lanes that facilitate counting.

In discussing frequency, it was pointed out that for this analysis plots may be considered too large if more than one species occurs in 100 percent of them, and needlessly small if at least one species does not approach 100 percent. The same guide applies to constancy.

Adequacy of Sampling

After the size and shape of the sample plots have been decided upon, the number that should be studied comes under consideration. Since homogeneity is relative, one must sample enough of the stand to reduce the error of the aggregate sample (as an estimate for the whole stand) to an acceptable level. Time spent in studying more area is wasted.

In 1902 P. Jaccard showed that as the amount of area studied increases, the total list of species included in the aggregate sample increases rapidly for a time; then new additions decline until a point is reached beyond which very few are added as more area is included. This came to be known as the "species-area curve" (Fig. 27). The choice of values for ordinate and abscissa have an important influence on the apparent sharpness of the break in the curve, and it has been claimed that in chaparral[1] and in tropical rain forest[363] such a break has not been demonstrated, regardless of ordinate and abscissa values.

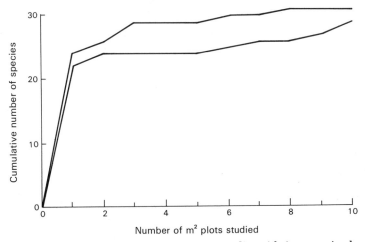

FIG. 27. Rate of enlargement of the species list with increase in the amount of area taken into consideration. Data are from two relatively homogeneous stands of rich steppe vegetation belonging to the same association.

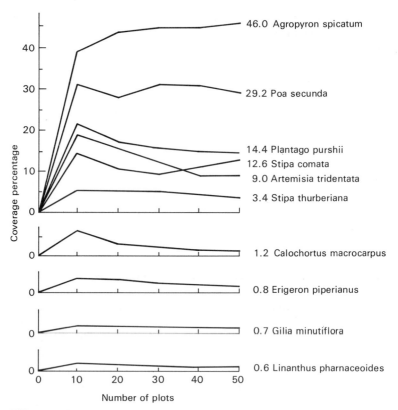

FIG. 28. Changes in canopy coverage as more and more of the same homogeneous stand is used in calculating the averages. The first ten plots happened to overestimate the coverage of such plants as *Artemisia, Calochortus,* and *Plantago,* and underestimated *Agropyron,* but by the time the data for forty plots were available, average relationships among species were rather well established. In this stand, efficiency (the amount of information derived from a given quantity of work) declined so markedly after forty plots were studied that further effort would better have been spent in the analysis of another stand.

(But in these studies only the canopy dominants were considered, and homogeneity of sample may be questioned.)

The principle shown by the break in the floristic curve, which usually defines the "minimal area" for an adequate representation of the floristic list, also applies to statistics other than the list, where it is much more important. Curves made by plotting density, dominance, or frequency against area may be expected to show a breaking point if homogeneous vegetation has been studied, and thus provide a visual basis for judging sample adequacy (Fig. 28).

Because sampling accuracy is increased more easily by studying more plots rather than by increasing their size, the simplest way to evaluate sampling adequacy is to average the plot data from time to time as the stand is studied, and ascertain the point beyond which changes in the average become insignificant. There are also a number of biometric tests which are commonly used for estimating the probable accuracy of a statistic, but these are beyond the scope of the present discussion.

The amount of area that must be studied to provide an adequate sample varies (1) from one type of analysis to another, (2) with the relative efficiency of plot shape, (3) whether the plots are systematically or randomly scattered, (4) from one association to another, and (5) from one species to another in the stand, being quickly attained for abundant species but impossible of attainment for rare species. The last problem may be minimized if one studies many plots, tallying abundant species in only alternate plots, with this taken into account when calculating averages.

Determinations of sampling adequacy are of use in four ways: (1) By determining the least amount of area that need be studied early in an investigation of a number of stands of the same association, one may accomplish more in the limited time available for field work. (2) Since homogeneity of environment decreases rapidly with increasing area, and every attempt should be made to correlate *specific* biotic assemblages with *specific* soil and microclimatic conditions, the smallest sample that is adequate is desirable. (3) Unless the sample used to characterize a stand is at least equal to the minimal area for the floristic list, one cannot use frequency or constancy as criteria of homogeneity.[345] (4) Since the minimal area for the floristic list varies with the association and provides an evaluation of floristic richness or species diversity, the minimal area serves as an additional character of an association.

In floristically impoverished arctic tundra, 1 m² may be adequate to sample a stand. Two hectares or more may be needed in floristically rich tropical rain forest.

There is one circumstance in which sampling need not be adequate in the above sense. It matters little whether the statistic is a close approximation of the stand parameter or not if the series of plots is to be used only for periodic reexamination to record changes in vegetation composition. In fact, if this is the sole objective, size, shape, and numbers of plots are of little moment. However, if sample size is not adequate to closely approximate parameters of the stand, it is imperative that the boundaries of plots used for such a purpose be relocated precisely at each visitation, and this is far more difficult than might be imagined, especially with small plots. Therefore, even in successional studies it is probably preferable to use an adequate sample rather than put much effort into the mere relocation of plot boundaries.

The amount of area required for a useful level of accuracy in sampling has no relation to the size of the stand. Only a minute fraction of a large and homogeneous unit needs study. On the other hand, some stands are too small to be entirely free of ecotonal influences, or too small to show the normal parameters for the larger plants. Any stand that is too small to demonstrate the average character of the association to which it seems to belong, i.e., is smaller than the area needed to allow a reliable assessment of one or more parameters, has been called an *association fragment.*

Earlier it was pointed out that constancy is definitely superior to presence as a study technique, and the foregoing discussion should clarify this point. Association fragments are too small to be adequate in a group comparison, whereas the inclusion of stands that considerably exceed the area necessary for floristic adequacy is undesirable since the species-area curve never becomes absolutely flat, and the more area studied the higher the constancy rating of rare species. The labor spent in laying out constancy plots of uniform size that equal or slightly exceed the minimal area for a floristic list is compensated by the time saved in not having to examine in detail all of the large stands, and certainly the data are more homogeneous as well as more capable of reproduction.

In tropical rain forest a peculiar enigma occurs with respect to sampling adequacy. With the large numbers of tree species having closely similar ecologic amplitudes, a large area is needed for an adequate sample (unless the site is floristically impoverished in consequence of some edaphic extreme). This size requirement is so large that rarely, if ever, can it be realized without encountering significant variations in either soil or topography. Therefore, if the character of the tree layers enters into the delimitation of associations, one must frequently recognize some climax associations in the tropics that have much wider than average ranges of floristic and environmental variation. However, thus far the herbaceous and shrubby vegetation of rain forest has been virtually ignored, and there is some evidence that the latter will provide criteria for discontinuities not readily demonstrable in the tree layers alone. An ecotone often does not involve discontinuity in all layers.

• THE PLACE OF STATISTICAL DESCRIPTIONS IN ECOLOGY

Provide Quantitative Records of Vanishing Phenomena

Since the last Ice Age, man's place in nature has changed gradually from that of a subordinate to that of an exceptionally powerful dominant who destroys preexisting ecosystems and maintains new ones of very different nature. Unfortunately, the serious study of natural communities (i.e., those unaltered by man) has been delayed until a time when this conversion is in an advanced stage. Soon the increasing demands of human populations still burgeoning unchecked will have put all the land surface under management and destroyed practically all natural ecosystems for eternity. Nature preserves offer the only means of counteracting this destruction. These are of value in many ways. They permit us to continue our incomplete search for principles that govern the distribution and behavior of organisms, to evaluate the checks and balances that operate in communities, and to test the validity of concepts not yet thought of. Only under natural conditions can many ecotypes persist, so a large number of alleles represented in virgin vegetation are lost to plant breeders when this vegetation disappears. Basic knowledge of the processes going on in undisturbed communities has much to offer in helping to manage land for timber, game, forage, water, and recreation uses.[14, 60, 404] Protected areas serve as reference points by which we can frequently appraise the degree to which various types of land use are altering conditions. They also provide information on the original habitat requirements of natural enemies of weed and insect pests which is of great value in devising ecologically sound control measures. For example, the use of insects to control *Opuntia* in Australia and Hawaii, and to control *Hypericum perforatum* in western North America, have represented more economic gain than the cost of all natural preserves that have thus far been established, and in both instances man had to search for natural enemies of the weeds in appropriate ecosystems which fortunately had not yet been too completely effaced.

Future generations are powerless to undo this destruction which continues apace, and which is depriving them of examples of landscapes that are priceless for their economic, educational, and aesthetic values. No one doubts the value of the usual type of museum for scientific study and general education, but few persons other than ecologists are aware of the similar need for the preservation of primitive areas as living museums. Fortunately, there has been a growing interest in the establishment of primitive areas, national monuments, etc., by government action, but the movement has been slow to get started and will undoubtedly prove inadequate in meeting the long-time human need. Furthermore, it is discouraging to observe that the condition of many parks and preserves reflects inadequate understanding of ecosystems as dynamic balances. Rodents or deer often converge on a "protected" area and create changes in vegetation equally as undesirable as the forces which "protection" was to have guarded against. Opening small areas to recreational use nullifies their value as primitive tracts. They should be carefully managed and used by none but serious investigators.

For many parts of the earth's surface, all we can ever hope to know of the pre-*Homo* conditions is contained in a vastly inadequate literature, and eventually the literature is all we will have. For this reason, all remnants of undisturbed vegetation should be subjected to exhaustive quantitative study while this can be done.

Utility in Studying Plant Succession

Quantitative methods of vegetation analysis are extremely valuable in studying plant succession, for changes in communities are the culmination of slow changes in the proportions of different species. These methods alone permit an investigator, or a series of investigators, to document changes through time on permanent plots with a high degree of accuracy.

The management of natural vegetation as a forage resource rests on a sound basis only when one knows the maximum potentialities of each ecosystem and has studied the processes of degeneration and recovery, thereby learning the degree to which vegetation can be used without reducing this productivity or at least jeopardizing recovery. We must not only evaluate the present vegetal composition in relation to this norm, but make the analyses in such a manner that they can be repeated to provide definitive information on changes effected by various land management practices. Density, dominance, frequency, vigor, and vitality have all proved useful in successional studies.

Provide Information on Autecology

Synecology and autecology are mutually supporting in many respects. Most of the techniques described earlier show something of the manner in which different species are affected by environment, and in this way reveal some features of autecology which cannot be easily recognized and evaluated by other means. For example, sociability studies provide a criterion of the relative effectivity of reproduction and dissemination and can reveal otherwise unsuspected antagonisms and dependencies. Life-form and leaf size analyses provide approaches toward the study of the impact of climate on evolutionary trends in the plant kingdom. Fidelity constitutes a measure of ecologic amplitude, and constancy aids in the evaluation of dissemination efficiency. Since each species has ecologic individuality, we may suspect every detail of change in floristic composition from one place to another as possibly indicating some environmental difference. In this way quantitative analyses have helped uncover correlations between plant distribution and soil factors. This is not to deny the truth of a common opinion that much variation in vegetation represents no more than accidents of dissemination, and that some variations in vegetation are products of conditions no longer extant, but unless we keep our minds open to other possibilities, valuable information on the indicator significance of plants cannot be uncovered.

Aid in Defining Plant Associations

The classification of plant communities cannot progress very far without resorting to quantitative studies, for no two stands have the same composition, and any serious attempt to evaluate the numerous similarities and differences among such complex units must take into account more details than the eye can readily perceive and the mind retain.

The initial recognition of associations is purely subjective, but when this is followed by objective analyses, the latter tend to correct impressions and bring out subtle facts which are of great value in distinguishing related communities. They either confirm or refute a working hypothesis that a series of stands exhibit consistent similarities among themselves, with consistent differences distinguishing them from all others. They give quantitative expression to association variability so that communication about vegetation is placed on a more precise basis.

Several attempts have been made to establish rigorous diagnoses for associations using some type of analytic data such as frequency, dominance, or constancy. These attempts have always been abandoned later because of their inflexibility in the face of biologic variability. One cannot hope to find consistent differences among a series of ecosystem types using only a single character of one phase of the complex. Recognition must instead be based on a number of characters, including potential floristic homogeneity and successional relationships, neither of which can be expressed quantitatively, as well as such characters as dominance and environmental characters which can be so expressed. The use of quantitative analyses is therefore to be considered an adjunct to a procedure that is fundamentally subjective. It is pertinent to note that, on the whole, species are more sharply defined than plant associations, yet the taxonomist has no set of objective criteria for distinguishing the former, and no longer confines his attention to the plant itself.

It has been proposed that a tabulation of detailed analyses of vegetation, topography, and soils from at least ten stands widely scattered over the geographic range of the association be considered essential to establish the nature and degree of variability that a worker is accepting when he recognizes an association. The implication here is that a reasonable amount of homogeneity in vegetation and environmental relationships is the most satisfactory written evidence that a series of stands have sufficient similarities to warrant a common name.

3 plant succession

Plant communities can be classified, mapped, and their structure described in minute detail, but unless we delve into their dynamic interrelations, much of the significance of the living world escapes us, for dynamism of widely varying kind and degree is an important attribute of all components of ecosystems. There is no fundamental understanding of a piece of vegetation until we know enough to give a reasonably accurate account of how it came into being and to predict its probable future. Since a community that is climax in one habitat is often represented in another habitat type by a community that is at least closely similar but is only temporary, one can hardly understand the ecology of vegetation without appraising its maturity status. Then too, the possibility of managing wildlands with maximum efficiency hinges directly upon the degree to which vegetation dynamics are understood. Most of the plants and animals that man continues to harvest from nonarable lands, as well as the yield of water from these lands, are most favored at some stage of development prior to the attainment of climax conditions, so that retarding or accelerating succession is frequently necessary. Distinctive habitat types have distinctive successional sequences, and in management we must either accommodate these trends or modify them. We must know the possibilities for modification and take into account the energy input required to achieve desired results. By trial-and-error methods we have discovered many empirical rules for effecting desired conditions, but the fundamental processes involved are as yet poorly understood.

Succession leading toward stability is a major unifying principle in synecology. This and ecosystem interrelatedness are the two most significant contributions which synecology has made to the natural sciences.

• DEVELOPMENT OF THE SUCCESSION CONCEPT

The natural replacement of one community by another can be so easily observed in so many places over the earth that the existence of this phenomenon has long been recognized. In Theophrastus' writings one finds references to vegetation sequences on fields and flood plains, and from time to time subsequent writers recorded similar observations. The successional relations of mire communities in Ireland were outlined by W. King in 1685, and in 1742 G. L. L. Buffon noted that *Quercus* plantations in France were more successful if shrubs or *Populus* were first allowed to modify the habitat. Excellent though only qualitative descriptions of plant succession on sand dunes, burned forest lands, and other habitats in central Europe were published by Anton Kerner in 1863.[91] Yet even to the end of the nineteenth century the dynamic aspects of vegetation had attracted the attention of relatively few botanists.

Shortly after the beginning of the present century, this situation changed abruptly in North America and much attention was focused on vegetation dynamics, largely as a result of effective research and teaching by H. C. Cowles and F. E. Clements. Cowles led this field of study during the first decade, but Clements soon became the more vigorous exponent. Observations, interpretations, and theories accumulated so rapidly that by 1916 Clements published a ponderous book devoted entirely to plant succession.[83] It was not until this detailed monograph appeared that the word succession came into wide use as a term for vegetation dynamics, although it had been used in this sense more than a century earlier.

In part this burst of interest in succession may have represented a delayed response of botanists to the Darwinian doctrine of dynamism that was destined to permeate the thinking of all branches of natural science. Yet the great wave of popular interest was almost wholly North American—Europeans for the most part continued to concentrate their attention on the structural and floristic aspects of vegetation, probably because ecologists with vigor and personalities comparable to Cowles and Clements happened to have different interests. During the past few decades the situation has become more balanced, with dynamism tending to be deemphasized somewhat in North America while getting more of its due share of interest elsewhere.

During the first third of our century succession studies were of a rather purely descriptive character, but subsequently interest has deepened to include such matters as determining rates of change, drift in the mode of cycling of matter and flow of energy as succession progresses, the roles played by different species in changing conditions, and forces regulating the sequences of populations. However, there are still opportunities in the area of pure description, for much of the earlier work was done with more enthusiasm than care, and if we become interested in explaining phenomena, the phenomena themselves must be accurately known.

• METHODS OF STUDYING SUCCESSION

A number of methods are available for studying plant succession. Usually each situation lends itself better to one technique than to others, but wherever more than one can be applied to a specific problem, it is highly desirable to do so.

Repeated Observations of Permanent Plots

Studies of one area that are repeated from time to time have often documented changes in vegetation such as follow the abandonment of

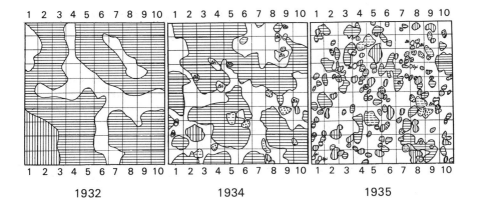

FIG. 29. Successive maps of plants in the same square meter over a 3-year period of increasingly severe drought in eastern Nebraska (see accompanying table). (Weaver and Albertson, 1936)

Composition of basal cover in percentages

Species, etc.	1932	1934	1935
Andropogon scoparius (horizontal hatch)	67.5	51.7	14.4
Bare ground (unmarked)	24.8	42.5	74.0
Andropogon gerardi (vertical hatch)	7.7	1.5	7.7
Bouteloua gracilis (dotted)	0.0	1.2	2.8
Bouteloua hirsuta (Bh)	0.0	1.1	0.5
Bouteloua curtipendula (broken horizontal hatch)	0.0	2.0	0.6

a field, the formation of a sandbar in a river, etc. One investigator studied the successional relations of attached organisms between tide levels starting on fresh rock surfaces which he prepared by chipping and found that changes leading to an approximate restoration of the previous natural balance were accomplished in about 18 months.[311] However, most vegetational changes are too slow for one individual to follow the entire sequence from pioneer to climax. One way of meeting this problem is to establish a series of permanent plots with the hope that they can be restudied over many years, perhaps by a sequence of workers. The success of such a project is strongly conditioned by the uniformity of methods employed by the series of workers, so that clear and detailed accounts of the procedures must be filed at the outset.

With relatively open communities of low stature, records of the permanent plots may be kept as detailed vegetation maps[439] (Fig. 29). The areas selected for study are marked with durable stakes, or with paint if rock surfaces are available, and new maps are constructed at suitable intervals. Making density or dominance determinations in plots along a line is an especially good plan, since two stakes are all that are needed to relocate the sampling units.

With little additional expenditure of energy, any plot studied in detail can be permanently marked, even though the possibility of revisiting it in the future may seem remote at the time. Most experienced synecologists will readily testify to the wisdom of this practice, having seen former study areas subjected to burning or grazing, or simply undergoing marked changes upon remaining undisturbed, but being unable to document the changes because the original plots were not staked permanently.

Comparisons of Existing Vegetation with Old Records

Descriptions published many years ago have sometimes proved valuable in dynamic synecology even though they were not intended for such use. For example, in the eastern United States the references which surveyors made to help relocate the corners of each mile-square section as the land was first being surveyed contain many allusions to trees by name.[51] Assuming the percentage of different trees cited within a given topographic sector or on a given soil type is indicative of the average composition of the original forest, the present tree populations can be compared with conditions a century ago or more. Thus, in a region in southern Wisconsin the land survey records indicate a scattering of *Quercus,* mostly *Q. macrocarpa,* associated with shrubs and herbs common in grasslands to the west. Today in the same area, there is a dense forest of *Quercus,* mostly *Q. alba, velutina, rubra,* and *ellipsoidalis,* beneath which *Acer saccharum, Tilia,* and *Ulmus rubra* are becoming established.[103] Here is excellent proof of conversion from one vegetation type to a second, with strong suggestion of a third stage to come.

Photographs taken years ago can show clear changes in vegetation, if the exact point is relocated and a camera of the same focal length is used[233] (Fig. 30). Even casual notations in the diaries of the first explorers and immigrants in the western United States have proved valuable in this connection. But a precaution in the application of this method that cannot be overemphasized is that the memory, especially of scientifically untrained persons, is usually unreliable as a record of past conditions. Only records written down shortly after the observation can be trusted, and in some instances even these must be interpreted in terms of the psychologic conditioning of the writer at the time.

FIG. 30. The lower picture of this ravine off the Snake River in Washington was taken 10 years after the top one. The large dark patches of shrubbery near the right and left margins are *Rhus glabra*. Below, a new and small clone of *Rhus* shows clearly above the large patch on the right, but the first few stems were actually established when the first photo was made. This increase of *Rhus* on the right side of the ravine has been more than balanced by a conspicuous thinning of the large patch on the left side.

Study of Age-Class Distributions in a Stand

The populations of species that make up a stand are not static—new individuals become established from time to time, and old ones die. If for one species the rate of addition exceeds mortality over an appre-

FIG. 31. *Populus tremuloides* with a stable population structure. Medicine Bow National Forest, Wyoming.

ciable time, its population density increases, and vice versa. Many variables affect this balance, some of which are intrinsic (seed production, life span, etc.) and some extrinsic (fluctuating populations of seed-consuming animals, above-average precipitation, etc.), so that population dynamics are complex.

In many types of vegetation, each stand contains a substantial record of its dynamic status that can be brought to light in a few hours. To do this, the proportions of various age groups present must be determined and interpreted autecologically.

Perennial plants usually produce a great quantity of viable seeds per individual, and frequently this is followed by abundant germination at favorable seasons. But mortality among the resultant seedlings is typically very high, especially during the first few weeks after germination, and at most only a few individuals out of each crop can be expected to attain reproductive age. If a climax community is defined as one which appears to have permanent possession of the habitat, one might expect a complete series of age classes for each species in the habitat, since for each plant that dies or advances in age a slightly younger one must be at hand to replace it (Fig. 31). But when the age-class series is interrupted or truncated at either end, the life cycle is not being completed and the plant usually cannot be considered as climax on the habitat. (Some exceptions will be discussed later.)

In Table 11 *Acer, Tilia,* and *Ostrya* and the four species below them

Table 11 **Population analyses of trees in 1 hectare of a forest near Lake Itasca, Minnesota**

(*Two methods of expressing density are compared. Note that mere "percentage composition" based on all individuals 1 dm and larger gives no hint of the significant interpretations which are made possible by keeping separate records of the size classes.*)

Species	Size Classes in Decimeters D.B.H.					Apparent Status	Percentage Composition
	0–1	*1–2*	*2–3*	*3–4*	*4–*		
Acer saccharum	220	86	35	6			20
Tilia americana	175	81	7	11	3		16
Ostrya virginiana	460	20	3[a]			Permanent	4
Ulmus americana	47	16	55			occupants	14
Quercus rubra	14	7	3	3			2
Fraxinus americana	100	10	3				2
Quercus macrocarpa	17	7					1
Populus tremuloides	39[b]	94	55	43		Disappearing	31
Betula papyrifera	53[b]	50	7	3		relics of an	10
Pinus strobus	260			3	3	earlier stage	1
Populus balsamifera			7			in succession	1
Betula allegheniensis		4					1
Picea glauca	3					Unsuccessful	0
Populus grandidentata	2					invaders	0
Ulmus rubra	30						0

[a] Approximate maximum size of the species in this region.
[b] Root suckers or stem-base suckers, rather than seedlings.

provide examples of a common type of size-class distribution, interpreted as an age-class distribution, for climax species. Seeds are produced in abundance, germination is satisfactory, and the initial high mortality is followed by ever-decreasing rates of mortality through a complete sequence up to trees of seed-bearing age. In populations with this structure the number of individuals in successive age classes presents a geometric series (Fig. 32) that tends to form a straight line when plotted on semilogarithmic paper.

In contrast with the above population patterns, the series of values

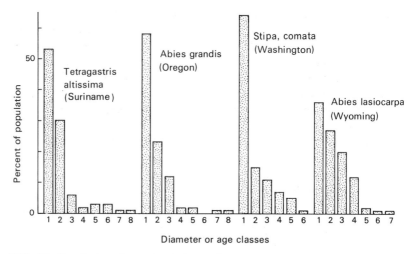

FIG. 32. Population structure of climax dominants which produce seedlings annually or with brief interruptions at most. Arbitrary size classes are equal for any one species. (Data for *Tetragastris* from Schulz, 1960)

representing the densities of *Betula* and *Populus tremuloides* in Table 11 are somewhat truncated at their lower ends. Habitat conditions must have become less favorable for their seedlings in recent decades, but the disappearance of these taxa from the stand is being long postponed by their special abilities to sprout from the roots or stem bases of old trees.

Pinus strobus finds conditions highly favorable for the production of seeds and seedlings, but seedling survival has been impossible for many years, as shown by the markedly disrupted sequence. When the few old trees die the species will promptly disappear from the habitat.

Mature trees of *Picea, Populus grandidentata,* and *Ulmus rubra* are obviously within dissemination range of the habitat, but thus far, at least, their life cycles are regularly terminated shortly after germination.

As a whole, the data in Table 11 provide evidence of a still incomplete change from an antecedent forest to a subsequent one that promises to be climax, but in Table 12 there is evidence of a sudden change in environment at some time in the past which was detrimental to the continued reproduction of the plants then dominant and allowed others to begin their replacement. Here the *Pinus* had been able to maintain its life cycle under the influence of frequent light burning which prevented the establishment of other trees. When burning ceased, fire-sensitive dicot woody plants invaded and conditions forthwith became inimical to the survival of pine seedlings. The dicot series are truncated at their upper extremities owing to the recency of the cessation of burning, but

Table 12   **Population analyses of trees in 1 acre of a forest near Gainesville, Florida**

Species	Seedlings	1	2	3	4	6	8	10	12	14	16
					Size Classes in Inches D.B.H.						
Pinus palustris					20	25	25	40	20	15	
P. elliottii elliottii				5		15	5	30	30	5	5
Quercus nigra	125	630	435	45							
Liquidambar styraciflua	100	20	5		20						
Myrica cerifera	1150	770	45								

SOURCE: Heyward, 1939.

the largest individuals are vigorous plants giving every promise of eventually growing still larger. Here again much information would escape us if we were to tally only trees 4 inches in diameter or larger, and present the results of the census only as "percentage composition."

The technique illustrated above is limited to those organisms in which ages are determinable relatively, if not absolutely. For trees and shrubs with active cambia, stem diameters are reasonably reliable indicators of relative age providing (1) the size classes are not divided too finely and interpreted too closely, and (2) one guards against an assumption that the same size range in different species indicates equivalent age ranges. While it is easy to demonstrate that age in years is but roughly proportional to diameter,[46, 173] a graded series of *sizes* has approximately the same successional significance as a graded series of *ages*, considering each species individually. A more precise technique is to count xylem layers on increment borings that terminate at the morphologic center of the stem and at the level of the original germinating surface, but even this laborious method is still subject to error, since xylem layers are frequently not formed at the rate of one per year. Furthermore, owing to past fires, the roots of a woody plant often reveal greater age for the individual than the base of the aerial stem, if the latter originated by sprouting from a root after a fire.[295] Caespitose grasses such as *Stipa comata* can be classified using basal diameter as a rough criterion of age (Fig. 32), while columnar cacti are better tallied by height than diameter.

Regardless of the technique, some understanding of the autecology of the species is essential for critical interpretations of the data, and at the same time population structure is so sensitive to environmental conditions that much new information is usually uncovered by its study.

Population dynamics among higher plants is simpler than among animals, for with plants reproduction and mortality alone are involved, whereas with many animals immigration and emigration must also be reckoned with. In view of its simplicity and informativeness, it is surprising how little use has been made of population structure in the study of plant communities.

Inference Based on the Nature and Occurrence of Relics

The earliest map of the vegetation of Minnesota showed isolated bits of forest dotting the grassland area of the southwestern third of that state, each tending to be of a crescentic form and fitted to the easterly margin of a lake, pond, or marsh. Each stand possessed a rather complete complement of forest undergrowth herbs and shrubs, but the stands were too widely scattered for such a distribution pattern to be explained on the basis of chance bringing the disseminules of so many species to each of these restricted plots. A more likely explanation is that the forest had once been continuous, then was broken up, and the remnants (*relics*) reduced in size by fires which spread under the influence of westerly winds. In the course of time these fires, originating in the extensive steppe to the west, eroded farther and farther into the forest, allowing small fragments of timber to persist only on the lee sides of natural fire barriers. Also along this major ecotone between forest and steppe it has been noted that the belts of timber along streams tend to be wide on the lee side but narrow on the windward side of streams. In places trees were found only on islands in rivers and ponds.

In the edge of the forest adjacent to the ecotone alluded to above, peculiar combinations of tree forms have been observed. Ancient *Quercus macrocarpa* trees with broad low-branched crowns, resembling trees in an old orchard, are widely scattered in dense forests of tall slender trees of other species which frequently show by the clustering of their stems a coppice origin (Fig. 33). Obviously the *Quercus* once dominated a savanna, then a dense sprout forest sprang up. *Quercus macrocarpa* is a tree not easily killed by fire and appears to have been the only arborescent species to maintain even a scattered population in the face of repeated burning. Then, after white man invaded the region, roads and fields stopped the spread of fires, allowing natural progress in succession toward forest. The new forest developed from sprouts of species which had been repeatedly killed back to the ground by fires, and as they grew up they forced the old *Quercus* trees to produce vertical risers from the old branches.

Still a third class of relic evidence corroborates the above two indications of succession related to fire history in the upper Mississippi Valley. Out in the grassland far from any trees are found occasional representatives of species of herbs (*Arisaema triphyllum, Dicentra cucullaria, Erythronium albidum, Podophyllum peltatum,* and *San-*

FIG. 33. This tree of *Quercus macrocarpa* with open-grown form has produced vertical branches on the main scaffold system as a vigorous forest of tall trees grew up about it. The clustered stems of the young trees suggest that they were frequently burned back to the soil surface during a long period of repeated burning that allowed the fire-resistant *Quercus macrocarpa* to mature with an open-grown form, presumably in savanna spacing. Hennepin County, Minnesota.

guinaria canadensis) which, so far as is known, can germinate and become established only in the moist microclimate beneath mesophytic trees.[53] Fire, sweeping over when the grass is dry and these herbs dormant, does not prevent their lingering almost indefinitely after the tree overstory has been burned away. In general, a relic status is by no means the only possible interpretation of a single species showing a disrupted range, but the odds are in favor of such an interpretation if the disseminules are not very mobile, which is true of these plants.

The above three situations illustrate very well how the autecologies of relics, their form,[280] and peculiar distribution patterns provide evidence of succession: change from forest to savanna or grassland, then recently a reversed trend. Even singly the points are rather substantial. Collectively they are convincing proof of a common sequence of events over a very large territory in the upper Mississippi drainage area.

Inference Based on Studies of Bare Areas of Differing Ages

If one starts at the edge of a glacier that has been retreating steadily and walks away from the ice at right angles to its front, he can assume that his advance will carry him across glacial till that has been exposed for successively longer periods. A series of plots laid out at intervals along such a transact should illustrate by their spatial sequence the probable time sequence for the plot nearest the ice, each plot in turn having vegetation representing a more advanced stage of succession. The plot records would be similar to a series of time-lapse photographs that might have been started at a point along the ice edge long ago. Since vegetation development parallels physiographic development, this technique can likewise be applied to stream terrace sequences, dune formation, pond margins, etc.

Another application of the method has been made in regions where the dates of abandonment of various fields can be ascertained. Analytic data from the fields are placed in series according to time since the last cropping, and the sequence may be assumed to indicate the direction and rate of vegetation change. A closely similar application is to study places in a forested area where the timber has been destroyed at different dates by fire, windfall, etc., the dates being indicated approximately by the number of xylem layers in the oldest woody plants in each.[165, 270, 271]

Some workers have applied the technique on a small scale to fallen trees in the forest, working out the sequence of changes in communities of lichens, mosses, herbs, etc., that takes place as a trunk slowly decays and finally loses its identity in the duff. Epiphyllous communities can be traced from newly unfolding leaves of evergreen plants, downward through the series of successively older leaves, to trace the origin and development of these miniature communities up to the time of catastrophe by abscission (Fig. 34). On woody twigs epiphytes can be dated at least to their earliest possible time of establishment,[341] and the succession of mosses and lichens on tree trunks at a given level can be determined by comparing stems of different ages studied in proper sequence.

The validity of this method in all its applications depends entirely

FIG. 34. Left to right, leaves from successively lower nodes of *Coffea arabica* showing the progressive development of a cryptogamic community. With substrates and microclimates strictly comparable, the space sequence here represents a time sequence.

upon a basic assumption that the areas studied differ *only* in age. This is hardly to be questioned where epiphylls on the leaves of one branch are studied. When applied to mosses and lichens on trees, it is necessary to confine attention to one species of tree as it grows in one association and take into account the influence of different degrees of shading.

A greater likelihood of error due to heterogeneity of habitat comes in applications such as studying succession on abandoned fields. Here it would be essential that the series of habitats aligned did not differ significantly in topography, parent material, or degree of erosional degradation, and it would be desirable if the agronomic system and size of the fields were uniform. Separate series of fields should be aligned and studied independently for each of these varying conditions to the extent that this is possible.

As a second limitation, the climate and flora must not have undergone significant changes since the oldest bare area was created. Changes in either climate or flora bring about a deflection in the subsequent course of succession, so that development originally leading to one climax ends in a different one. Thus it is extremely improbable that the vegetation development now to be observed on the bottoms of freshly dug gravel pits in the Great Lakes region bears much resemblance to the development that was initiated on the same kind of raw gravel some

11,000 years ago when the last continental ice sheet was starting to melt away. The composition of the flora has changed, the macroclimate has changed, and the microclimate determined by the surrounding forest now influences even large areas of newly exposed gravels. The longer it takes to complete a developmental sequence, the greater the likelihood that present successional tendencies have not prevailed in the past, or may not continue in the future. In fact, we may suspect that to a limited extent, the results of any successional study are somewhat conditioned by the phase of the climatic cycle in which the work was done.[3]

Fossil Sequences

Frequently water or wind deposit sediments over a long period of time so that a series of superimposed strata accumulates. Any plant or animal remains that may be found in one of these strata may be presumed to belong to organisms which were living at the time the layer was deposited (except under rare circumstances in which they represent redeposition of older fossiliferous material). Thus if a series of sedimentary strata accumulates over a long period, and the proportions of different species change during the period of deposition, this may be clearly reflected in the fossil content of successive strata. Working up through such series, paleontologists have been able to demonstrate changes in the composition of faunas and floras at many places over the earth's surface. Stream deposits, varves, marine sediments, peat accumulations, and even forest soils[107, 139] are examples of deposits that have yielded fossils indicating plant succession.

Since Lennart von Post introduced the technique in 1916, studies of fossils in peat strata have proved especially rewarding.[163] The recentness of the last continental glaciation, which left millions of ponds scattered over the cool and cold parts of the northern hemisphere, coupled with subsequent climatic conditions favoring peat accumulation and fossilization, have provided fossil sequences showing many details of biotic change during the past 11,000 years or so. Pollens, some of which can be identified as to species, and most as to genus or family at least, are especially well preserved, but fragments of wood, strobili, seeds, moss shoots, diatoms, etc., are also present in sufficient quantities and adequately preserved to be useful. Where layers of volcanic ash, or debris from prehistoric villages are intercalated between peat strata, valuable time scales can be established that help relate archaeologic, geologic, climatic, and vegetational history. Radiocarbon dating is useful in the absolute dating of sequences involving up to about 35,000 years.

Special peat borers have been devised which enable the researcher to obtain a complete core of peat to almost unlimited depths in a few hours' time. And methods of preparing samples for study, with keys for pollen identification, have been worked out. As a result of hundreds of studies of peat fossils in eastern North America, we know that the following major changes took place in the periphery of the glaciated area. (1) Taiga vegetation dominated by *Abies, Picea, Larix,* and *Pinus* soon invaded the deglaciated surfaces, apparently without a well-defined tundra phase intervening, as in Europe. (2) Taiga was then slowly replaced by steppe in the midcontinental region or temperate forest in more moist regions. (3) This warming trend culminated in a warm-dry period, the *hypsithermal,* when xerophytic vegetation types encroached markedly into areas formerly supporting mesophytes. (4) A final period of a few thousand years ensued, during which the xerophytic vegetation has been receding for the most part (Fig. 35).

Pollen fossils in Europe indicate a similar sequence of postglacial events there,[184] except that a well-defined tundra belt bordered the ice as it receded. Near the middle of the pollen record charcoal appears in quantity, suggesting man's clearing of forests by fire to provide crop-lands. Above this level the pollen of climax dominants of the preceding forest (*Quercus, Tilia, Ulmus, Fraxinus,* etc.) is poorly represented, while that of *Betula, Alnus,* and *Corylus,* invaders of fallow land, is well represented. Herbaceous weeds such as *Plantago* and *Rumex* also become conspicuous above the charcoal layer.

It is a commonly accepted principle that a fossil flora with a close counterpart in a modern flora indicates past climatic conditions similar to those of the modern flora. Thus the fossil sequence method is not only of interest in pushing our knowledge of plant succession back into pre-historic time, but it is also of at least equal importance for suggesting climatic history.

Without denying the great value of fossil sequences for tracing suc-cession and climatic changes through geologic time, a number of limitations to the method should be noted:[348]

1 Mistaken identity (a hydrophyte being interpreted at first as a cactus)
2 Production of pollen of different species being far out of proportion to the relative densities of the individuals
3 Complete absence of some species from the record only because their pollens decay quickly (e.g., *Thuja*)
4 Loss of sections of a record by fire which may burn off the peat sur-face during very dry summers
5 Regular and abundant production of pollen by certain species, whereas others that are equally represented in the flora may produce pollen only at irregular intervals
6 Unreliable results for entomophilous plants whose pollens vary widely from one sample of peat to another owing to inequal dispersal,

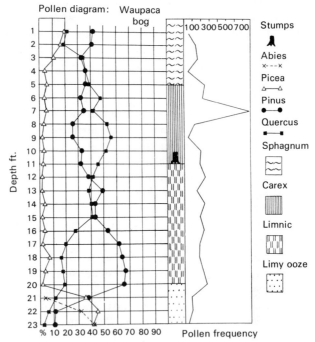

FIG. 35. Vertical changes in the proportions of different tree pollens in a peat deposit 7 m (23 feet) deep in southern Wisconsin. A *Picea-Abies* forest apparently surrounded the pond as sediments began to accumulate, but this forest soon waned and was replaced by *Pinus* and *Quercus*. The record is interpreted to indicate subarctic climate for perhaps more than a millennium (*Picea* with *Abies*), followed by temperate climate that persisted to the present. A hypsithermal interlude is indicated by the temporary ascendence of *Quercus* over *Pinus*. Since in this region the recent activities of man are not likely to have increased the abundance of *Picea*, its increase near the surface suggests a distinct cooling trend that commenced in the not-too-remote past. (Voss, 1934)

whereas anemophilous pollens are deposited rather uniformly over a peat sample if they are represented in the local flora

• TERMINOLOGY

Succession. The term *succession* will be used for any unidirectional change that can be detected in the proportions of species in a stand or for the complete replacement of one community by another. Later on it will be possible to further amplify the intended usage.

Sere.   Succession typically begins on a bare area soon after it has been created. An initial group of pioneers appears, then this is usually replaced by other communities in turn until the area comes under the control of plants that seem capable of perpetuating themselves indefinitely, these forming the climax association. All temporary communities in the sequence are collectively referred to as a *sere* (or "chronosequence") ; the adjective *seral* is used for particular communities or organisms. It is possible for two or more seres involving different community sequences to terminate in the same climax.

Stage.   Any floristically or structurally distinctive segment of a sere may be called a *stage*, but the transition from one stage to another is always part of a gradual process rather than an event, so that each stage becomes recognizable only as the dominant which characterizes it gains ascendancy. Even so, many seres cannot be divided into stages.

Primary and secondary seres.   The character of the bare area has a very important bearing on the kind of community which invades it, as well as on the rate at which the sere advances. *Primary bare areas* are those which are formed by recently active physiographic processes such as deglaciation or erosion, and the seres which begin on such habitats are called *primary seres* (or *primary successions*). There is always an invasion of a relatively unweathered parent material, the surface of which has never before borne a plant cover.

  Secondary bare areas are those which result from the destruction of preexisting vegetation by fire, smelter fumes, cultivation, etc. Community sequences on such areas are referred to as *secondary seres* (or *secondary successions*). Frequently the catastrophe which creates a secondary bare area does not exterminate all of the preexisting vegetation. Thus residual species may be mingled with invaders. It is most convenient to extend the use of the term bare area to include such habitats as have been only partially depopulated. However, if fire sweeps a grassland during its season of estivation, and the same plants put up new shoots from subterranean buds as usual at the start of the next growing season, the scorched surface is not considered a bare area in the sense of plant succession.

  The importance to be attached to this distinction between primary and secondary bare areas lies in the fact that in secondary succession early seral communities in particular benefit tremendously from the soil having been previously occupied by plants. It already contains humus with nitrogen which supports an active microbiota, its minerals have been altered by acid secretions, it contains a supply of dormant seeds and spores, it is permeated by root and earthworm channels that promote aeration and allow water to enter the soil readily. As roots, and sometimes the litter too, of a devastated community decay, nutrients may become more plentiful than previously, with a consequent increase in the environment potential. In primary succession, on the other hand, the soil is nearly sterile and structureless, certain nutrients may be seriously deficient, or solutes may be physiologically unbalanced, and the rate of vegetational development is limited by the rate at which these limitations are overcome.

It should be clear that the communities involved, as well as their rates of replacement, usually differ to a marked degree between primary and secondary succession.

Xero-, meso-, and hydroseres.   Wholly independent of the structural-nutritional aspects of their soils, bare areas may be classified according to their characteristic water relations: wet or *hydric*, as a pond bottom; dry or *xeric*, as a rock surface exposed to the sun; or intermediate *mesic*, as a glacial moraine. These special terms are adjectives that describe environment in relative terms.

The seres that begin on each of these three types of bare areas are also given special designations, compounded logically of terms already introduced. Those starting in xeric habitats are called *xeroseres*, with the corresponding terms being *hydroseres* and *mesoseres*.

Still other terms utilizing the same basic roots are *xerophyte*, any plant growing in a habitat in which an appreciable portion of the rooting medium dries to the wilting coefficient at frequent intervals; *hydrophyte*, any plant growing in a soil that is at least periodically deficient in oxygen as a result of excessive water content; and *mesophyte*, any plant growing where moisture and aeration conditions lie well between both extremes.

• SUCCESSIONAL PATTERNS

A survey of the descriptions of seres that have been published reveals infinite variety in the details of vegetational development in different climatic areas and in the diverse habitat types to be found within each area. Plant succession in lakes, for example, varies considerably from one part of the continent to another; it differs between oligotrophic and eutrophic lakes in any one region, and even in different bays of the same lake there may be remarkable differences in development. Fortunately for the sake of classification, there exist relatively few fundamental patterns of development, despite the diversity of expression of each pattern. Since seres starting on a particular kind of bare area exhibit many similarities, it will be convenient to discuss succession according to types of bare areas.

Primary Succession

Rock outcrop succession. An exposure of rock usually constitutes a very severe type of bare area, yet in all but the driest regions one can find plants invading such habitats. Crustose lichens are the most common pioneers, but *Selaginella* or mosses such as *Bryum* and *Grimmia* are also abundant on rock outcrops. Unlike the lichens, however, most higher plants require at least a small crevice in which a trace of mineral soil has accumulated; therefore succession in crevices differs from succession on the plane surfaces that intervene.

Lichens, and certain mosses as well,[252] have several significant ecologic adaptations which enable them to colonize rock surfaces. Not only can some of them get established without the least vestige of soil, but they can endure prolonged desiccation to the point of becoming brittle, in this respect contrasting markedly with leaves where death usually follows when their water content drops below about 50 percent. This adaptation is crucial, for rock surfaces, even if porous, hold water for only a very short period following a rain, so that where freely exposed to insolation, long periods of drought separate brief intervals when water is available to the lichens. Shortly after the start of a shower, however, enough water is imbibed to permit photosynthesis, and with osmotic pressures up to 1000 atm,[24] even air with high relative humidity can reactivate desiccated thalli. Also, since their cardinal temperatures for photosynthesis decline in winter, these plants can take advantage of the usually more favorable water balance prevailing then.

With photosynthesis usually confined to brief and widely separated intervals, lichens growing on exposed rock surfaces make very slow and sporadic growth. Replicate photographs of rock surfaces on Isle Royale in Lake Superior showed no net change in the sizes of lichens over a 17-year period.[98] Where the growth rate of a particular species has been studied in a particular environment, the results can be used by extrapolation to determine the time zero for similar bare areas.[31]

It is a universal principle of ecology that any community entering upon a habitat alters the primary factors which originally characterized that habitat. These changes may or may not be to the advantage of the plants that bring them about. Often they are of indirect disadvantage in that they allow other plants to gain foothold, with these proving to be superior competitors. Thus as a rule, each community in a sere contributes a definite part to a major environmental metamorphosis.

Lichens tend to disintegrate a rock surface mechanically through the wedgelike action of their rhizoids and weaken the rock by secreting corrosive carbonic acid.[168] They may accumulate a loose film of debris, and in some instances there appears to be a replacement of the pioneer

FIG. 36. Quartzite rock with *Grimmia* clones expanding from crevices. Crustose and foliose lichens cover most of the surface elsewhere.

by one or more subsequent lichen communities. But in general, pioneer lichens exert so little influence upon rock surfaces that no more than secondary lichen communities at most are able to invade the plane surfaces between crevices.[415] Thin films of soil accumulating next to the rock surface only make them more vulnerable to erosion by wind or precipitation.

What appear to be bare rock surfaces have sometimes been found supporting algae and autotrophic bacteria that live in pores just beneath the surface, but the extent to which these plants may be antecedents for lichen colonization is unknown. In some places it has been shown that the roots of the first woody plants to invade limestone outcroppings will dissolve their way directly into the rock as perhaps lichen rhizoids do.[324]

An examination of rock crevices, rather than the plane surfaces between, usually reveals an entirely different story of succession. Windborne materials fill a rock fracture as soon as it opens and keep it filled as it is widened by weathering, so that edaphic conditions there are distinctly better from the start and development is not so slow. Not only does the crevice sere commonly begin with a higher type of plant, e.g., mosses, *Selaginella*, or sometimes even herbs, but the shoots of these taller pioneers projecting from the crevice intercept material moved by wind or gravity, building up the soil above the level of the crevice (Fig. 36). Mat-forming plants, and those with basal rosettes of leaves, are especially constructive in such a situation. The crowded shoots are well suited to accumulating aeolian particles, and in mosses or *Selaginella* the habit of the shoots in growing upward while decaying pro-

FIG. 37. Successively wider rock crevices from right to left suggest stages of succession from herbs to low shrubs to tall shrubs as the fracture planes weather. The stabilized lichen-covered surface tends to be overriden by vascular communities expanding from the crevices. In the background is a suggestion of a still later stage consisting of conifer-dominated forest. Cadillac Mountain, Mt. Desert Island, Maine.

gressively at their lower extremity makes for a steady accumulation of organic matter. Ants living in the crevice sometimes aid materially by assembling nest materials.

On gently sloping and unfractured rock surfaces, randomly located pioneers may provide foci for development which spreads centrifugally as the mat thickens, with the most advanced stage being centrally located in each expanding island.[323] By spreading outward either from such foci or from crevices, or at the margin of the outcrop, mats of higher plants encroach on adjacent rock surfaces, overriding any lichen communities they may encounter (Fig. 37). As the rock surface disappears beneath a coalescing cover of vegetation and soil, other communities in turn may enter as rapidly as the rooting medium thickens. Finally, there enters on the habitat a community which seems able to maintain its characteristic composition and structure regardless of further increases in depth or changes in the character of the soil. This, the climax, is in approximate equilibrium with all the incident factors of the environmental complex.

The microclimate of a rock outcrop frequently sets definite limits to the extent of encroachment over the unfractured surfaces, and even if there is coalescence the habitat is usually too dry to foster a climax as

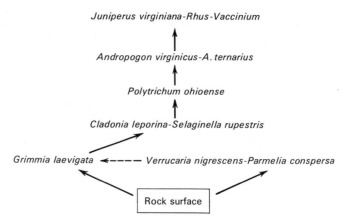

FIG. 38. Principal stages of succession starting in shallow depressions in granite rock in eastern North Carolina. The *Verrucaria-Parmelia* lichen crust is overridden as *Grimmia* colonies expand from independent starting points. (Based on data from Oosting and Anderson, 1939)

mesophytic as those on deep loams in the same region. For example, on sandstone outcroppings in southern Illinois, soil accumulation may lead to forest development only in places well protected from sun and wind, whereas a few meters distant, exposure results in a climax consisting of lichens and mosses only.[469] But in the humid climate of southern Florida, forest can develop quickly on coral limestone with virtually no soil present.

Successional diagrams such as those in Fig. 38 constitute a graphic means of illustrating the main features of a sere. They usually involve many compromises, however, for although the communities which comprise the sere have a characteristic order of appearance, many deviations, including occasional omissions and sometimes reversals of sequence, must be omitted or the diagram becomes too complex to serve its purpose. Certain of the deviations from the usual pattern may reflect only chance operating on the availability of different species with similar ecologic amplitudes, and determining whether they occur singly or in varying combinations at a particular stage. Other deviations are ecologically based, representing minor environmental variations, such as depressions that collect water, direction of exposure, steepness of slope, etc., which evoke parallel floristic peculiarities. The point at which these become significant enough to recognize must always rest on the judgment of the individual, but in any event interest in exceptions must not be allowed to obscure the most frequent sequences of events.

The primary controlling factor in any xerosere is the initial degree of dryness of the habitat and the relative rapidity with which this is ameliorated. On a rock outcrop drought tends to be extreme, owing to lack of a rooting medium that retains enough water to satisfy transpiration demands between storms, and the rate of vegetation development is limited by the rate of accumulation of such a water-retaining medium. Stage after stage in the xerosere improves edaphic conditions, but in so doing ensures its own destruction by making it possible for superior competitors to invade. Here as in all seres, the major role of the changing environment is to determine first which species can germinate, then which of these can continue to develop. Then it is a matter of which of these can, through size or numbers, achieve dominance over the others.

On sloping surfaces crevices are especially important even late in the sere, from the standpoint of anchorage. Mats of vegetation with soil tend to develop weight in excess of the strength of their anchorage, and unless sizable crevices are abundant, the mantle of organisms plus soil slumps to the base of the incline, although there the plants may continue to grow in a situation where they could never get established directly.

As a very broad generalization, it is true that as primary succession advances, dominance shifts from small plants low in the phylogenetic scale to large plants which are evolutionarily higher. In rock outcrop succession the pioneer communities are commonly dominated by lichens and mosses with vasculares eventually taking over through a sequence of herbaceous, shrubby, and arborescent communities, if climate and parent materials permit. It should be noted, however, that the shift in dominance seldom eliminates the life-forms characteristic of preceding stages. Thus there may be epigeous lichens in a climax forest, but they will be species vastly different in ecology from those that pioneered the site.

In comparison with other seres, the rate of succession on rock surfaces is extremely slow, many centuries being required for the completion of a sere in all but very wet climates. Because of the thinness of the layer of debris accumulating over rock, and its high organic matter content, a hot fire can easily destroy this product of centuries of plant activity. Erosion is then free to wash the rock outcrop completely bare once more. Clearly, it is desirable to give special protection to vegetation which has developed on thin soil overlying rock, for nowhere does the revegetation of denuded land present a problem so difficult of solution. In parts of Florida where very little soil has accumulated, ponderous machinery has been developed to comminute the soft coral bedrock and provide a rooting medium that is satisfactory for growing crops, but this much manipulation of rock outcrop environment is indeed unique.

Dune succession.   Sand dunes form continuously along many seacoasts, lake shores, and stream banks, owing to wind removal of sand

FIG. 39. Foredunes captured by *Abronia maritima* and *Franseria*. Baja California.

FIG. 40. Desert along the western edge of the Salton Sea in California. Each dune supports a single plant, or clone, of *Prosopis pubescens* that has grown to keep pace with sand that collects in the still air beneath the branches.

that is deposited at the water's edge. In dry regions sand may be released by rock weathering. Also, dunes may form or be rejuvenated wherever the vegetation cover of outwash plains or other sandy soils is destroyed so that the surface can be scoured by wind.

On flat topography in arid regions sand may simply spread out as a rather flat sheet, or it may ruffle up to form bare and mobile mounds of a variety of forms, some of which migrate with the wind.[257] Wherever wind carrying sand encounters an obstruction, its carrying power is reduced so that sand becomes lodged about the obstruction. In this way shadowlike mounds of sand, called embryo dunes, or foredunes, accumulate about nuclei of rocks, driftwood, or plants. When inanimate objects cause the accumulation of sand mounds, their size is limited by the fixed magnitude of the obstruction offered to the wind. But this is not true of phytogenic dunes.

Sand accumulating about an annual or a biennial is dissipated when the plant completes its functions and dies. But if a perennial causes a foredune to accumulate, the dune is likewise perennial, increasing in size as the plant grows, and often migrating slowly downwind over a long period (Figs. 39, 40). Erosion on the gradual windward face desiccates the plant progressively, as deposition on the steep lee slope stimulates vegetative propagation there.

To be successful as a sand accumulator a plant must be tolerant of atmospheric desiccation, resist wind breakage and sand abrasion, and what is especially important, it must accommodate worsening aeration about its root system due to sand deposition. The last is accomplished by producing adventitious roots along the rhizomes of grasses or erect stems of woody plants at successively higher levels. *Ammophila arenaria*, a common sand-binding grass, can maintain itself in habitats where the deposition of sand amounts to as much as 90 cm/year.[353] It not merely tolerates burial; it requires it to maintain vigor. In another dune grass with similar characteristics it has been shown that the older roots are very short lived so that new sand increments above are essential to provide substrate for new roots upon which continued functioning of the plant as a whole depends.[293] A cessation of sand deposition starts the deterioration of such plants, and if the clone is not quickly invaded by plants of a different ecology, the dune surface again becomes susceptible to rapid blowing.

The characteristics of dune-forming plants and the sand mounds they accumulate are closely related. If the plant grows upward with exceptional vigor the dune tends to increase in height rapidly. If the plant spreads laterally at a rapid pace the dune will be low and broad. Most successful dune-formers are perennial grasses and shrubs whose growth in many cases is definitely stimulated by covering. Some characteristic native and naturalized members in the North American flora are:

Shrubs	**Grasses**
Hudsonia tomentosa	*Ammophila arenaria*
Mesembryanthemum aequilaterale	*A. breviligulata*
Prosopis juliflora	*Calamovilfa longifolia*
P. pubescens	*Elymus mollis*
Prunus pumila	*Redfieldia flexuosa*
Salix spp.	*Uniola paniculata*

An embryo dune forming about a single plant continues to increase in size until conditions arise which bring about the death of the plant. The latter may become elevated higher and higher above the water table as sand accumulates, so that the water supply becomes less secure, and all the time transpiration stress is increasing. As the plant weakens and loses its control, vigorous erosion starts on the windward side and soon the freed mound of sand is moving rapidly downwind.

A dune lacking vegetation moves when wind speed reaches about 4 m/sec, giving enough force to roll sand grains up the gradual incline of the windward slope (about 5°) and drop them just over the crest so that they roll down the precipitous lee slope (about 30°), or cause an oversteepening that is corrected by shearing from time to time. Small dunes move rapidly, overtaking and becoming part of larger dunes. Owing to differences in constancy of winds, depth of sand, etc., dunes may take the form of parallel ridges in harmony with wind direction or, especially along seacoasts, at right angles to it, but usually they take the form of a crescentic "barchan" that moves downwind with the two horns directed forward. These may coalesce to form a complex.

Moving at rates up to 25 m/year, wandering dunes have a tremendous effect upon whatever vegetation they encounter (Fig. 41). Plants of low stature are overridden and destroyed. Many are killed without being completely covered due to reduced oxygen about their roots. Migration continues until the movement of the sand is diminished by a period of below-average wind, or by above-average precipitation, which permits aggressive colonization by plants. Sometimes the approach or development of a new dune in a windward direction may lessen the activity of a dune long enough for it to become captured by vegetation (Fig. 42).

A bare sand surface exposed to wind presents some unique and formidable conditions to invading plants. Sand particles blown along by wind are highly abrasive and this must extract a heavy toll among seedlings. Burial is often fatal even to seedlings of plants which as mature individuals require deposition to maintain vigor.[268] If they escape these two hazards, the high temperature of the insolated sand increases transpiration and respiration and frequently scorches the hypocotyl at

FIG. 41. Dune overriding and killing a stand of *Picea sitchensis*, and encroaching on a pond. The dune may fill the pond and continue its march if there is enough sand above the capillary fringe. Florence, Oregon.

the sand surface.[105] Small wonder that successful germination and establishment are practically confined to rainy seasons.

Although drought at the surface of bare sand is critical, below the surface the sand is commonly moist to field capacity. Only a little rain is sufficient to penetrate below the reach of atmospheric evaporation, capillary water rises rapidly if only a short way up from any water table, and it has been suspected though not proved that internal dew formation may help maintain this water supply below the surface. Whereas early in the sere, developing shade and humus accretions tend to progressively reduce the severity of drought at the soil surface, roots make increasing demands on subsoil moisture. Also, mineral weathering and dust accumulation may reduce infiltration and reduce moisture supplies by favoring surface runoff.[200]

In contrast with foredunes, the pioneer community that invades a large mass of sand that has slowed its movement initiates a developmental sequence.[106, 200] It stabilizes the surface, provides lodging for wind-borne disseminules, and shields the resulting seedlings from sun and wind. The humus accumulation allows a microbiota that becomes active and aids in the development of soil structure. Because windward slopes are more exposed to desiccating winds, and much of their precipitation is transferred to lee slopes, they normally support seres differing from those of lee slopes.[106] When H. C. Cowles made his classic study of dune succession at the south end of Lake Michigan he wondered if the amelioration of drought as the *Quercus velutina* forest developed on wind-exposed dune surfaces would continue to the point of allowing the invasion of the more mesophytic *Acer-Fagus-Tsuga* forest to be found

FIG. 42. Dune surface near Minneapolis that has been quiescent for several years, resulting in the establishment of many young plants of the coarse *Calamovilfa longifolia*, with the diminutive annual *Cenchrus pauciflorus* also aiding stabilization.

on well-protected slopes, but he found no evidence for such a conversion. Apparently intrinsic microclimatic differences between the two slopes cannot be effaced by vegetation influences. In fact, vegetation influences seem to entrench initial differences in many respects.

Woody dune plants are notable for their extensive root systems. Aeration makes deep rooting possible, and the limited supplies of water and especially of nutrients gives an advantage to plants that can produce long roots.

Once a dune is stabilized by vegetation (Fig. 43), creep, rodent activity, and slope wash slowly reduce the sharpness of its contours as the centuries pass, so that in the continued absence of major disturbance a dune system tends to become an undulating plain.[400]

Disturbance of dune vegetation and its significance. At any time during the development of its plant cover, sand may be set in motion again

FIG. 43. Dunes well stabilized by *Ericameria ericoides* and other shrubs along the California coast near Santa Maria.

if the vegetation is destroyed even in part. In fact, the usual history of sandhills is one of alternate breakup and restabilization of the complex as a whole, with no dune retaining its identity for long. Fire, drought, windfall, logging, overgrazing, recreational use (Fig. 44), the trailing of livestock, etc., have all been known to break the vegetal cover and allow wind erosion to get started. A trough- or bowl-shaped "blowout" can be quickly excavated, developing an active rim on all but the upwind side (Fig. 45). The blowout increases in size, sometimes up to a kilometer in length, until a large area of sand is once more on the move, unless a period of above-average precipitation favors restabilization. Each blowout effaces all soil development (Fig. 46), the humus and small aeolian particles that have accumulated separating from the sand and blowing away.

Erosion may go so far as to remove sand down to the capillary fringe that lies above the water table, so that flat, moist *slacks* (or *pannes*) are commonly interspersed among moving dunes. In such situations it is the upper surface of the capillary fringe that determines the floor of a dune complex below which the sand cannot be removed. In the gypsum dunes of White Sands National Monument, New Mexico, all of the 62 species of vasculares comprising the flora must germinate in the slacks, and of these only seven have the ability to grow upward later at a sufficient

FIG. 44. Stabilized sand along seacoast near St. Petersburg, Florida, where the only shade has attracted picnic parties (note debris) that have destroyed an area of grass cover. If this were a windward slope, wind erosion would have been active by now.

FIG. 45. Active blowout among low coastal dunes stabilized mainly by *Elymus mollis*. Near Florence, Oregon.

FIG. 46. Slack among dunes of steppe region near Roggen, Colorado. *Salix* and *Carex* have invaded sand that is kept moist by the capillary rise of moisture from the water table.

rate to keep above the surface of a dune advancing over the slack.[154] In some regions a rising water table during the wet season creates a temporary marsh or pond in each slack (Fig. 46).

Controlled succession on dunes.[410] Moving dunes result in much economic loss. They override (or associated erosion undermines) forest, pasture, cropland, highways, railways, buildings, and other valuable properties. They fill in harbors and channels so that navigation, fish migration, and natural drainage are impeded. For these reasons, coupled with the slowness and uncertainty of natural succession, stopping the movement of sand and stabilizing its surface has long been attempted by mankind. Great stone walls built along either side of the Nile Valley show clearly that the Pharaohs of Egypt fought the encroachment of sand onto fertile croplands. At the present time, using newly developed combinations of engineering and ecologic techniques, many areas of hazardous or at least worthless shifting dunes are being converted to

land of high value. Golden Gate Park in San Francisco represents a fine
example of such conversion.

In any sand-stabilization project a study of the natural dune seres of
the particular region where control work is to be attempted provides
valuable clues as to the best species to use and the order in which to
plant them to ensure success in the operation. Even though the natural
sequence may be somewhat emulated, with special planting techniques
and the judicious use of mats or fences the artificial sere can be made
to advance with abnormal rapidity. As with any erosion problem, most
of the effort expended at first should be directed to the point where the
sand is originating rather than at its leeward edge where the damage
may have reached serious proportions.

On the coast of Oregon where dune stabilization has been under study
for many years, the following schedule was worked out for fixing the
sand.[287]

Step 1. An initial sand binder such as the native *Elymus mollis* or the
exotic *Ammophila* spp. is planted, using 2-year-old nursery stock representing clonal divisions. It has been found that the layer of virtually
calm air produced by friction next to a bare sand surface is only about
0.03 cm thick, but after a stand of grass is established the layer
increases to about 1 cm thick, which is enough to stop erosion and
start deposition.[318] It is this initial sand-stilling step that is always the
most difficult one, and to increase chances of success the planting is
done at the onset of the rainy season.

Step 2. Two years later the area is sown with leguminous herbs
(*Lupinus littoralis, Lathyrus japonicus*) and grasses (*Poa macrantha,
Festuca rubra*) in order to (1) fill in poorly vegetated spots, (2) maintain stability in the face of declining vigor of the pioneer grasses as the
surface becomes stable, and (3) augment the nitrogen supply of the
ecosystem.

Step 3. After the herbaceous cover is fairly complete, woody species
are planted to lift the winds higher and thus better ensure stability of
the surface. *Cytisus scoparius* and *Lupinus arboreus* (both nitrogen-
fixers) with *Salix hookeriana* are planted on the seaward side of the
stabilized belt, with *Pinus contorta* on the landward side. The native
Tsuga heterophylla or *Picea sitchensis* may be expected naturally to
enter the habitat slowly, but their advent is inconsequential for control.
Step 3, in fact, is considered essential only where topography is irregular, hence conducive to local intensification of wind scouring. But
because of the longevity and superior wind-lifting influence of the tree
growth-form, forest provides the most permanent and safest type of
dune cover, and hence is usually the goal of revegetation projects
wherever climate permits.

In some areas native vegetation can be depended on to invade and stabilize after no more than an initial planting has been made, and in still other areas, trees (usually *Acacia, Casuarina, Eucalyptus* or *Pinus*) may be planted directly in sand if brush barriers are formed in an open network. Should the wind be too strong for any planting, as just above the littoral zone along seacoasts, windbreaks of open reed or lath fences, or brush piled in rows, may be erected at right angles to the wind as an aid in establishment, but these must present a continuous front of uniform height.[77] By erecting a series of fencelike structures successively above one another as each in turn becomes buried, the crest of a dune may be quickly brought to a height that cuts off most of the sand coming from the sea. Thereafter new fences erected on windward slopes can be used to broaden the sand ridge before all is stabilized with a living cover. By this technique dunes have been shaped to serve as dikes along the coast of Holland.[65, 77]

In selecting species for planting, the chemical as well as the physical features of dune environment need consideration. Foredunes originating on seacoasts have a fairly good supply of nitrogen, calcium, phosphorus and other nutrients accruing from plant and animal remains cast up by waves. But as dunes move away from the shore, wind-sorting removes the nitrogenous materials, and with time the calcium and other nutrients are lost by leaching, so that fertility becomes critically low.[462] Where urgency of stabilization counterbalances the importance of cost, nitrogen fertilizer is dependable for stimulating growth. Fertilization becomes imperative if any harvesting of established dune vegetation is permitted.

Along seacoasts, saline spray carried onshore by winds imposes added limitations to the variety of species suitable for planting.[321]

Palatability is another point to consider. If grazing pressure is likely to be appreciable and not easily controlled, unpalatable plants are to be preferred, at least as pioneers. For the final stages, however, plants that improve the habitat for wildlife may be favored as a means of realizing another benefit from sand stabilization.

All use of stabilized dune vegetation must be limited and subject to constant surveillance, in order to prevent the start or at least the expansion of blowouts.

Lake and pond succession. Inland bodies of water vary in area from pools that one can step across, to vast expanses of water that one cannot see across; they vary in duration from vernal pools which desiccate completely each summer to those that maintain reasonably constant water levels for centuries; some are deep enough to be thermally stratified and some are not; some extend below the depth of effective light penetration and some do not. Because such important features are so varied, many ways of drawing a distinction between lakes and ponds have been proposed, depending on the use to which the classification is put.[450]

From the standpoint of the ecology of macrophytes, there is much merit in classifying bodies of water as *ponds* when they are so small that there is insufficient wave action to prevent a continuous cover of plants extending from shallow water onto the uplands. *Lakes* are then distinguished from ponds by having a wave-beaten marginal zone which is permanently devoid of macroscopic vegetation, so that the communities of hydrophytes growing below the water surface have no connection with terrestrial vegetation that begins well back from the lake.[421] Using this criterion, protected bays off a large lake must be classed ecologically with ponds on account of the identity of their vegetation, whereas small bodies of water lacking marginal vegetation owing to steep rocky shores are ecologically lakes. As a result of wave inhibition of vegetation in the shallow waters of a lake margin, where productivity would otherwise be at maximum, lakes are normally much less productive of dry matter than are ponds.

Lake seres.[421] When a lake originates through some geologic accident such as blockage of a drainageway, glaciation, etc., the outline is ordinarily quite irregular, but waves and wind-induced currents at once begin to wear away the headlands, depositing the eroded material in bays, with a result that the shoreline is progressively smoothed. There is also a vertical component of the wave-induced remodeling of a basin, involving an encroachment of water on land by erosion, accompanied by a filling of the basin with the sediments produced. The back and forth surge of waves usually cannot move large boulders, but smaller stones are dragged downslope in inverse proportion to their sizes, with silt and clay being held in suspension so long that these particles are carried far out from the shoreline before settling out. Thus the deepest parts of a lake accumulate layers of fine mineral sediments derived in part from erosion of the shore, in part from atmospheric dust, and in part from streams which discharge into the basin.

In regions of high rainfall, the above processes of erosion and deposition cause most lakes to increase in area, while the deeper places are slowly built up to a plane surface, the height of which is determined by the wave base, below which turbulence is feeble and allows fine sediments to come to rest permanently. Early in the history of such a lake there typically appears a relatively high type of plant community on that part of the sloping bottom which is just below the level of strong wave action, for it is only there that fairly good illumination accompanies freedom from destruction by turbulence. Submerged anchored hydrophytes such as *Chara, Elodea, Myriophyllum,* and *Potamogeton* are characteristic dominants. At successively greater depths there are usually one or more communities arranged somewhat in belts along the contours, each in turn composed of dominants more tolerant of decreasing illumination, and of sedimentation. Mosses and blue-green algae are common constituents of the deepest zones.

As the depositional terrace extends into deeper water, each vegetation zone can extend farther from the shore because of improving illumination, and so encroaches on territory formerly held by the adjacent zone. Since sedimentation ceases only after the bottom builds up to a plane surface corresponding with a level just below severe turbulence, the communities of deeper waters become extinct, each in turn, and one community tends to assume dominance over most of the bottom.

In shallow water, where wave action is too strong for most macrophytes, there may be a few species that can grow here and form a zone or two despite turbulence and slow erosion. Succession progresses in this centrifugal direction only as an erosional terrace expands shoreward. Thus one of the communities of submerged anchored hydrophytes which early occupied a narrow zone on the lake bottom tends to form a climax which extends its area in either direction so long as erosion and deposition continue. The lake bed habitat eventually becomes a flat plane in equilibrium with wave activity. In freshwater such benthic climaxes are dominated by herbaceous angiosperms or *Charales*; in seas the corresponding dominants are thallophytes, especially *Phaeophyta*.

A lake approaches senility when the deeps are filled to the level of moderate turbulence, and the water becomes so shallow that wave action decreases and erosion consequently declines to a very slow rate. This results typically in a long-enduring condition, and the wavering balance between erosion and deposition on the bottom may destroy the macroscopic vegetation and result in the formation of a deep layer of unstable ooze.

Geologically, lakes are short lived, disappearing as a result of filling with debris dumped where the feeding streams enter, combined with downward erosion of the outlet—a process which may overtake the widening and shallowing phase at any point, and which usually prevents completion of the theoretical developmental sequence described above. When the lake bed eventually dries, a new sere leading toward a terrestrial climax is initiated.

The foregoing outline of developmental trends in physiography and vegetation applies chiefly to regions where rainfall exceeds evaporation. In arid climates the sequence is different. Here silting is slower and there is usually little or no overflow from the lake. Because of the latter condition the lake level fluctuates widely with seasonal and long-term variations in rainfall. Salinity gradually increases so that any freshwater vegetation disappears, to be replaced by salt marsh or other halophytic communities.

FIG. 47. Recession of the valley glacier in the distance has been so recent that the developing plant life of moraine and pond shows negligible order, owing to the still-limited flora and lack of significant competition. Alberta.

Pond seres.[191] Where wave action is feeble, as in ponds, embayments of lakes, or sheltered lagoons along tropical seacoasts, the vegetal cover is continuous across the shore line. Silt brought by flowing water, together with peat and marl from organisms growing in the water, build up the bottom progressively so that succession is entirely a centripetal process of development from hydrophytic vegetation to a terrestrial community that first makes its appearance at the original margin of the water. When a pond or embayment is first formed, physiographic processes dominate and sediments move about slowly by water currents so that the deepest parts fill most actively, but after aquatic vegetation is well developed, deposition of organic matter near the shore tends to become dominant, owing to the high productivity of shallow-water habitats.

Examination of a newly formed pond reveals that the invading plants have only slightly different requirements with respect to water depth (Fig. 47). But as competition intensifies, most species are drawn into conformity with a series of narrow belts, each characterized by some species or life-form that dominates a well-marked sector of the environmental gradient (Fig. 48). Since water depth exerts the major control, all belts must creep toward the center of the pond as sedimentation progresses (Fig. 49). Thus each belt from the center to the pond margin may be interpreted as a stage of succession. From any given point on the

FIG. 48. Pond in northern British Columbia formed by deglaciation several thousand years ago. Competitive elimination and mutual adjustments have produced narrow but sharply demarked vegetation zones (*Nymphaea, Carex, Betula-Salix, Picea mariana*) on a gradual environmental gradient. Too little peat has accumulated to have much effect on the zonal pattern.

bottom, all zones will pass to the shore in definite sequence. Succession is brought about by shallowing, which throws the competitive balance in favor of plants of the next zone above.

Some common types of hydrophytes and the successional roles they play in pond habitats are as follows:

FIG. 49. Pond near Puget Sound that has supported vegetation for at least 11,000 years. A wide floating mat of *Carex* is being invaded patchwise by shrubs, with *Tsuga heterophylla* entering the shrub patches. Extension of the mat as a shelf appears to have eliminated emergent vegetation that probably once encircled the basin, and left only small remnants of a *Nuphar* belt. *Tsuga* is the major climax dominant on peat as well as on adjacent mineral soil in this area, but permanent differences in undergrowth mark distinctive associations on the two soil materials. Note free-floating segment that has become detached from the *Carex* mat.

Plankton and floating macrophytes.   Communities composed chiefly of algae, bacteria, protozoa, and other minute animals which are suspended in the upper layers of water comprise *plankton*. Floating vascular plants include *Eichhornia, Lemna, Pistia, Salvinia, Spirodela,* and *Wolffia*. Depth of water is of no consequence to any of these plants, so they occur all over the water surface unless wind pushes them to one side of the basin or another. In comparison with other groups of hydrophytes, their environment is unique for its homogeneity.

Except where the floaters are abundant, this class of hydrophytes usually has limited influence on succession in the way of helping build up the bottom, for the substance of plankton organisms is easily decayed, producing nothing more substantial than ooze. But because of their superficial position in the water they have an important if indirect influence on succession by intercepting light, and thus restricting the

FIG. 50. Pond surface completely occupied by a floating mat of *Eichhornia crassipes*. Florida.

development of communities on the pond bottom. Where these hydrophytes are very sparse and the water contains virtually no other suspended matter, aquatic mosses or algae can extend to a depth of 120 m before reaching their compensation points. But where there is a continuous sheet of floaters (Fig. 50), all green plants are eliminated below and oxygen levels drop so low that fish cannot survive.[378] The significance of the shade factor is well illustrated by the finding that artificial fertilization of ponds with nitrogen and phosphorus may be used to favor plankton which makes the water so opaque that submerged macrophytes are killed,[217] or promotes such a copious development of epiphytic algae that the same result is achieved.[399]

Submerged anchored hydrophytes. In cool and cold climates the genera *Ceratophyllum, Chara, Elodea, Fontinalis, Isoetes, Najas, Pota-*

mogeton, Vallisneria, etc., provide many species which grow entirely submerged in water. They are the first macrophytes to advance over the bottom, as a rule, and so usually comprise the innermost zone of vascular plants in pond margin vegetation, extending to a depth of about 7 m, which makes their study rather difficult.[471] In comparison with plankton, submerged anchored plants more actively advance the sere. During photosynthesis freshwater vasculares soon exhaust the free CO_2 in the surrounding water, then must turn to the soluble bicarbonates as a source of CO_3^{--}. Withdrawal of this ion from the water causes insoluble carbonates to precipitate in the adjacent water or to accumulate as brittle coatings of lime up to several millimeters thick on the epidermis. These coatings flake off and settle out, together with other precipitates, to accumulate on the pond bottom as *marl.* Where parent materials provide a rich supply of carbonates, the bottom sediments are marl (up to 30 m thick) or at least a limy ooze.

Submerged anchored plants also promote the deposition of silt, for currents of water penetrating the stands are slowed and their silt-carrying capacity is reduced. The deposition of marl and silt are also characteristic of other types of anchored macrophytes as well as this group.

In another way, the completely submerged plants tend to resemble plankton in their influence. With their feebly developed xylem and lack of cutinization, their decaying remains produce sediments more like ooze than like the fibrous peat formed by plants exposed to air.

Floating-leaved anchored hydrophytes.   Communities dominated by species in *Brassenia, Nuphar, Nyphaea, Nymphoides,* or *Sparganium* frequently form a zone in water which is no deeper than about 3 m. As the water becomes shallower and plants of this life-form migrate toward the center of the pond, their broad leaves form so continuous a cover at the water surface that submerged species are put to a disadvantage by shade. Exposure of the upper blade surface promotes the development of a cuticle as well as lignification of xylem, with a result that the dead tissues of these plants have more substance and are slower to decay.

Emergent anchored hydrophytes.   In water no deeper than about a meter there may be communities dominated by herbaceous plants which are rooted in the pond bottom but project well above the water surface. These are sometimes referred to as "amphibious" plants or, collectively, as "reed swamp," in contrast with "aquatics" of the categories discussed above. Representative genera are: *Carex, Eleocharis, Glyceria, Mariscus, Phragmites, Sagittaria, Scirpus, Sparganium, Typha,* and *Zizania.* As the water becomes more shallow, these plants are able to encroach on the floating-leaved plants by sending shoots up into the air between their blades.

Mangroves might be included in this category. These thicket-forming

FIG. 51. Pond with an anchored zone of *Carex*, and with a stable *Salix* scrub growing where firm peat has accumulated. Trees in the background, mainly *Abies lasiocarpa*, are growing on mineral soil and are unrelated to the pond sere. Medicine Bow Mountains, Wyoming.

shrubs found in tropical and subtropical lagoons or bays have conspicuous prop roots which enable them to advance over accumulating mudflats.

Marginal mats. Originating on the moist soil at the edge of the water where both light and oxygen content of the water favor maximal productivity, a narrow belt of vascular plants or mosses may expand toward the pond center at a relatively rapid rate. These plants form a tangled peat-accumulating mat which either remains anchored to the bottom and fills the basin as it advances, or pushes out over the water surface as a floating shelf which is attached only to the shore.

The anchored type of mat in the cold or cool parts of the northern hemisphere is usually dominated by *Carex* (Fig. 51). Floating mats may likewise be dominated by *Carex* but sometimes by *Decodon, Mariscus, Phragmites, Sagittaria, Sphagnum,* or *Typha* (Figs. 52, 53).

A floating mat of *Carex* may attain a width of many meters and is usually so firm that a person can walk across it to within a few meters of its outer (thinner) edge, whereas the opposite edge is occasionally firm enough to be cropped while still floating. Fluctuations in the level of pond water commonly follow fluctuations in rainfall, but the unanchored edge of the shelflike mat maintains its position relative to the water surface by floating,[61] which gives this type of community somewhat of

FIG. 52. A floating mat dominated by *Sphagnum* with *Myrica gale* on a pond in southwestern British Columbia. The substitution of *Sphagnum* for *Carex* here indicates nutrition too low in divalent cations for fen.

an advantage over anchored plants. Abundant air channels in submerged organs of the dominants give the mat this buoyancy.

Whether of the anchored or the floating type, mats are very constructive in succession through the active formation of peat. Although peat derived from submerged and emergent communities usually begins to accumulate in the deeps early in the sere and may form a continuous mantle over the pond bottom before the mat is well formed, the latter commonly becomes the major contributor to sedimentation (Fig. 35). Floating *Carex* mats in Minnesota are accumulating litter at the rate of about 1.5 cm/year,[273] but radiocarbon dating shows the average rate of peat accumulation during post-Wisconsin time to be about 0.6 mm/ year, owing to compression as the litter increments become buried.[367]

Sometimes portions of a floating mat are torn off to become floating islands (Fig. 49) that shift from one side of the pond to the other as the wind changes, becoming attached if they remain in one position long. Mats may also start on floating bits of debris, and in southeastern North America these develop to the point of allowing invasion by trees.[234]

Expanding in a centripetal manner, a floating mat overrides communities of emergent and submerged anchored plants (Fig. 49). In the opposite direction, as the older (shoreward) edge of the mat becomes

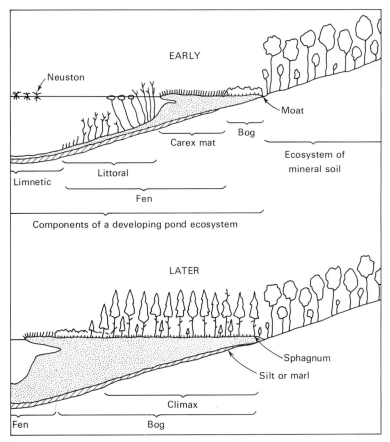

FIG. 53. Some terms applicable to an area having a pond in an active state of development.

thicker and firmer with age, it builds up above the water table and becomes a suitable habitat for invasion by communities which may be dominated by shrubs or trees, each of which in turn appears to demand a greater degree of firmness and drainage of the peat. As a result of this inward advance of the zones, open water eventually disappears and finally a relatively mesophytic climax becomes established even over the center of the peat lens.

In cool and cold climates, at least, an abrupt and ecologically very important change takes place when the germination surface becomes elevated to the point where rain keeps the surface of the peat leached, and the relatively high nutrient content of the pond water is no longer available to seedlings and sporelings. A decline in calcium and an increase in acidity in turn lessen the availability of nitrogen and

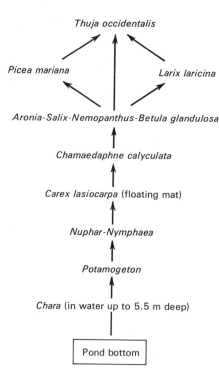

FIG. 54. Common sequences of dominants in pond succession in lower Michigan. The replacement of *Carex* by *Chamaedaphne* marks the transition from fen to flat bog (for definitions see p. 148) in which the ground beneath the woody plants has a carpet of *Sphagnum* throughout. (Gates, 1942)

phosphorus at this time. A *Sphagnum* carpet develops and subsequent communities are sharply different in their floristics, this point along the sere marking the distinction between *fen* and *bog* (see p. 148). Aside from the chemical implications of its presence, *Sphagnum* grows upward with sufficient rapidity to smother slow-growing seedlings of potential community components, and this heightens the distinction between fen and bog.

Pond seres are usually much less uniform than a useful successional diagram (Fig. 54) can indicate. Certain zones may be locally unrepresented whereas elsewhere they may be telescoped, and the specific composition of a given zone may vary. Variation is especially characteristic of zones rooted on the bottom and seems to reflect several factors. The pond bottom is commonly heterogeneous, and various members of a life-form group may grow best in silt, sand, cobble, marl, or peat.[343, 426, 467] Topographic irregularity begets variation in the speed of water currents, and certain species are sensitive to currents.[455] Locally there are differences in wave action and rates of erosion or deposition. And finally, since the environment is rather extreme and the species few, a low level of competition puts more species on an equal footing.

The chemical nature of the pond water, which depends largely on the chemical nature of the parent materials forming the basin, is a factor of importance governing the complexion of the sere as a whole, at least up to late stages of peat accumulation. As some ponds develop fertility declines, owing to the progressive immobilization of nutrients that were abundant in the newly formed basin, whereas in other ponds nutrients may slowly accumulate, starting from water originally low in fertility.

Early in hydroseres, both freshwater and saline,[160] the dominant environmental factor controlling development is depth of water in relation to light availability on the bottom. Later the nutrition, aeration, and temperature of the rooting medium tend to take precedence.

Pond hydroseres involve change from a saturated toward a fairly well-drained substratum, which is the reverse of the trend in rock outcrop and dune xeroseres. Thus in both hydro- and xeroseres succession proceeds from extremes of wetness or drought toward a climax which is the most mesophytic community to appear on the habitat. Although *mesotropy* is evident in the early stages of hydro- and xeroseres, it becomes difficult to demonstrate toward the ends. Furthermore, as will be pointed out in a later section, the principle does not seem to apply to certain seres at any stage.

Climatic fluctuations have a very pronounced effect on plant succession. Wet phases retard, stop, or even reverse hydroseres,[238] whereas dry phases speed up the rate of change. With xeroseres the reverse is true. Water is so important a factor everywhere in terrestrial vegetation that we might suspect the conclusions from any successional study to have been colored somewhat by the weather peculiarities of the years immediately preceding the time the study was made.[63, 93]

Thousands of ponds with clearly zoned vegetation, as in Figs. 47 and 48, attest a common pattern of vegetation sequences over a wide area, and the stratification of peat types, as in Figs. 35 and 55, prove the persistence of such vegetation trends through thousands of years. But there are circumstances that allow progression and retrogression to alternate frequently in time or space. For example, during drought periods fire originating on uplands may extend varying distances into peatlands, burning out pockets in which succession starts anew when the water table again rises (Fig. 56). The active growth of peat-formers at the lip of a basin can produce peat dams that flood and cause retrogression in the entire basin. On gentle slopes peat accumulation may be very rapid only locally, so that drainage is impeded frequently and a large area may consist of small units in varying stages of succession and retrogression due to impoundment; such a complex enlarges without apparent end.[215, 396] Also, where permafrost causes unequal interference with drainage, one can observe a mosaic of areas, each at a slightly different stage of succession or destruction by impoundment. In all such

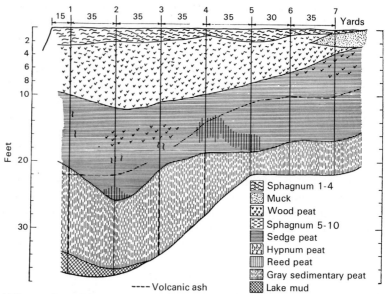

FIG. 55. Stratification of peat types in a bog near Puget Sound. The stratigraphy shows a regular and uninterrupted sequence of stages such as might be inferred from the present community zonation about ponds in that region (see Fig. 49). (Rigg and Richardson, 1938)

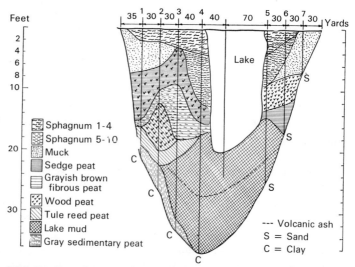

FIG. 56. Stratification of peat types in another (see Fig. 55) bog near Puget Sound. A turbulent history is indicated, but there is nothing to cause doubt that the same successional process was renewed after each interruption. (Rigg and Richardson, 1938)

situations succession still follows a common pattern that is normal to the climate, the nature of the water supply, etc.

Relation of zonation to succession. In the preceding discussion, the concentric zones of vegetation seen about a pond were given a dynamic interpretation. It is appropriate at this point to look into the justification for such an interpretation and consider its implications for other zonal patterns as well.

Wherever the intensity of any important factor of environment varies progressively across the landscape, plants form beltlike communities, or zones, each of which reflects a fairly definite range of tolerance for the factor. Should the course of physiographic development, or manipulation by man, bring about a progressive change in the intensity of the factors controlling the belts, the latter must migrate in an appropriate direction, and at a speed commensurate with the rate of change, if they are to remain in a suitable environment. The mere juxtaposition of communities on a gradient, then, is only an indication of possible successional relationships that may proceed in either of two directions. Conclusive proof that the belts are dynamically related must be based on one or more (preferably all) of the following types of evidence: (1) Young plants of one community should appear and maintain their position in the older part of the adjacent belt. It is essential here that a distinction be made between young and vigorous invaders and small but old plants which are stunted and barely able to maintain themselves in an ecotonal environment which may never allow them to rise to dominance (Fig. 57). (2) Relics of a preceding belt should persist for a time in the younger portions of a succeeding belt. It must not be overlooked here that the abundance of individuals often declines gradually across a perfectly stable ecotone only as a consequence of decreasing probability of establishment. To indicate retreat, the most remote individuals must all be old and exhibit by their vigor and vitality that they have lost their ability to complete their life cycles at these extreme locations and so will no longer be represented there when the existing individuals die. (3) The vertical stratification of any types of decay residues (e.g., peat types) or fossils (especially pollens) must conform to the successional hypothesis.

In peat-filled basins there is a situation in which the indicator significance of zonation may be more apparent than real. In Michigan a *Thuja occidentalis-Sphagnum* association has been interpreted as the typical climax on mature peat deposits,[172] but on well-drained mineral soils of the surrounding uplands the climax is entirely different from that which obtains on even the oldest peat deposits. Superficially the adjacent upland forest seems to be the last in a series of zones connected with the hydrosere, but the upland trees (*Acer saccharum,*

FIG. 57. Ecotone between *Populus tremuloides* grove and surrounding grassland east of Crookston, Minnesota. The size gradient of *Populus* may be interpreted as active advance upon grassland only if successively smaller plants are younger, rather than merely being dwarfed.

Fagus, Tilia, Tsuga, Quercus) are unable to grow on peat except perhaps as rare accidentals. In other regions, as around Puget Sound, upland climaxes and peat-filled basins may have the same tree dominants, although the undergrowth is always distinct. Therefore the space sequence at the margin of a peat area appears never to represent a time sequence.

Near seacoasts the zones of terrestrial vegetation that occur in parallel series are relatively permanent so far as direct evidence is concerned.[322] They are controlled primarily by wind in conjunction with salt spray, both of which decrease in intensity inland. Should there be indirect evidence that the coast has been elevating or subsiding, the direction of long-term changes in position of the zones in the immediate past is not much in doubt, but the future depends on very slow geologic processes whose direction and intensity cannot be foretold, so that a successional interpretation is unsatisfactory.

Altitudinal zones of vegetation on mountain slopes may likewise be considered members of a successional series only in the event of climatic change which through geologic time causes slow upward or downward displacement.

Special terminology. Since bodies of water and wetlands are so varied and have been studied extensively with a consequent elaboration of special terminology, it is desirable to present an outline-glossary to define more critically some of the terms used above and relate them to others in common use. In so doing, additional significant aspects of the ecosystems may be brought out.

Mineral content. Saline wet areas can be divided into *coastal saline, brackish* (diluted seawater), and *inland saline.*

Freshwater containing relatively little salt has long been classified according to the nutritional requirements of the average plant. Lakes and ponds resulting from deglaciation tend to be relatively *oligotrophic* when first formed, the clear waters held in the newly formed basins containing very little of at least some of the essential plant nutrients and so supporting a sparse flora. An oligotrophic condition is also favored by deepness of a body of water, which restricts the development of highly productive rooted vegetation, or by wave action or stoniness sufficient to inhibit marginal vegetation. On account of the paucity of decaying material, the dissolved oxygen remains unconsumed.

Gradual accumulation and retention of nutrients by aquatic ecosystems commonly change oligotrophic water, especially in ponds, to a relatively *eutrophic* condition with abundant nutrients, but with low oxygen content, due to active decay processes. These waters are said to have a high "biochemical oxygen demand" (BOD).

In contrast with the above trends, ponds formed by the blocking of valleys, settling of the land surface, etc., may be highly eutrophic at first because of materials dissolved from a developed soil and from the decay of drowned terrestrial vegetation. In part these nutrients subsequently become bound up in organic matter so that effective fertility declines, yet the water remains in the eutrophic class unless it is mostly too deep for rooted plants.

Whether eutrophic or oligotrophic, some ponds develop a special condition referred to as *dystrophic.* The water becomes brown as a result of suspended organic colloids, and the carbon to nitrogen ratio rises above 10.

Sediments.[163] The sediments that accumulate in pond and lake basins may be classified as: (1) *lake silt,* inorganic material brought into the basin from outside, or eroded from shallows and shores and deposited in deeps; this comprises the bulk of sediments in barren oligotrophic waters; (2) *marl,* $CaCO_3$ precipitated from eutrophic water by plants through photosynthetic use of bicarbonates, and commonly forming a layer at or near the bottom of a sequence of sedimentary strata; (3) *ooze,* either (a) *dy* (*gel mud*), structureless blackish-brown colloids, soluble in KOH, which are precipitated by Ca salts as a gelatinous layer from dystrophic waters, or (b) *gyttja* (*necron mud*), a semireduced particulate ooze, not soluble in KOH, representing mostly planktonic remains that accumulate at the bottom of eutrophic waters and frequently rest on marl; or (4) *peat,* fibrous, partly decayed fragments of vascular plants which retain enough structure so that the peat can usually be designated as having been derived principally from *Carex, Sphagnum,* woody plants, etc. *Limnic peat* is laid down by plants that grow submerged, and owing to their lack of cutin and lignin, this type is the most nearly structureless of the peat types. *Humified peat* is the blackish oxidized surface of a mature peat deposit which represents the attainment of an equilibrium between accumulation and oxidation. Alternating blackish and brownish layers reflect alternating dry and wet climatic phases, with oxidation favored by dryness and a new brown layer accumulating upon a return of wetter conditions.

Ecosystems.[326] Wetland ecosystems may be classified ecologically as (1) saline, brackish, or freshwater *marsh,* which is an herb-dominated ecosystem in which the rooting medium is inundated for long periods, if not continually, and is composed chiefly of mineral materials that are sometimes high in humus content; (2) saline, brackish, or freshwater *swamp,* that differs from marsh only in that woody plants are dominant; (3) *mire* (moor), which includes all ecosystems with wet peat serving as the rooting medium. Mires comprise two categories.

Fen (topogenous, minerotrophic, or soligeous mire; eutrophic moor) is distinguished by the seedlings or sporelings having available to them water which has been in contact with mineral soil and which consequently has a much better supply of nutrients than is contained in rainwater. *Cyperaceae, Gramineae,* or *Juncus* usually dominate in early stages of fen succession, with forbs and nonericaceous shrubs or trees (the *carr* of British literature) invading later, and appearing first on the centrifugal margin. Mosses, when abundant, seldom include *Sphagnum.* The surface of the peat is flat or slightly concave. Fen occurs in basins or on slopes with seepage, in areas of low to high rainfall. In the latter, fen is superseded by bog. *Eutrophic fen* is relatively fertile, has a *p*H usually above 4.5–5.0, and the flora is relatively rich. *Mesotrophic fen* is somewhat less fertile, nutritionally little superior to bog,* and has a poor flora.

Bog (ombrogenous or ombrotrophic mire; muskeg; moss; oligotrophic moor) includes mires in which seedlings or sporelings have

---

* Although fen is more fertile than bog, it is still nutritionally inferior to normal upland soil, so the term eutrophic is used only in a relative sense. It should be noted too that water low in nutrient content can still sustain good plant growth if it flows past the plant sufficiently fast to offset nutrient depletion through uptake. Fen substrata, at least in cold climates, tend to be rather consistently different from bog substrata in having higher *p*H, higher adsorbed calcium, magnesium, potassium, iron, and manganese and lower adsorbed phosphorus, while nitrogen nutrition is at least locally better.[192, 291] Fen water has a higher conductivity than bog water.

available to them scarcely more nutrients than are contained in rain-water (which has approximately 12–18 ppm electrolytes, with an electrical conductivity of 0.02–0.03 mmho/cm) as a result of the continual downward movement of water in consequence of a surface built up well above the water table, and high rainfall.[189] Bog is limited to cold and wet climates well beyond the influence of ocean spray. It is usually preceded by fen and hence marks a second phase in the nutritional relations of the developing ecosystem.[191] *Sphagnum* is usually conspicuous, forming closely spaced hummocks about 0.5 m high, usually accompanied by low ericaceous shrubs, and sometimes stunted coniferous trees as well. Floristically, bog tends to be more impoverished than fen. The pH is generally less than 5.0–4.5. *Blanket bog* (or climbing bog) is a type that is initiated in locally wet spots, from which it spreads to cover all topography except steep slopes, often overwhelming forest. Blanket bog is conspicuous in wet foggy climates along cool-temperate coasts, e.g., Ireland and southern Alaska, but is also common in continental interiors at high latitudes. *Raised bog* (raised moss, or high moor) is a type confined to the area of a wet basin as a result of only moderate precipitation. The surface becomes convex so that the feeble drainage channels (*lagg*) that run across the basin are pushed to one or both sides of the peat dome. Since lagg water represents drainage from adjacent mineral ground, as well as from the raised center of the bog, it tends to be eutrophic, hence is commonly bordered by a narrow belt of fen on the centrifugal side. The steeply sloping margins of the dome tend to be vegetationally differentiated and have been referred to as the *rand* habitat. The convexity of the dome may result from bases in the drainage waters damaging *Sphagnum* along the rand, from high rates of peat decomposition there, or from a fluctuating water supply. *Flat bog*, the third type of bog, is not only confined to the limits of a wet basin, but it remains flat without developing convexity (except locally as hummocks develop). This type is characteristic of drier climates than is raised bog.

Some practical problems. In temperate and cool climates eutrophic bodies of water used for domestic purposes or recreation may become highly distasteful and odorous, if not toxic,[373] as a result of periodic appearances of *water bloom,* an exceptionally abundant growth of plankton algae during hot weather that turns the water greenish. Adding sufficient $CuSO_4$ to bring the concentration up to about 1 ppm (providing there is no excess of $CaCO_3$ or P to precipitate the Cu ions) virtually stops algal growth, but is not injurious to fish or man.[328] However, to apply an algicide after a bloom has reached full development kills so many cells at once that for a time an even more undesirable situation is created than with the slower natural rate of population turnover. The interesting suggestion has been made that a removal of as

FIG. 58. Three years after it was dug, the efficiency of this unlined irrigation canal, designed to carry water 46 cm deep, is clearly being reduced by
the invasion of *Typha latifolia*. Central Washington.

many fish as is compatible with maintaining high fish reproduction
might be used as a means of reducing fertility indirectly, and this would
in turn reduce algal production.[331] Algae bring about an initial concentration of nutrients, with the effect compounded at successive steps
in the food chains, so that each fish removed from the ecosystem
contains a large quantity of nutrients.

The natural eutrophication of waters with consequent loss of clarity,
frequency of odorous blooms, and reduction of oxygen in the cold
deeps which would otherwise favor choice game fish, is accelerated
enormously by sewage pollution. Steady increase in the human population about an attractive lake creates an almost insurmountable problem
in the disposal of human wastes, even with the best sanitation, because
the area slopes toward the lake.

In Europe, and recently in Arkansas, too, many ponds have been
managed for the production of warm-water fish (bass, catfish, carp,
etc.), and here fertilization is deliberate as a means of increasing the
algal food of invertebrates upon which the fish feed. Sometimes the pond
is periodically drained, a green manure crop is planted, and then the
basin is flooded again, which results in a great increase in fertility that
favors the next fish crop. In Arkansas, where the fish yield exceeds $\frac{1}{4}$
ton per acre, rice crops are grown in alternation with impoundment.

Rank growth of vascular vegetation often becomes an economic problem in warm, moist climates where canals become clogged (Fig. 58),

filters blocked, reservoirs filled, the water tainted, or birds attracted that foul the water.[234] Notable among the plants causing such trouble is *Eichhornia crassipes* which grows in ponds, ditches, canals, and rivers in tropical and subtropical latitudes around the world. This floating plant covers the water surface rapidly by vegetative propagation, impeding navigation, the use of seaplanes, drainage, fish and waterfowl production, and mosquito control. It was introduced into southeastern North America in 1884 and soon became a pest. Introduced into tropical Africa only recently, in 1958 plants of this species floated down the Congo past Elizabethville at the rate of 150 tons/hour.[207] Much effort has been spent in searching for a cheap and efficient technique for eradicating *Eichhornia*, but only the use of hormonal sprays has shown promise. In some areas aquatic weeds of this type can be raked onshore to dry, and the material then sold as fertilizer to compensate part of the cost of raking.

In temperate regions sporadic interest has been shown in the possibility of mowing aquatic vegetation and using the fresh cuttings to feed livestock.[193] Although some of these plants are relatively low in protein, compared with terrestrial forage, this is not serious for cattle because the bacteria of the rumen produce enough protein to meet a cow's needs. In recently deglaciated areas where much of the land surface is occupied by ponds, this endeavor, if successful, would appreciably increase the economic potential.

It has been shown that the stage of succession is a criterion of malarial hazard in many places, for insect populations change as vegetation and habitat evolve, and the mosquito vectors of this disease are favored by a particular stage of the hydrosere.[292] Water levels therefore can be manipulated to cause maximum damage to the plant community most favorable to mosquito breeding.[336] In tropical Africa, by taking advantage of the high and sustained transpiration of evergreen *Eucalyptus* trees that are adapted to swamp habitats, afforestation has been successful in drying up areas that are in a stage favorable to mosquitoes. In recent years insecticides have become cheaper than ecologic methods of mosquito control, but there is good likelihood that after insecticide-resistant strains of mosquitoes have had time to develop, ecologic control may again find favor. Also because the sprays harm many kinds of insects, some of which may be beneficial, the ecologic method may be the safer in the long run. But, as in most land-use technology, the use of sprays tends to become widespread without an initial exploration of all the indirect influences they may have on ecosystems.[75]

Game preserves and fur farms are generally established in areas where the vegetation provides optimal environment for a specific animal species or group. For example, in North America waterfowl favor *Lemna, Polygonum, Potamogeton, Scirpus,* and *Zizania,* whereas muskrats find *Carex, Pontederia, Sagittaria,* and *Typha* favorable. Owing to inexorable successional tendencies, effort must often be expended later to counteract trends that reduce the amount of the desirable plants. Succession may be reversed by flooding a basin to the necessary depth by damming the outlet,[370] by blasting holes in peat to create small ponds over its surface,[350] or by careful removal of some of the peat with fire.[335]

Where water levels in ponds, lakes, and artificial reservoirs are controlled for the purpose of storing water at one season and using it for irrigation at another, there is a regular summer drawdown which results in a barren and erodable apron on that part of the bottom which is exposed a part of each year. Not only is the apron unsightly, but it contributes much silt each year toward filling the reservoir and reducing its storage capacity. High-water periods prevent the establishment of plants requiring drained soil, whereas low-water periods desiccate the seedlings of any aquatics that may have appeared during the winter and spring, the efficacy of this alternation being further demonstrated by the use of fluctuating water levels to control vasculares in other situations.[335] Work in some areas has shown that reservoir margins can be revegetated with artificially propagated, long-lived perennial grasses or trees that grow naturally in wet soil.[393, 418]

Although considerable peat is mined for use as a soil conditioner and as fuel, the principal uses of peat lands are for cropping and pasture. High crop yields are obtained without much difficulty, but the resource is not very enduring under this type of use since drainage and cultivation greatly accelerate oxidation of the peat, and peat production has stopped completely. On the San Joaquin River delta, the peat surface has been subsiding at the rate of 3 inches/year.[133] Thus the practice of peatland development for agriculture runs counter to our welfare in the long term, whereas the resource could instead serve man indefinitely in the capacity of a water reservoir, a wildlife refuge, as a recreation site, and even as pasture.

River terrace succession. Early in its history a stream in a humid region cuts downward, rapidly forming a **V**-shaped channel, but later when the gradient has been reduced sufficiently, more and more of the erosive force is directed against the valley sides, with a result that a relatively flat valley floor begins to develop. Unless there is some interruption, the floor continues to broaden, with meander loops migrating slowly down its length. Commonly, geologic events result in periodic renewals of active down-cutting, each time leaving a portion of the last-formed valley floor stranded as a shelflike terrace along the sides. In this way uplifts of the land, increased precipitation, or loss of a stream's load, individually or collectively may result in a series of terraces that are in essence a series of closely similar habitats of varied ages. The youngest members in this series are the sand or gravel *bars* that are being deposited at water level on the inside of each meander loop. Benches which lie slightly higher, but still low enough to be inundated at high-water periods are called *floodplains*, and among the series of *terraces* above the floodplain, the greater the altitude the greater the age. Since all members of this physiographic series have a common origin, all are likely to be of similar mineralogic composition. While each bench is in the floodplain stage, a thick mantle of silt is commonly accumulated, but texture may vary considerably among the different subtending layers.

If the climate and flora have remained constant through a period of terrace accumulation, and the water-laid deposits have not been smothered with colluvium from the canyon walls, there is available a series of habitats which may afford a picture of the sere which began long ago at the river's edge when the uppermost terrace was but a gravel bar, each successively higher level representing an advance in vegetational development.

In a study along the Mississippi River near Minneapolis, gravel bars were found to be colonized by annuals belonging to genera such as *Eragrostis, Mollugo,* and *Polanisia.*[175] Their water-borne disseminules are left on the surface each year when the floodwaters of spring recede, and the plants are well at home on this coarse substrate despite its high water table and frequent inundation. Along with the annuals, the seeds of *Salix fluviatilis* and *Populus deltoides* germinate, and these, being woody perennials, have by far the greater influence on the development of the ecosystem despite their slower rate of growth the first summer.

Within a few years *Salix* forms a dense thicket with vigorous root suckers (Fig. 59) and, in contrast with the herbs, it promotes the deposition of silt and organic debris. *Populus,* being a tall tree, eventually forms an overstory and helps bring about the disappearance of the light-demanding *Salix.* Some aspect of the environment beneath the *Populus* is in turn unsuited to its own seedlings, but a group of more shade-tolerant trees, including *Acer saccharinum, Ulmus americana,* and *Fraxinus pennsylvanica subintegerrima* succeed here. In this sere edaphic factors seem more critical at the start, with differing degrees of shade tolerance becoming decisive in promoting succession later.

Several hundred miles farther south along the Mississippi River, *Platanus occidentalis* is conspicuous as a pioneer tree in a homologous river terrace sere, but comparative tests of light requirements of seedlings showed that during their first year at least, *Platanus* seedlings are fully as shade tolerant as seedlings of those trees which appear later.[285] The tentative conclusion was drawn that the failure of *Platanus* reproduction later in the sere is a consequence of change in the character of the soil surface. Elimination of one successional stage by another may be

FIG. 59. Before *Salix* could stabilize this sandbar, shifting river currents started its active erosion, exposing the horizontal roots that often ensure the successful invasion of this shrub.

a result of a wide diversity of vegetation influences and their interactions.[406]

In pond seres, it will be recalled, each community invades its neighbor laterally, but in the river terrace hydrosere all parts of a single terrace may be at approximately the same successional stage at the same time. Invaders and relics therefore tend to be evenly dispersed over a terrace, so that the ecotones between contiguous terraces are not dynamic tension zones here, as they are in pond seres.

Any assumption that the precursors of the present-day vegetation of upper stream terraces are indicated by communities now to be found on floodplains and lower terraces is valid only if climate and flora in the past have been essentially the same as at present. In the sere in central Minnesota, both climate and flora have changed since deglaciation permitted the reexcavation of the drift-choked Mississippi Valley. Paleobotanical evidence in this region indicates that *Picea* and *Abies*, rather than dicot trees, were characteristic dominants in early postglacial time, probably as the upper terraces were being laid down.[99] Thus present community replacements which can be demonstrated indicate no more than successional tendencies at this point in geologic time, and we can expect succession to continue along this route only so long as the climate and flora remain much as they are now.

River terrace seres begin anew with the formation of each bar and island along the river bed (Fig. 60), but it is the fate of most of these,

FIG. 60. Part of a gravel bar in a river near Indianapolis. *Justicia americana* is the emergent rooted forb in the shallow water. *Populus deltoides* seedlings are emerging through a grass-forb community higher on the bar, and a plant of *Salix* has become well established at the right edge.

and many floodplains as well, to be undercut and washed away. Economically it is sometimes desirable to prevent the normal course of erosion along the outside of a meander loop. Minor mechanical stabilization to this end may be sufficient if immediately supplemented by planting woody species with suitable ecologic requirements. Frequently, however, it is necessary to construct substantial rock or concrete weirs to deflect the current away from an eroding bank. Straightening of the stream course is to be avoided, however; otherwise the gradient of the stream bed is steepened and a vigorous new erosion cycle is artificially induced.

Talus succession. Once geologic processes produce a cliff, the weathering of its face may allow loose rock to accumulate at its base as a body of *talus* or *scree.* Accumulation is rapid at first, but with the passing of time the growing mass of debris covers more and more of the cliff with the rate of wastage progressively declining and becoming extremely slow as the receding brow becomes covered with loose rock. Throughout this process the angle of slope of the growing accumulation remains rather constant, depending on the character of the rocks composing the cliff, as this determines average particle size (the coarser the particles the steeper

FIG. 61. Garlands of relatively mesophytic shrubs encircle talus slopes in arid steppe region. Grand Coulee, Washington.

their angle of repose) and the activity of vegetation in retarding the gravitational pull of loose material. The chemical character of the substrate varies from one region to another according to the kinds of rock composing the cliffs.

A critical ecologic feature of talus as a habitat is its unstable surface over which stones and finer material slide or roll so frequently as to bury or crush small plants. Isolated trees becoming established on a talus slope, or about its lower margin, often show scars made by bounding rocks. Except in very wet climates, drought is another severe condition associated with talus and more stable rock accumulations called rubble. Water penetrates so quickly as to be available to only deep-rooted plants, and seedling establishment is therefore extremely difficult (Fig. 61).

In Fig. 62 are diagrammed two seres described from opposite sides of a ridge, both being on identical substrata of loose rock within a few hundred meters of each other.[130] On the cool, moist north-facing slope mosses growing in the angles between the rocks provide a seed bed for herbs and shrubs with deep root systems, and these promote the accumulation of organic matter which eventually permits a forest climax to become established. In this sere *Menziesia* and *Xerophyllum* precede the appearance of the climax trees, then persist as the forest undergrowth (Fig. 63), showing clearly that subordinates are not always dependent upon the presence of climax dominants, and that a taxon may be present in both climax and antecedent communities of the same sere.

On the drier south-facing slope crustose lichens alone can invade

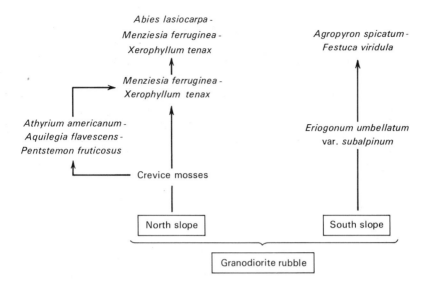

FIG. 62. Diagram of succession on loose rock on two slopes of the same ridge in the southern Selkirk Mountains. Compare with Figs. 63 and 64.

FIG. 63. North-facing rubble slope being invaded by *Xerophyllum, Vaccinium,* and *Menziensa* with *Abies lasiocarpa* becoming superimposed. Rate of plant invasion is here conditioned by rate of accumulation of duff. Bonner County, Idaho.

FIG. 64. *Eriogonum umbellatum subalpinum* at the margin of a south-facing rubble slope in Bonner County, Idaho. Severe microclimatic limitation to organic matter accumulation limits the rate of succession to the rate of rock weathering, which here is extremely slow.

the stones directly, significant colonization by vasculares being accomplished entirely by very slow lateral encroachment from surrounding areas where a soil has accumulated. *Eriogonum umbellatum,* a prostrate woody plant, is well suited by its vigorous vegetative spread and by the slow decomposition of its litter to lead the invasion (Fig. 64). The climax in this microclimate, where soils of the entire slope desiccate regularly and deeply each summer, is a grassland dominated by *Festuca viridula, Agropyron spicatum,* and other perennial herbs.

Extensive tracts of colluvial material that are so common at high altitudes in mountains have recently been recognized as being very important regarding water supplies. Here where precipitation is relatively high, it is desirable to have the most complete cover of vegetation possible to aid in the retention of water at times when it is in good supply, to be slowly released later. Each time the forest on such steep slopes is destroyed by fire or logging there is initiated another cycle of rapid downward movement of soil materials, resulting in the quick dissipation of stored water in spring. Succession leading to a new forest is very slow because of substratal instability coupled with slow growth at low temperature. Large areas of timber on these soils are classified as more valuable for watershed benefits than for wood.

FIG. 65. Vegetation development on glacial till in front of Nisqually Glacier, Mt. Rainier National Park, Washington. Foreground: fresh till surface. Middle ground: *Alnus* thicket forming the first closed vegetative cover. Background: seral conifer forest.

Succession on glacial till. In several respects the debris left by a receding glacier is a rather favorable habitat for plant invasion. It consists of a mixture of mineral particles grading from coarse to fine, all kept moist by water from the melting ice (Fig. 65). Since such a habitat is best described as mesic rather than xeric or hydric, and the pioneers are mesophytes, vegetational development on it may be referred to as a mesosere.

On freshly deposited glacial till in fjords in the vicinity of Glacier Bay, Alaska, some of the climax dominants may become established concurrently with the first seral plants[218] (Fig. 66). The very heterogeneous group of primary invaders includes *Epilobium latifolium, Lupinus nootkatensis, Alnus* spp., *Salix* spp., *Populus trichocarpa, Picea sitchensis,* and *Tsuga heterophylla.* This mixture, in which the herbs are most conspicuous at first, is superseded physiognomically by an *Alnus* scrub, through which the *Populus* may later emerge, with *Picea* then replacing the deciduous tree. As the A_O horizon and a moss layer develop, the slow-growing shade-tolerant *Tsuga heterophylla* that started slowly to

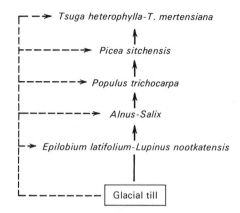

FIG. 66. Diagram of common successional trends following deglaciation in the area northwest of Juneau, Alaska. Solid areas indicate sequence of attainment of dominance, and dashed arrows show that seedlings of even a climax dominant may appear among the first invaders or in any stage thereafter. (Based on data from Heusser, 1954)

invade at the outset is joined by *T. mertensiana*, the two ultimately sharing dominance in the climax. Along with this change in the substrate, seral herbs and shrubs are replaced by shade-tolerant sciophytes of the climax, such as *Menziesia ferruginea*, *Vaccinium membranaceum*, *Cornus canadensis*, and *Rubus pedatus*. Because fresh till is very deficient in nitrogen, *Alnus* is especially constructive in this sere through its ability to bring fixed nitrogen into the ecosystem by means of microbes in its root nodules.

While there is a continuous evolution of environment throughout a mesosere, in contrast with rock outcrop and pond seres, the habitat changes are not necessary to enable subsequent communities to invade or to assert dominance. Apparently mesoseres are confined to temperate and cold climates, for under the intense solar radiation of tropical latitudes, the seedlings of climax species, even in rain forest areas, require the protection of a temporary community that is tolerant of direct exposure to the sun.

With the water balance favorable from the beginning, yet with soil aeration presenting no problem, mesoseres are completed in relatively short time as compared with xero- and hydroseres. Time to equilibrium is most directly dependent on the longevity of the principal dominants of the different stages.[147, 218] In a tundra mesosere at the head of a glacial valley in Austria, two of the three climax dominants (*Festuca varia* and *Helictotrichon versicolor*) became established the third year after deglaciation, with a complete plant cover formed by the thirteenth year.[329] At Glacier Bay, Alaska, climax trees are well represented on a deglaciated area within a century, although equilibrium requires perhaps 10 centuries for approximation, owing to the long life span of the trees involved. *Picea sitchensis*, the dominant of the penultimate stage, may live for 764 years. In another mesosere on mudflows in California, where the long-lived dominants include *Libocedrus decurrens* and *Pseudotsuga menziesii,* 10 centuries is again the estimated time to climax.[137] Xero- and hydroseres are slower by comparison.

The kinds and numbers of disseminules that fall on any area are determined mostly by the proximity of the area to other vegetation and by the richness of the total flora. Initially, the most critical character of a bare area is its roughness, as this influences the lodgement of disseminules and determines whether or not they may be moved out of the area as easily as they arrived. Then for those that lodge permanently, environmental pressures destroy selectively most of the disseminules, or the seedlings and sporelings they produce. In xeroseres and hydroseres this selection by physical factors of the environment is drastic, favoring only xerophytes and hydrophytes, respectively, as pioneers. In mesoseres this type of selection is weak, and eliminates only the most obligate xerophytes and hydrophytes, with climax species often among the first colonists.

Secondary Succession

Succession following fire. Nearly all terrestrial vegetation in which plants are spaced closely enough to carry fire are susceptible to burning. Fire usually kills or damages some of the plants, thus initiating immediate readjustments in species relationships, with an eventual trend toward reestablishment of the preexisting balance. Fire may remove trees, leaving the forest undergrowth essentially intact (after the plants sprout),[122] or it may alter the forest undergrowth without evident effect on the trees.[87]

The intensity of heat liberated when vegetation is burned varies according to the quantity and type of fuel, its degree of desiccation, the intensity of insolation at the time, wind velocity, the degree of slope of the land surface, etc. Fires are sometimes infernos that consume everything above ground and oxidize humus in the upper part of the mineral soil. At the other extreme, if the ground is covered with only a thin stand of partly dried grasses, the blaze may be scarcely more than a flash that kills few, if any, of the current crop of seeds still held by the maturing inflorescences (Fig. 67).

On most burned areas, even though superficial organic debris and part of the humus may be destroyed by fire, the remainder of the soil profile is not necessarily degraded.[15] In fact, if erosion does not assume serious proportions, fertility is at least temporarily improved by the nutrients released in the ash, by the more rapid nitrification that follows removal of shade, and by the green-manuring effect of decaying roots belonging to the plants killed by burning. Reduced transpiration demands by surviving plants typically raise the available soil moisture status in moist climates. On the other hand, the aerial component of en-

FIG. 67. Edge of an area burned the preceding August, as photographed in May. In this stable community dominated by *Bromus tectorum*, small changes in the relative development of species are conspicuous the first postfire season, but negligible thereafter. Dry matter production increased temporarily after burning. Lewiston, Idaho.

vironment is definitely more rigorous. Insolation is increased at the soil surface and the resulting heat and dryness of both air and germinating surface may prevent direct regeneration of many climax species until antecedents have produced moderate shade and thereby tempered the microclimate. However, if the new vegetation is too sparse to take up the abundant supply of nutrients from the ash, this material may be lost to the ecosystem by leaching.

In northern Idaho on habitats where *Tsuga heterophylla* is the climax dominant, conditions following fire are often not so severe that dominants of all the seral communities cannot become established during the first subsequent growing season, along with some seedlings of the climax trees. However, each of the communities in this mesosere needs a different length of time to attain maturity and assert dominance. *Marchantia* and *Funaria* are conspicuous the first year before seedlings of invaders, or root sprouts of herbs and shrubs that grew in the previous forest, can make much of a showing. Among the invaders *Epilobium* and/or *Cirsium* attain sufficient size and abundance within a few years to definitely dominate the physiognomy. Shrubs, among which the invading *Ceanothus, Physocarpus, Ribes, Rubus,* and *Salix* are conspicuous, overtop the tall forbs after a few years, then later the seral trees emerge through the shrub canopy. Climax trees, some of which may have germinated as early as the first season following burning, are the slowest in growth and consequently the latest to assert dominance. As in the Alaskan fjords, there is little evidence here that the dominants of any of the stages require environmental change to make their establishment possible. Only a few plants, mostly parasites, epiphytes, and sciophytic bryophytes of the forest floor, must await advanced stages of development before they can reinvade the habitats. Since the heliophytes which invade these deforested sites are commonly more drought-tolerant than the climax species which ultimately eliminate them, disturbed vegetation related to mesoseres commonly has a relatively xerophytic stamp, but this site preemption by xerophytes is not to be construed as meaning that vegetation development has become conditioned by a drier environment. The sequence of events in this particular fire sere, as well as the primary sere following deglaciation in southern Alaska, illustrates a general principle that where environment is not severe, succession may be largely accounted for by nonecologic factors. But by no means are all seres following fire mesoseres.

Telescoping of stages and rapid development of a sere reflect an absence of extreme conditions. Not only does the soil of a burned area retain good structure and fertility, but there is less competition for the same amount of rainfall as before.[405] Rodent and cutworm populations are at their lowest ebb. Furthermore, the "bare area" is far more apparent than real. In forest habitats the subterranean organs of many woody and herbaceous plants survive hot fires, sending up sucker shoots which then share the habitat with an influx of weedlike species, until redevelopment of an overstory eliminates the latter (Fig. 68). In grasslands nearly all the plants may regenerate in this way, and sometimes even the climax dominants of scrub and forest regenerate from roots (e.g., *Populus tremuloides, Quercus dumosa, Sequoia sempervirens, Tilia americana*).

Climax species are often fire resistant (e.g., *Eucalyptus* spp., *Pinus ponderosa*) and so persist through successive cycles of minor readjustment that follow surface fires. On the other hand, there are primarily seral species that get established abundantly on a fresh burn but persist in small numbers in the climax until it is burned again. *Betula papyrifera,* most conspicuous as a seral tree in the *Picea glauca* forest regions of North America (Fig. 69), persists indefinitely as scattered individuals among the shade-tolerant conifers, owing to its ability to sprout from the roots if accident befalls the stem. It is also able to occasionally take

FIG. 68. Evergreen shrubs, normally subordinates in climax *Pinus ponderosa* forest, assume dominance and greatly retard reinvasion of the climax tree following fire. Shasta, California.

FIG. 69. An early stage in fire succession north of Lake Superior where forest dominated by *Picea glauca* and *Abies balsamea* with small amounts of *Betula papyrifera* has been burned. *Epilobium angustifolium* and many *Betula* seedlings now dominate the habitat.

advantage of very small openings that are formed when a climax conifer dies. Depauperate individuals of *Epilobium angustifolium*, too, may persist for centuries in climax forests until another fire allows them to rejuvenate and produce an abundant crop of seeds that quickly populates the area.[302, 423]

In most of the seres discussed previously, one community facilitated the development of its successor. The reverse influence is illustrated by stands of *Betula papyrifera* or *Populus tremuloides* where *Picea glauca* follows them in fire succession. The whipping action of wind-tossed dicot canopies in winter tends to disbud a conifer understory, and since the excurrent *Picea* depends on one apical bud for continued height growth, this postpones its emergence into full sunlight.[374]

Seeds of *Ceanothus* and other plants may fail to germinate so long as they remain in cool shaded soil, but the heat of a fire, or subsequent strong insolation, stimulates them to do so. This phenomenon is especially common in chaparral vegetation, but not unknown elsewhere.[423] Conifers such as *Pinus contorta* retain viable seeds in persistent fruits, releasing these seeds within a few weeks after the tree is killed by fire, this materially aiding prompt recolonization (Fig. 70). Fire-resistant bark and vigorous sprouting from roots also favor the assumption of dominance by certain species following fire.

Since species differ in their susceptibility to fire, burned areas of equal age often develop somewhat differently, owing to different intensities of burning, or to differences in the degree of vegetational development since a preceding burn. In grasslands the heavier the grazing the more limited the amount of fuel and so the less intense the heat generated. Surface fires in woody vegetation frequently consume mostly litter, but in so doing they kill many green plants, and when these dry a great quantity of fuel becomes available for a much more devastating second burn.

Rock outcroppings or swampy spots sometimes allow one or a few trees to survive a burn, and their advantage in subsequent repopulation of the area gives the new forest a special complexion, at least for one tree generation. This phenomenon provides frequent illustration of the ecologic principle that alternative communities frequently represent the same stage of secondary succession.

Even the size of the burn has an important bearing on the course of subsequent development. Fire may run through a stand only as tongues, burning a fraction of the surface and only partially modifying the vegetation. At the other extreme, the burn may eliminate all potential tree dominants over an area many miles in diameter, with a result that for many decades only seral plants with highly mobile disseminules can gain representation beyond the periphery of the unburned area. Large stands of *Pinus contorta* in the northern Rocky Mountains are self-reproducing

FIG. 70. Intermediate stage in forest succession. Over wide areas in western North America one sees *Pinus contorta* forming pioneer forests on burned areas, with an understory of slow-growing shade-tolerant trees that are destined to replace it. *Pinus banksiana* plays the same role over wide areas across Canada.

only because superior competitors lacking serotinous cones have been eliminated over large areas and can reinvade only by extending their ranges slowly, generation by generation. If a species requires 30 years from germination to seed production and has a maximum dissemination range of 0.5 km, it can encroach centripetally upon a burn at a rate of less than 2 km per century.

In conifer forests of northern and western North America, rodents are an important deterrent to tree invasion following fire.[216] Immediately after a fire the burned area offers so little food and cover that many rodents abandon it, but quickly as new vegetation redevelops they return, often in greater numbers than before. Reforestation by sowing seed on burned land is feasible in some areas, but elsewhere it is a failure even when the sowing is done immediately after the fire with the intent of getting seedlings established before rodent pressure builds up.[414] It is sometimes helpful at first to scatter poisoned grain, dyed green so as not to attract birds, to reduce rodent density before scattering tree seeds. Also there has been encouraging progress in developing rodent-repellent coatings for tree seeds.[11] In southeastern North America bird consumption of seeds poses the same problem.

Where vegetation is fired at frequent intervals, fire-sensitive species are kept in subordinate roles if not excluded from the area. Thus on the coastal plain of southeastern North America ecosystems dominated by *Pinus palustris* or *P. elliottii* with undergrowth of equally fire-resistant grasses or shrubs can be maintained in dynamic equilibrium with burning at about 5-year intervals. Should burning stop, climaxes dominated by fire-sensitive species of *Quercus* develop (Table 12).

It is a curious fact that most of the economically valuable forests in temperate latitudes are dominated by seral trees, with natural stands owing their existence to accidental fires in the past. To perpetuate such trees in abundance without burning has not proved practical. Intentional burning after logging seems essential to remove thick accumulations of litter and duff that are so detrimental to the establishment of seral trees, and to eliminate small climax trees not taken in the harvest. The recently started practice of clear-cutting a few isolated blocks of timber each year, followed immediately by burning and planting, is an ecologically sound means of providing favorable environment for fire-sere trees, and at the same time it keeps the landscape as a whole in essentially continuous production. There are other desirable features of this system too. It promotes a steady flow of timber from a region, which is sociologically desirable, and it creates small areas of seral vegetation that are essential for the maintenance of game animals (deer, elk, moose, grouse) which indirectly are dependent on fire for favorable food and cover. Controlled burning can sometimes be used to reduce tree diseases as well as providing such other benefits.

FIG. 71. Relic *Pinus strobus* in a young forest of self-
reproducing *Acer saccharum* and *Tilia americana*
(data in Table 11). The xylem layers in the *Pinus*
would provide a minimal estimate of the number of
years that have elapsed since the fire, because the
reproduction of this tree becomes unsuccessful soon
after a pioneer community becomes established. Itasca
Park, Minnesota.

But the above advantages to the use of fire tend to be offset in varying
degrees by unfavorable effects. There is always some loss of fertility
(volatilization of nitrogen and sulfur, subsequent leaching loss of potassium, etc.), and soil erosion, runoff, and flooding hazard are increased.
It is always necessary to balance probable losses against probable benefits, and each of the elements involved varies from place to place.
Whereas burning at frequent intervals has become a standard land
management technique in forests of southeastern North America, absolute protection from fire is most desirable in southwestern California.

There the flooding and silting hazard is so serious a consequence of fire that an annual *Brassica* is commonly sown on burned areas by aircraft immediately after an accidental fire. This establishes a temporary cover protecting the soil until root sprouts from the burned woody plants can be relied upon to provide enduring protection.

In most grasslands the slow accumulation of litter in vegetation that is not grazed or mowed usually leads to a striking deterioration of vigor and vitality of the grasses. Burning at intervals of 1–15 years, depending on the particular region, is essential for maintaining maximal productivity, and in tropical climates essential for maintaining satisfactory levels of forage quality.

Owing to the long life span of trees, most forest stands do not have time to reach complete equilibrium following one fire before the area is burned again. Those stands in which the present dominants have clearly reached a state of self-perpetuation nearly always contain relics (Fig. 71) of a preclimax stage (even if these are only decaying logs or bark plates), and the character of the xylem layers of the present dominants shows that they started life under favorably open conditions in contrast with the shade-suppressed growth of their offspring. Frequently the trees are still too dense for the demonstration of complete replacement cycles. Under these circumstances our concept of climax must be based on a projection of current population trends that are clearly evident 100–200 years after the last fire, and may be somewhat inaccurate, but since fire will always be with us, the details of an equilibrium requiring perhaps 600 years to develop are of little more than academic interest. Equilibria predicted on the basis of trends in near-climax stands are entirely satisfactory for most purposes, especially for vegetation management.

Succession on abandoned fields. In regions where the natural fertility of the land is low and difficult to maintain, tracts are often cultivated for a time until economics force abandonment. This has been true of much of the forest areas of the northeastern United States, and of the area surrounding the southern Appalachians, and is essentially a universal practice in the moist tropics. Also, where rainfall is low, such as on the plain just east of the Rockies, the acreage put under cultivation tends to expand during periods of above-average precipitation, but during the dry years that inevitably follow, crops fail and the land is left idle. In all cases secondary succession begins immediately when tillage stops.

Two or more years of close cultivation usually destroy all vestiges of preexisting vegetation and create a habitat favorable not only to crop plants but also to weeds, especially introduced annuals which on other habitats cannot compete successfully with indigenes.

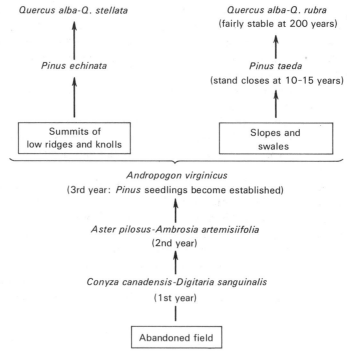

FIG. 72. Successional trends on the Piedmont plateau near Durham, North Carolina. (Based on data from Oosting, 1942)

Even the most diligent cultivation does no more than keep the populations of such weeds reduced to a low level, and tillage spreads their disseminules, mixing them well with the soil. Consequently, when cultivation ceases, the pioneer community which immediately takes possession is dominated by those annuals which were able to set seed despite cultivation. Analyses of soil in fields have shown that a square foot of soil down to the depth of plowing may contain 7000 viable seeds representing a number of species.[371]

Because different crops and cropping systems favor different ecologic groups of weeds, the pioneer community tends to be related to the character of the last crop.[142, 371] The timing of the last cultivation, past use of fertilizers or weedicides, past and current rates of erosion, and proximity to appropriate seed sources also have a bearing on the composition of at least the early stages. Studies of succession on abandoned cropland in North Carolina have been especially complete (Fig. 72), with considerable attention having been directed to controlling factors.[34, 88, 251]

Digitaria is an important dominant at first (Fig. 73) as it is always present in the cultivated fields, but it dwindles after the first year, owing

FIG. 73. *Conyza canadense* and *Digitaria sanguinalis* dominating an abandoned field on which *Zea mays* was grown the preceding year. Florence, South Carolina.

to its low stature. *Conyza*, another annual sharing dominance with *Digitaria*, is tall but the decaying roots of the first generation of this plant seem to have an autotoxic effect that inhibits a second generation. *Aster*, a perennial disseminating its fruits in autumn, does not germinate until early summer of the *Digitaria-Leptilon* year and so cannot assert dominance until the next summer. *Andropogon* disseminules are relatively immobile, so that the population of this perennial is slow to build up. By the third year, however, *Andropogon* threatens the stand of *Aster-Ambrosia* by creating dense shade that stops *Ambrosia* reproduction, and by its intense competition for water (Fig. 74). *Pinus* seedlings can get established only on mineral soil, and although the reason for its delayed appearance is obscure, an explanation of its demise lies in the thick layer of litter and duff that accumulates beneath the trees. This material, however, serves as a protective medium for *Quercus* fruits and drought-sensitive seedlings,[34] once squirrels introduce these trees. After a time shade thickens to prevent pine establishment even where disturbance happens to lay bare a small patch of mineral soil.

In the study of an homologous sere some 600 miles to the north, it was observed that succession is much more rapid in those parts of a

FIG. 74. *Andropogon virginicus* dominating a field abandoned several years previously. Near Lancaster, South Carolina.

field that are closest to a tract of relatively undisturbed vegetation which can serve as a seed source. Here species representing the climax forest (e.g., *Cornus florida*) sometimes become established within 5 years after land abandonment.[23] Also in this sere birds spread the seeds of *Juniperus* widely over a field, and once the *Juniperus* is well established it lures squirrels which bring nuts from nearby *Quercus* forests that they cache and sometimes fail to recover.

On the midcontinental plain where the prevailing climax is steppe, low fertility of old cropland may play a role in delaying natural revegetation.[361] Here the earlier stages are floristically impoverished yet more variable from place to place than is the climax, in which a few species come to dominate uniformly a large number of subordinates.[398] In this steppe the kinds of animals and their relative abundance change in accord with the evolution of the plant community, but at no place do they seem to influence the direction or rate of change.

Where highly preadapted weeds have been introduced by man, they may greatly retard the return to climax conditions, if not prevent it.[427] In Michigan a field that became thickly populated with introduced herbs supported only a thin scattering of trees 50 years after abandonment.[158] In eastern Washington *Bromus tectorum* has become a minor member

FIG. 75. Farmed land abandoned in the face of drought has eroded to the depth of plowing before being stabilized by natural means. Near Chadron, Nebraska.

of a number of kinds of undisturbed vegetation and seems able to prevent the return of native dominants once it becomes well established on severely disturbed land.[120]

Owing to deteriorated soil structure, abandoned fields are usually subject to severe erosion by wind or water, and loss of topsoil after abandonment may reduce the habitat potentiality far more than mere exhaustion of readily available nutrients during the cropping period (Fig. 75). It is often necessary to use special planting techniques and carefully selected species in order to stabilize old fields once erosion has set in.[16, 100, 264] But in the steppe east of the Rockies, where 50–100 years are required for the natural redevelopment of climax on abandoned fields,[48, 101, 458] it has been shown that if climax grasses are planted promptly in fields as they are abandoned, by the third year forage production may equal that of virgin grassland.[100]

Cultivated crops reduce soil fertility because man keeps removing those parts of plants having the highest nutrient content (especially seeds and fruits), and at the same time repeated tillage oxidizes humus and destroys soil structure. Timber crops are less exhausting. Even if trees are removed as fast as they mature, fertility is scarcely reduced, for trees do not make heavy annual demands on nutrients (Table 13), the

Table 13   **Quantity of certain minerals taken up annually by field and forest crops, as pounds
per acre**

Constituent	Average of 9 Field Crops	Average of 4 Forest Types
K_2O	78	11
CaO	43	62
SiO_2	37	29
MgO	17	10
P_2O_5	28	8
SO_3	11	3
Total ash	235	126

SOURCE: Wheeting, 1938.

boles that alone are removed have low nutrient content, and harvesting does not necessarily degrade the soil. There are a few areas, however, where fertility is so low that any timber harvest causes a significant reduction of fertility,[356] and even some areas too infertile for any tree growth.[315]

Where soils are highly podsolized, as in high latitudes, it is possible for man to replace natural vegetation with crops and by suitable management raise the level of soil fertility. But in temperate latitudes virgin land is often relatively fertile, and cropping degrades it. However, maintenance of soil fertility by soil amendments is relatively less expensive here than to the north.

In the moist tropics man is largely dependent on natural vegetation to maintain the fertility of cropland. Newly cleared land is indeed fertile but loses its fertility quickly, and it is customary to practice a rotation in that the natural regeneration of rain forest over a period of 10 years or more is relied upon to restore fertility between cropping periods of 3 years or less (Fig. 76).[92] This system is basically a form of managed secondary succession. If clearing is done as a sequence of contiguous and parallel strips, these are always adjacent to a good supply of disseminules as they are abandoned, so that reinvasion is prompt (Figs. 77, 78) and soil improvement is clearly evident from the start of succession following field abandonment, whether causally related to the vegetation sequence or not.[313]

Grazing succession.[152]   When a number of herbivores are confined in a unit of vegetation not previously subjected to heavy grazing pressure, succession is initiated mainly because the balance of competition among the plant species is soon upset. Each kind of herbivore has its distinctive food preferences when offered a given mixture of plant species, and this results in considerable damage to those plants which are most palatable. Heavy and repeated removal of foliage reduces

FIG. 76. Fields in varying stages of secondary succession following crop-ping compose most of the vegetation of this hillside in montane rain forest of Costa Rica. Even the forested area at the upper left was undoubtedly once a field. The family living in the small house needs only a small cultivated area for its sustenance, but the location of the planting must be changed every few years.

photosynthetic capacity and food reserves, and in turn dwarfs root systems, so that the grazed plants are weakened and their populations dwindle. Many changes in both soil and atmospheric conditions are effected by close grazing, and these environmental changes usually per-mit other species to gain foothold on the area. Plants increasing in domi-nance under the new conditions are the "increasers" of the range tech-nician. Those which wane are "decreasers," and those which can enter the ecosystem only after grazers have effected changes are "invaders."

The net effect of heavy *grazing* (of herbs) or *browsing* (of woody plants) is to bring about a change from a community in which some or all of the plant species furnish food for the herbivores, to a new com-munity in which the plants are relatively unpalatable, or unavailable owing to growth-form (spiny or prostrate) or phenology (green for but a brief period), or are remarkably capable of rapid regeneration when grazed (e.g., *Poa pratensis*) (Figs. 79, 80). In limited areas trampling may be so excessive that even this community is destroyed. Manuring, reduction in the amount of plant litter, compaction of soil, and increased erosion are other measurable changes in the ecosystem as the vegetation is altered.[129] Impalpable reduction of nutrient resources is also involved wherever herbivores are removed from an area by

FIG. 77. Eighteen years after the last cropping, a tall dense forest has developed. Some of the tree species that invaded at first are already dead or decadent. Only one species of the rain forest climax has invaded as yet. Costa Rica.

herdsmen or hunters, the effect being greater on those elements of the landscape mosaic that are most heavily grazed.[220]

The term *pasture* is often restricted to small areas of highly productive herbage that is used intensively, and commonly plowed up and replanted as often as necessary to maintain high forage output of a few species. *Range,* in contrast, refers to extensive areas of uncultivated land supporting complex vegetation of lower productivity that cannot be easily renewed by artificial means, and so must be used cautiously to minimize damage. The art of range management is to maintain the

FIG. 78. Forty years after the last cropping, the structure of the seral forest resembles climax rain forest, but in species composition stability is far from being achieved. Costa Rica.

productivity of desirable forage plants at the expense of undesirable species. Our discussion below will concern only range, since it is here that undesirable vegetation changes are hard to reverse and synecology is so very important.

Efficient range management depends on (1) a knowledge of the potentialities of every habitat type in the grazing unit, (2) an understanding of the grazing autecologies of both desirable and undesirable species in each habitat type, and (3) an ability to predict what changes in each ecosystem, and in the mosaic as a whole, would follow change in the current type and intensity of grazing.

Moderate grazing is not necessarily detrimental to range vegetation, and in fact may increase productivity (1) by keeping the LAI from rising much above the optimum, rather than allowing the accumulation of leaves with negative net photosynthesis, (2) by shifting dominance toward species with relatively high productivity,[146] (3) by stimulating

FIG. 79. Virgin steppe of *Andropogon scoparius*. For some consequences of excessive grazing of this vegetation see Fig. 80.

vegetative reproduction, or (4) by preventing plant senescence.[240, 420] Moderate browsing commonly increases the productivity of shrubs (at the expense of flowering) since it prevents the accumulation of senescent shoot tissues which are a drain on the production of the young and active organs.[57] Moderately grazed steppe too is usually more productive than ungrazed steppe, owing to the effect of accumulated litter in weakening grasses. If light grazing allows a wider variety of species to gain representation in a habitat formerly dominated by one or a few, total productivity may increase as a result of efficiency gained by the complementary use of resources by the mixture.[254]

Since range improvement requires that at least half of the net annual production be left ungrazed, the average herdsman nearly always permits too intensive grazing. The vegetation can be considered overgrazed if (1) unpalatable plants have increased at the expense of palatable ones, (2) the foliage has been thinned so that the utilization of light is well below maximum, or (3) if the physical environment has been degraded.

Grazing succession is complicated by many variables. When a community is subject to heavy grazing, the sere initiated usually proceeds in a direction that differs according to the type of grazing animal. Horses, cattle, sheep, goats, deer, rabbits, birds, etc., have different food preferences and hence do not induce the same change in vegetation.

FIG. 80. Vegetation dominated by *Poa pratensis*, which has remarkable abilities to endure grazing, and *Verbena hastata*, which is avoided by cattle, has replaced the *Andropogon* community (Fig. 79) that undoubtedly occurred here before the advent of the white man.

From an ecologic standpoint it would be most efficient to use different kinds of grazers on the same area, at least in succeeding years. In African savannas where half a dozen or more native mammals use an area simultaneously, they produce up to 15 times more meat per unit land area than could be produced by converting the same area (at considerable expense) into a cattle ranch.

The season of grazing is also critical, for different kinds of plants may be utilized intensively at different seasons, this determining which ones can assume dominance.[247, 387] In some ecosystems it is practical to let each of several parcels of a range rest for a month or so each year, with the period of rest for the same parcel being progressively delayed in succeeding years. The aim of this "deferred rotation" system is to allow processes such as seed-setting, germination, and establishment, occasional periods of freedom from interference so that life cycles can be continued. The range technician can also improve a plant community by grazing it rather heavily (i.e., concentrating animals on small area) at a time when chiefly the low-value plants are susceptible to damage, then giving the community respite (maximal herd dispersal) at a time when minimal use will be of most value to the desirable species. It should be clear that the terms increaser and decreaser are not appelations that are fixed for a species; the type of response to grazing differs with the season of grazing, type of animal, intensity of grazing, habitat type, etc.

Fire may complicate the changes in vegetation wrought by herbivores. As an example, when white man first saw southern New Mexico and adjacent areas there was much shrub-steppe or savanna in which woody legumes, yucca, cacti, and so on, were scattered over a rather continuous cover of grass. Indigenous herbivores had grazed this vegetation very lightly, and occasional fires together with grass competition had kept the woody plants few in number and small in size. With the advent of heavy grazing by domestic animals, the grass was thinned to a point where it would no longer carry fire, and at the same time competition was reduced for fire-sensitive woody plants. In consequence, much of this type of vegetation became converted to dense stands of shrubs or low trees with negligible grass beneath. Thus grazing and fire must be considered jointly in understanding the dynamics of this vegetation.[233, 358]

Studies of grazing succession provide most of the examples of animals assuming dominance in ecosystems. But there are many other ways in which animals play conspicuous and important parts in plant succession. For example, by constructing dams, beavers frequently convert a drained valley bottom into a flooded bare area and thus initiate secondary succession. Insects may completely destroy a conifer forest so that a new sere is initiated. Colonial birds may destroy a community by trampling or nesting (Fig. 81). Other animals may unwittingly do much to promote succession by promptly introducing seeds in a habitat as rapidly as an environment becomes suitable for their establishment. For example, fructivorous birds bring *Rubus* into deforested areas with surprising promptness and uniformity, for the birds that inhabit forest openings fly directly from one of them to another. Also, cattle feeding on the sweet pods of *Prosopis* deposit the hard seeds in viable condition in their dung, thus they have the potentiality of reintroducing this shrub into any area where it might have been eliminated by fire.

In forests where *Pinus* is being replaced slowly by other conifers, porcupines often speed up the conversion by girdling the pines, whose bark they prefer. Moose may retard or set back pond hydroseres by cutting up the marginal *Carex* mats and dispersing them with their hooves.

The above are but a few of the spectacular ways in which animals influence plant communities. They are always at work in many subtle but important ways.

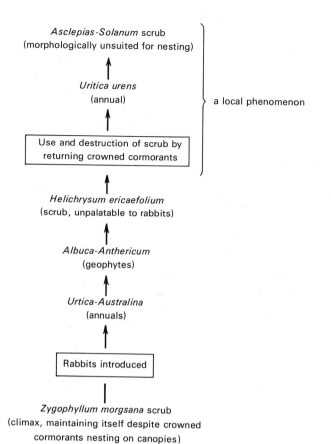

FIG. 81. Origin of one zootic climax following the introduction of rabbits, with a second arising locally through the interaction of rabbits and cormorants. (Based on data from Gillham, 1963)

• ANALYSIS OF PLANT SUCCESSION

The foregoing discussions of representative types of seres have provided a background of facts and concepts which now will be used as a basis for a subjective analysis of the principal phenomena involved in plant succession. F. E. Clements presented the first treatment of this type in 1916, and his outline will be followed below, although many of his hypotheses and tentative conclusions require modification as a result of subsequent research.

Formation of a Bare Area

The immediate cause of origin of a sere is the appearance of a raw geologic formation that is suitable as a rooting medium for plants, or

FIG. 82. The form of the dead *Pinus strobus* here indicates a previously different configuration of the dune surface. In the wind remodeling of this landscape all humus and other influences of the preceding forest community are lost. Dune State Park, Indiana.

the destruction of vegetation, resulting in an area supporting less than its potentialities warrant. New situations available for invasion are produced by:

1 Physiographic processes, producing mostly primary bare areas:
    a. Erosion, by water, wind (Fig. 82), gravity (Fig. 83), or glaciers
    b. Deposition, by the above agents plus vulcanism[150] and the precipitation of travertine or sinter
    c. Emergence, producing barren land surfaces
    d. Submergence, producing barren submersed surfaces
    e. Congeliturbation, producing unstable substrata of silt or stones, and thaw ponds (Fig. 84)
2 Climatic phenomena, producing mostly secondary bare areas
    a. Drought, creating openings in established vegetation by weakening or killing the most drought-sensitive species (Fig. 29)
    b. Wind, knocking down trees individually or in groups
    c. Lightning, starting devastating fires
3 Biotic agents, producing mostly secondary bare areas:
    a. Man, destroying vegetation by cultivation, logging, dredging

FIG. 83. Secondary succession in progress in the path
made by an avalanche that cascaded down this shallow
ravine many years ago.

(Fig. 85), strip mining,[110, 383] releasing poisonous fumes from
smelters or refineries, firing vegetation, bomb devastation
  b. Other vertebrates, creating overgrazed areas, trampled areas,
     beaver impoundments, excavation mounds
  c. Insect and fungus outbreaks that destroy components of a vegeta-
     tion

The above outline embraces all the types of bare areas discussed
earlier, and includes many others. Practically all parts of the earth's
surface may be identified with one of these categories, although a few
minor kinds (e.g., areas devastated by volcanic gases or weedicides)
could be added.

FIG. 84. Local thawing of ancient permafrost has created a pond that extends gradually. Note the roots of trees that have toppled into the water and the posture of others on their way. Tanana Valley, Alaska.

FIG. 85. Gravel washed free of silt and clay by a gold dredge is providing a type of bare area very difficult for plant invasion.

FIG. 86. At upper timberline the slow progress of primary succession is marked by conspicuous clonal expansion of the dominants. Olympic Mountains, Washington.

Invasion (Colonization)

Almost no bare areas on earth are inimical to plant invasion. The closest approaches are the ocean depths, the mountain summits of Antarctica, permanent snowfields, and nearly rainless deserts, but even these inhospitable places support nonvascular vegetation of some type.

The genesis of a plant community on a bare area normally involves three processes—immigration, establishment, and multiplication.

Immigration is the entry of living reproductive structures into a habitat where the species was not formerly represented. Such structures have been called *disseminules* if they are detached units carried through air or water, or *propagules* if they remain attached to the parent plant while extending through a substratum or over its surface. Immigration accomplished by disseminules results in the appearance of individuals at many points scattered over the habitat (Fig. 86), whereas immigration accomplished by propagules results in a mass invasion from the margins of the bare area (Fig. 87).

Pioneer plants are intolerant of one or more conditions that arise as a dense plant cover develops, so that their tenure is normally limited to a single generation after such a cover develops. They tend to be relatively xerophytic, light-demanding, heat-demanding, frost-hardy, deep-

FIG. 87. Abandoned field in Turkey Run State Park, Indiana, dominated by *Solidago, Fragaria, and Rubus,* with trees starting to invade. *Juniperus virginiana* immediately to the right of the stake is introduced by birds. *Sassafras albidum,* farther to the right, is invading by means of sprouts from horizontal roots.

rooting, and not exacting as to soil.[59] Where environmental amenities permit a dense vegetation to develop, the survival of pioneer species in the landscape depends on their abilities to produce highly mobile disseminules in great quantities and at an early age, these characters permitting them to avoid intense competition by taking advantage of every new bare area as soon as it is created. Such pioneers as *Epilobium, Funaria,* and *Salix* have been referred to as "nomadic" or "fugitive" because of this enforced mobility. By contrast, climax plants with heavier disseminules (*Agropyron, Pinus, Quercus,* etc.) generally spread into new territory slowly. In mesoseres where environment is conducive to rapid succession toward forest, rapidity of growth is especially conspicuous among pioneers (Fig. 77).

Establishment involves the development of immigrants to maturity. Certainly many more living structures arrive in a habitat than can succeed there, and failure may occur at any time in the life cycle.

Multiplication refers to additions to the young community which represent progeny of the immigrants. Most immigration is accomplished by means of disseminules, and as a result the pioneer individuals tend to be widely and randomly scattered. Some of these early arrivals increase their numbers by vegetative reproduction, e.g., mosses, *Salix fluviatile,* and *Ammophila.* Others must produce a crop of seeds to multiply, and for these to gain dominance their life cycles must be short. This helps account for the abundance of annuals and biennials among pioneers. Whether by propagules or disseminules, each pioneer individual tends to produce isodiametric families of offspring about itself, the initial points of establishment serving as springboards from which remaining gaps in the bare area are filled (Fig. 86). As a consequence, from initial randomness there is a rapid shift toward extreme gregariousness, but then as families increase and coalesce the degree of clumping is often reduced.

Aside from increase in numbers from within, the pioneer population is constantly augmented by a rain of disseminules of the same and different species which arrive from adjacent habitats.

By means of all these processes, collectively designated as invasion, a bare area normally accumulates a complete plant cover—one which uses the environmental resources ever more fully, which is increasingly capable of ensuring the stability of the recently created surface, and which usually renders the habitat favorable for the establishment of plants with different requirements or tolerances. While each of the invasion processes starts successively later, once started they all continue to operate to the climax.

Changes in Environment

No less striking than the changes in plant and animal populations during succession are the changes in the nonliving components of the ecosystem. In part this environmental metamorphosis is due to the activities of the organisms themselves (the *autogenic influences*), and in part to certain other processes that operate to some extent, at least, independent of the character of the plant cover (the *allogenic influences*).[413] Normally both groups of forces are at work at the same time, but one or the other usually seems to exert the stronger influence.

Although changing environment is a universal accompaniment of succession, and always has a strong selective influence on species, it is not always necessary for the sequential appearance of the communities, especially in mesoseres. Nor does invasion, with its necessary alteration of environment, always result in succession, as in extreme deserts.

Autogenic influences.[259] The manner and degree of vegetation influences depend on the details of the taxonomic composition and structure of the community, for each species contributes in its own individualistic way to the sum which we call vegetation influences. Even though dominants by definition exert the most influence, subordinates often rival them closely in this respect.[69, 386] Since dominants or subordinates, if not both, change as the sere develops, each stage in the sequence plays a distinctive role in the gradual evolution of edaphic and aerial conditions. Where succession advances by abrupt stages, this may be a result of cumulative change in environment that passes a threshold required by dominants of the next stage.

The importance of plant influence on environment has been very simply illustrated by tallying the occurrence of small annuals in relation to the position of large shrubs in the desert of southeastern California.[451] Some annuals succeed only in the proximity of one or a few species of shrubs, with others dependent on different kinds of shrubs. Still others are oblivious to the quality of the necessary shrub influences, and finally there is a group unable to tolerate the proximity of any shrub. Not only is the distribution of most of these annuals related to the positions of shrubs, but their height and number of flowers are also influenced by the taller plants.

Soil accumulation.   Plant life plays important roles in the weathering of rock, in the entrapment and stabilization of solid particles that are being moved by wind, water, or gravity, and in making organic additions to the rooting medium (which as a matter of convenience we will refer to as "soil").

Early in succession the substrate is often unstable, but after the first community brings about stabilization, it then serves as a trap for materials moved in from contiguous areas that are not yet stabilized. Soil accumulation is especially rapid in aquatic habitats where currents carrying silt and clay are slowed in moving through rooted plants. Along the coast of the British Isles much new land has been formed by *Spartina townsendii,* which promotes silting and protects the accumulation against subsequent wave erosion.[35] Mangrove thickets along tropical coasts play a similar role.[78] The formation of natural levees along the margins of mature streams is largely due to trapping of sediments by vegetation; and through the effects of the levees on runoff, silting is promoted over a broad belt behind the levee. In the positions of their stem bases in relation to the soil surface, coupled with their ages, woody plants often provide a record of the amount and rate of deposition on the surfaces where they germinated.

In many seres at least a part of the advance from pioneer to climax is primarily dependent on additions of metabolic products to the substrate by the plants (e.g., peat, marl). In other seres organic accumulations are significant products of vegetative evolution, even though succession is not primarily dependent on them (e.g., humus accumulation in marsh soil).

The first clearly defined influence of vegetation on raw parent materials such as till or dune is the production of a layer of litter, which then starts to decay and thereafter continually adds humus to the mineral part of the profile. Collectively, these forms of organic matter constitute a large pool of bound nutrients in cold wet climates where the accumulations tend to be thick, with many years intervening between the addition of a unit of litter and its complete mineralization.

Trees that cast heavy leaf litter during a brief span of weeks are especially important to low-growing subordinates. In temperate climates it is well known that the leaves of deciduous trees must be raked off a lawn (or at least finely shredded) before they are softened by autumn rains and settle down to form a compact layer of overlapping units; otherwise, even well-established lawn grasses are seriously damaged. Slow-growing tree seedlings[216] and bryophytes[44] commonly do not gain sufficient height during their first summer to endure this smothering effect on a heavy autumn leaf cast. The survival of such small plants therefore tends to be restricted to elevated parts of the microrelief as provided by fallen logs, tree bases, summits of boulders, mounds caused by wind-thrown trees, etc.

Litter accumulation may be detrimental to seedlings in still other ways. When seeds germinate in the upper layers of litter, the seedlings are suspended well above the relatively constant moisture supply of the mineral soil and their survival depends on rapid elongation of the radicle, for only a few warm days dry out the porous litter and duff. The accumulation of thick surface layers of organic debris always places a drastic restriction on the list of species that can cope with it, thereby contributing to the floristic simplification and unification that characterizes the climax.[212, 444]

Litter, duff, and humus accumulate until each attains an equilibrium with its respective rate of decay, and all are in adjustment with the annual rate of litter production. In tropical rain forest the thin superficial organic deposit may attain its permanent thickness within 10 years after a secondary bare area is created,[241] but in primary succession under *Pinus ponderosa* in the relatively dry temperate climate of California it continues to build up for 100–600 years.[137] Farther north in the wet temperate forest of southern Alaska in an area where dominance was shifting from *Picea sitchensis* to *Tsuga heterophylla*, the purely organic layer had a thickness of 4.5, 10, and 16 cm at comparable sites where the maximum ages of the trees were 125, 230, and 300 (+?) years.[195] In this region of podsol soils the thickness of even the humus-containing part of the mineral profile generally becomes stabilized before vegetative equilibrium is attained.[137] In certain prairie-podsolic profiles it has been estimated that time to equilibrium for humus contents of the A_1, A_2, and B_2 horizons is 110, 420, and 590 years, respectively.[116]

As humus becomes incorporated into a parent material, a microbial population develops, and with the passing of time the latter makes increasing demands on the limited oxygen supply of the soil air. The significance of this for vegetation dynamics was suggested by an experiment in which additions of starch plus ammonium sulfate to a soil so stimulated microbes that wheat plants rooted in that soil died, apparently from lack of oxygen.[249] Since the soils of grass-dominated ecosystems develop especially high humus contents, poor aeration attributable to microbe activity may at times be a significant factor militating against invasion by woody plants requiring better aeration. Also, it has been suggested that humus, serving as a necessary medium for a root-rot fungus, may account for the restriction of *Sequoia sempervirens* seedlings to microsites with mineral soil exposed.[305]

Soil structure. The soils of all primary bare areas, as well as many types of secondary bare areas, have their mineral particles haphazardly arranged, with structure developing largely as a consequence of vegetation influences. When roots take up water the soil dries and shrinks in many places at once, and this sets up strains resulting in many small cracks, or at least planes of weakness, that establish aggregate boundaries. Then as roots thicken, pressure sets up shearing stresses which emphasize the distinction between aggregates and their boundaries. Also within the aggregate, humus, and especially the metabolic products of microbes, tends to bind grains more firmly together than is accomplished by clay colloids alone.

When well developed, aggregates are rather compact clusters of adhering particles separated by pores and intermittently open planes, with a consequence that the proportion of air to solids in a given volume is increased as aggregates form (i.e., bulk density is reduced). This improved aeration facilitates the mineralization of humus and the respiration of soil organisms. Earthworms and larger invertebrates enter a sere only after considerable plant debris has accumulated, but then, by bringing subsoil to the surface each year, they create many channels which further reduce bulk density. Progressive decrease in bulk density with advancing succession has been demonstrated in both primary[109, 137] and secondary[34] seres.

In loams or heavier soils, with which the above discussion has been primarily concerned, the slow infiltration and poor aeration that characterize their raw state are alleviated as structure develops. Sand, in contrast, loses some of its dryness as a result of grains becoming bound together in clumps. Here again may be noted a tendency for community influences to alleviate extremes.

But not all species have the same influence on soil structure, and not all are beneficial. In one experiment it was shown that *Bromus* promoted aggregation at twice the rate of *Medicago sativa*, whereas *Zea mays* effected no change under similar conditions.[22] *Beta vulgaris* var. *macrorhiza* has a deleterious effect on succeeding crops planted in the same field, and at least part of this influence appears to be a result of degraded soil structure.

Soil moisture. Except for fog interception, vegetation has no significant influence on how much water an area receives from the atmosphere, but it has a powerful influence on the fate of such moisture.

Several vegetation influences tend to increase the efficiency of water use by plants in upland ecosystems. Prompt infiltration, with consequent reduction of water loss due to runoff, is favored by the porosity usually promoted by plants in fine-textured soils. Then in coarse-textured soils humus increments materially raise the critically low water-retaining capacity. The cooling effect of shade furnished by a plant cover retards snow melting, raises the viscosity of water and thereby field capacity, and reduces evaporation from the soil surface, all of which delay the inception of progressive soil desiccation in summer or after a rainstorm. Where foliage intercepts fog that would otherwise drift on beyond a habitat, vegetation can greatly augment soil moisture through fog drip. Studies showing that *Araucaria excelsa* may precipitate an extra 76 cm of rain annually led to the establishment of plantations of this tree on the island of Lanai to increase its water resources.[74] This may well happen naturally when succession leads to a forest climax. In contrast with all the above, other influences of vegetation on soil moisture tend to have the opposite effect.

The canopy of each vegetation stratum in turn, as well as litter and duff, extracts a toll of precipitation in that drops or frozen particles are held aloft until evaporated. Thus after a habitat becomes clothed with vegetation, much less rain and snow reach the mineral soil than before. Added to this is the heavy demand of the root systems upon soil moisture to replace transpired water. Owing to interception and use, the water content of a soil profile (but not of the surface horizon) commonly declines as succession advances, even in some xeroseres.[475]

Several economically important phenomena are involved with these influences. It has been shown that the balance between water-conserving and water-dissipating tendencies of a forest may often be shifted in favor of conservation by thinning the canopy so as to reduce interception, but not so much as to lose the benefits of shade. On the other hand, in some regions after a hydrosere has progressed to a forest stage, logging the trees leads to a resurgence of the water table and initiates a new hydrosere, which is very undesirable from a silvicultural standpoint. This shows plainly that the lowering of water tables, so critical in hydroseres, is aided materially by transpiration demands after a heavy vegetal cover has developed, especially if the latter is evergreen. Other evidence of heavy demands of vegetation for water has been provided by converting native vegetation with low water-use characteristics to an exotic community with a higher water requirement, which resulted in a depression of the water table and drying of rivulets.[221, 459]

Although there is commonly a net desiccating effect of vegetation on soil, the development of a plant cover on a bare area usually prevents excessive drying of the surface (which is crucial for seedling ecology) and at the same time prevents excessive wetness below, thereby tending to equalize the vertical distribution of moisture in the profile.

Just as vegetation types as a whole have distinctive influences on the water regime, so do the individual plants in one stand. Species differ as to the proportions of water draining centrifugally off the canopy or running down the stems, and where large plants grow scattered, small snowdrifts may accumulate under individuals or groups at one season, with rainshadows conspicuous at another season. Thus soil moisture increments within what must be considered a homogeneous stand of vegetation tend to have a mosaic pattern, creating diversity among microsites that can be significant in governing the pattern of subsequent invasion.

Mineral cycling and nutrients.[8] Whereas energy flow involves space, with solar energy coming from space and eventually being returned into space as heat loss, the cycling of matter involves use, release, and reuse of elements that remain in the vicinity of the earth's surface. Probably all elements enter into the cycling of matter through ecosystems, but at the one extreme some are very important (e.g., calcium and nitrogen), whereas others (helium, titanium) are so rare that they can be ignored. Some cycles are quickly completed, such as cations leaching from leaves in raindrops, then being taken up from the surface soil by roots, and possibly returning to the same leaf within a month's time.[470] Other cycles are so slow they involve geologic time, as the chemical constituents of peat and coal.

Each species of plant tends to have distinctive propensities for taking up the different soil solutes, and this in turn gives chemical individuality to the foliage drip from its canopy and to its litter. Then the ions are released from the litter in definite order and are adsorbed or used at different levels as they percolate through the soil. These vegetation influences have been well documented by comparing soil analyses under contiguous planting of different tree species some years after they have been established,[327] and by agronomic research showing that the same land may differ considerably in its fertility as a consequence of changing the type of crop grown.

There has been a widespread assumption, perhaps usually well founded, that the dominants of a phytocoenosis have the greatest influence on soil fertility since they usually produce the greater share of the annual litter crop. Even if this should be the rule, it is not safe to ignore subordinates, for in some phytocoenoses at least, the nutrient content of the litter of the subordinates is of superior quality.[70, 386] These plants may account for much of the difference in fertility of the soil from one habitat type to another within a series that shares the same type of overstory.

One of the first important changes a pioneer community makes in a previously unoccupied body of parent material is to bring about a redistribution of many minerals. Solutes taken up throughout the rooting area are mostly returned to the soil surface in foliage drip or litter, so that the fertility of the surface soil increases at the expense of the subsoil. Starting from an originally diffuse and uniform distribution then, the solutes taken up by vegetation tend to become concentrated in well-defined horizontal strata near the soil surface. In a dune sere in England, for example, it was found that depletion of the subsoil continued for 15–20 years after invasion before uptake below was balanced by leachates derived from mineralization of the humus above.[475] This uptake of ions by roots tends to counteract fertility losses by leaching. Also, the vigorous removal of soil water reduces the volume of percolate that otherwise would tend to carry ions below the root zone and away from the area in streams.

Nitrogen is unique among plant nutrients for not having its ultimate origin in the weathering of common rock minerals. Hence except for certain types of volcanic materials, and for shorelines that have been enriched by flotsam, nitrogen deficiency is usually a limiting factor at the start of primary succession. For the most part, primary invaders must be able to grow where nitrogen is no more plentiful than in rainwater, whereas other species may not be able to invade until nitrogen is plentiful.[178] Frequently, invaders show nitrogen deficiency symptoms, unless they happen to contain endophytic microbes that provide available nitrogen, or at least grow so close to plants having an endophyte that their roots can absorb excess nitrogen which is secreted.[5, 429] The slender supply of nitrogen continually received from rainfall and from symbiotic fixation is augmented by free-living nitrogen fixers that appear soon after the first litter is cast and provides a substrate. Thus the forces bringing nitrogen into the ecosystem gain momentum, and since the uptake of the mobile nitrogen ions is prompt, relatively little is lost in the percolate. However, where rainfall is high, enough nitrogen may be produced as the ecosystem develops so that there is an excess to leach away, as is shown by increases in fertility of streams flowing from such areas.

Early in a sere, nitrate commonly is the main source of nitrogen, but often as climax is approached, ammonium may be the dominant source.[132]

Sulfur and especially phosphorus are commonly deficient in parent materials. Like nitrogen, these deficiencies also tend to retard the growth rates of early invaders, then accumulate as succession advances.[203]

In two ways plants enrich soil more directly than through the decay of the litter they cast. Many studies have shown that raindrops hanging onto foliage briefly before dropping to the ground leach a surprising quantity of nutrients and organic compounds from the leaves. Foliage drip may return as much or more phosphorus and potassium to the soil as does leaf cast, and it has been demonstrated that the luxuriant growth of *Hylocomium splendens* on the ground directly beneath the canopies of *Picea abies* can be attributed to calcium, nitrogen, phosphorus, and potassium that are leached from the tree foliage.[412] Then below ground small amounts of nutrient ions, sugars, amino acids, etc., diffuse from rootlets into the surrounding soil.[472] These must surely be of importance to rhizosphere microbes, if not to associated higher plants.

Where high rainfall promotes leaching there is clear evidence that as succession advances soil fertility builds up to a peak which may be followed by a significant decline as equilibrium is approached. For example, in coastal southern Alaska, recently exposed till that has become covered with *Alnus* accumulates nitrogen from this shrub at the rate of 26 kg/ha/year. Later, when *Picea* replaces *Alnus*, mull changes to mor and soil nitrogen begins to decline, although carbon continues to accumulate. Nutrition consequently becomes less favorable (to the average plant, at least) as the carbon to nitrogen ratio increases from 13 to 35 and succession continues toward a *Tsuga* climax.[109] What little nitrogen remains in such strongly podsolized profiles is mostly in the litter and duff, which explains the development of a superficial mat of feeding rootlets, together with an increase in the proportion of highly mycotrophic species. In California the nitrogen content of recent mudflows reaches its peak at about 200 years, which is well before climax is reached.[137] Even in warm-temperate climates where podsolization is weak and does not involve coniferous climaxes, decline in soil fertility,[88, 189, 437] and consequently in productivity has been demonstrated late in seres. In part the phenomenon may reflect leaching losses promoted by plant acidification of the soil, and in part increasing amounts of one or more essential element becoming tied up in the accumulating litter, duff, and humus, and cells of living plants and animals. It might also reflect an increase in the proportion of nonproductive cells, which depresses net primary productivity. In Georgia the long-term trends in cycling and fertility do not progress smoothly, for each time one dominant supersedes another there is a temporary spurt of productivity.[186]

Changes which become detrimental to a group of plants in possession of a site are commonly of at least indirect benefit to others, and declining fertility may be essential for the appearance of later stages in a sere. *Tsuga canadensis*, for example, is a climax species characteristic of podsols. It becomes very susceptible to *Rhizoctonia* root-rot if fertilized,[316] and possibly its assumption of dominance depends on a natural decline of fertility. Similarly, *Cynosurus cristatus*, a grass characteristic of infertile soils, loses out in competition with other grasses when soil phosphorus is brought up to normal levels.[52]

Whereas the quantity of nutrients per unit of land area varies little over the land surface, the proportions contained in the soil, in living organisms, and in superficial organic debris vary widely. In some situations the proportions of nutrients in soil and in vegetation tend to remain constant throughout the long period of their accumulation as the sere progresses,[415] but commonly there are striking redistributions. In Ghana rain forest the top 3 dm of the soil profile, which contains the bulk of the humus and consequently of soil nutrients, holds 8206 kg/ha of nitrogen, phosphorus, potassium, calcium, and magnesium, with the tissues of the living plants on the same area containing 6400 additional kilograms of these nutrients.[194] In semiarid Australia the nitrogen content of living plant tissue is relatively much lower, with 2278 kg/ha in the solum, and only 398 kg in plant tissue.[202] Earlier it was pointed out that during primary succession in Alaskan fjords a striking redistribution of nutrients takes place with large stores accumulating in the mineral horizons in early stages, then being transferred to a thick mat of superficial litter and duff as *Picea* and *Tsuga* replace *Alnus*. Where there is so much transfer from the rooting horizons to superficial debris and/or living tissues, the removal of some peculiarly critical material from the soil may well play an important role in the replacement of one group of species by another.

Growth activity may remain high in an ecosystem that is low in nutrients if turnover is rapid, so that few mineral resources get trapped in an inactive, slowly decaying body of litter and duff. This seems to explain the high sustained productivity of rain forest on soils that are generally not too well supplied with nutrients, and the high rate of productivity that characterizes only the early stages of certain seres.

Toxins.[162, 198, 468] For more than a century it has been suspected that the roots of certain plants secrete substances that are toxic to associates, but conclusive proof that this operates in nature has proved extraordinarily difficult, although it has been easy for the physiologist to demonstrate that tissue extracts of one species are frequently toxic to another under laboratory conditions. One plant may be damaged by chemicals that are liberated either directly by another, or which result from a decay of the tissues of the other. These substances may be effective by reducing germination, root or shoot growth, dry-matter accumulation, disease resistance, or the efficiency of use of water.

Toxins may diffuse out through the cuticle of living leaves of one species where they can be washed to the soil and damage the roots of an associate. Foliage drip from *Camelina* spp., for example, is particularly damaging to *Linum* roots, reducing the yield of flax fields to about 20 percent of normal where *Camelina* is an abundant weed.

The leaves of other plants (e.g., *Artemisia, Eucalyptus, Mentha, Salvia*) liberate volatile oils or terpenes that damage neighboring plants without first becoming part of the soil.[307]

The roots of established plants of the desert shrub *Parthenium argentatum* secrete an organic acid that is suspected of causing the death of seedlings appearing in the vicinity of old plants, which results in the maintenance of wide spacing in the stands.[47]

Horticulturists in southeastern North America have observed that when a peach orchard becomes old and unproductive it is not advisable to remove old trees and replant young ones in the same ground.[349] The new trees would be stunted, apparently by alcohol-soluble constituents of root bark that are released when the old roots decay. What may prove to be another indirect type of damage is the observation in Australia that *Eucalyptus pilularis* litter seems to favor a microflora that prevents the establishment of new seedlings of this tree.[166] Such findings raise the possibility that one-generation seral species may sometimes owe the brevity of their tenure to the accumulation of auto-toxic substances, and in fact strong evidence of this has been presented for *Conyza canadensis* in abandoned-field succession.[251]

Fairy-ring phenomena, involving temporary but severe damage to grasses and forbs as the clone of a fungus or a vascular plant expands centrifugally, may also depend on toxic influences of the invader.[112] And the filtrate of water in which one species of alga has been growing can strongly influence the development of other species of algae, which may explain the reciprocal phases of development of algal synusiae in ponds.[248]

Although bioassays have demonstrated that a surprisingly high percentage of vascular plants produce toxic substances that could find their way to the soil in litter or as foliage drip, rarely have these proved effective outside the laboratory. For the most part they seem to be destroyed when the protoplasm disintegrates, neutralized by adsorption to soil colloids, decomposed by microbes, or kept very dilute by continuous leaching of the soil.

Extremely little definitive work has been done with toxic interactions except for crop plants, but interspecific influences through toxic products could well affect the floristic composition of some or all successional stages, as well as the balance among species at climax.

Soil evolution.   Plant life exerts powerful influences on the direction and rate of development of soil profiles. Surface stabilization often prevents erosion that would otherwise prevent the development of an A horizon; minerals are dissolved by acids secreted by roots; altered temperature affects the type of weathering of minerals; and more water gets into the soil as a result of reduced runoff, but then the downward movement of solutes and clay thus favored is curtailed deeper in the profile by roots taking up the water.

Commonly, raw parent materials contain compounds such as $CaCO_3$ or $CaSO_4$ that are very soluble, hence in the first few decades loss of these substances by leaching is the prevailing mineralogic process, provided rainfall is adequate. Once the highly soluble materials are leached out, alteration of primary minerals to clays (which began at time zero) remains as the most conspicuous chemical process. These clays provide additional adsorptive surfaces for ions, but in the course of millennia they in turn tend to be converted into extremely stable oxides or hydroxides with little or no capacity to hold ions. The second and especially the third of the above processes operate so slowly that there is increasing probability that either climatic or physiographic changes will interrupt the process, or at least deflect the direction of trend. The details of all these major pedologic processes are strongly influenced by the character of the vegetation, so that there is a high degree of correlation between seral stages and soil evolution.[474] The amount and disposition of the organic horizons is also strongly influenced by plants (Table 14).

Table 14   **Soil changes during dune succession on the Isle of Man**

Stage	pH	Loss on Ignition, %	Carbon-ate, %
Embryo dune	7.6	0.9	2.7
Stabilized dune	7.0	1.2	0.8
Complete grass cover	6.4	5.5	0
Calluna vulgaris scrub	5.8	10.9	0

SOURCE: Moore, 1931.

If grazing of *Calluna* scrub is prevented in England, *Betula pubescens* invades and within 60–100 years a podsol with a thick A_0 changes to a brown forest soil with mull characteristics.[138] In the Alaskan fjords the reverse change (from mull to mor) which is associated with a change from *Alnus* to *Picea* dominance requires a few centuries, but about 1000 years are then required for the development of the mature podsol. This is approximately the time required for the *Tsuga* forest to approximate equilibrium, for although the climax trees may appear relatively early, the longevity of the seral *Picea* (to 764 years) necessitates many centuries for its complete replacement.

At Chicago 95 percent of the development in dune soils that may be expected at 8000 years is completed in 1000 years, which is the time required for the climax *Quercus velutina* forest to first become established in the habitat.[317] A still longer sequence of correlated vegetation-dune changes has been reported for Australia,[64] where on marine sands half of the $CaCO_3$ is leached from the solum in 50 years after the sand comes to rest, and all of it by 200 years. This permits pH to drop from 8.8 to 6.0, with a result that iron begins to move downward. By 2000 years a well-developed iron-podsol has developed, and at 2500–3000 years the tree *Angophora intermedia* is replaced by *A. lanceolata* with a corresponding change to a humus podsol. Time to equilibrium is not indicated by the materials available for study there, but it is obviously at least 3000 years.

In forest communities it is a common observation that the characteristic undergrowth becomes stabilized earlier than the overstory, with treetop epiphytes arriving still later. In pedology there is an interesting parallel in that there are great differences in the time required for different horizons and pedologic processes to attain equilibrium.

Plant succession and profile development are inextricably interrelated, but the relation between the stable end products stands much in need of clarification. Some conceive of an ideal situation where soil types and vegetation types are coextensive, whereas others doubt if this obtains very often. But to argue this point involves an assumption that the current systems of soil and vegetation classification are both as natural as is possible to develop. If appropriate soil characters were emphasized, there is every likelihood that the two classifications would be parallel.

Light. In terrestrial habitats the first plants to appear on a bare area are subjected to the full intensity of sunlight. As succession advances, the replacement of plants of low stature by others that are taller, and the increasing number of superimposed canopies usually result in a gradual reduction in the quantity of light which filters to the ground. Thus while all stages of the life cycle of pioneer invaders must be completed with the plants exposed to full sunlight, in subsequent communities the seedlings of each stage in turn must be able to develop under increasingly denser shade. Where vegetation grows dense it is an essential qualification for climax status that seedlings be capable of growing under low light intensities, but in the open vegetation of desert and tundra climax dominants may not be tolerant of shade even as seedlings.

On account of the wide variation in light requirements among plant species, the decrease in light intensity as succession advances is one of the most critical of the autogenic forces which determines the floristic composition of each stage. Yet light does not explain all. Seral species are sometimes shade tolerant, their disappearance during succession being attributable to such factors as the development of an unfavorable seed bed,[285] or to increasing root competition. And climax species may be retarded by shade after their first year.[12]

Light, heat, relative humidity, and wind all tend to vary concomitantly, so experimentation is essential to determine which element of the complex is most critical. For example, the death of seedlings in shade may be as much a result of high humidity favoring parasitic fungi as the result of insufficient light energy.[424]

Temperature. The diurnal pattern of gain and loss of heat by radiation, convection, and conduction is greatly changed as plants colonize a bare area. In an unoccupied terrestrial habitat temperature conditions change markedly with the rising and setting of the sun, the most critical intensities of heat and cold obtaining at the soil surface where seedlings or sporelings must endure them if plants are to get established. Thus thin shade often seems necessary for sensitive species, especially on dunes where heat-girdling of the hypocotyl is commonly fatal.

As the pioneer community develops appreciable stature, but before the canopy closes, the daily heat supply is received over enough vertical surface so that the high temperature hazard is considerably mitigated. However, at this stage nocturnal chilling may be intensified, for scattered tall plants tend to prevent breezes from mixing warm air with cold, yet the canopies are ineffectual in retarding rapid loss of heat at night by radiation. Once a canopy closes over, shade reduces warming of the soil surface by day, and loss of heat at night.

Experience in reforesting frost pockets has shown that trees with frost-sensitive seedlings can be planted on such sites only after a primary cover of frost-tolerant species has become established. Perhaps elsewhere too, plants high in seres, if not terminal, may be unable to invade earlier on account of temperature extremes, but the degree to which this is common is unknown.

Changes in temperature below the ground surface that result from the development of a plant cover are also important. A moss-lichen mat only 1–2 cm thick may reduce soil temperature by 10°C even at a depth of 7.5 cm.[364] In relatively mesic steppe the accumulation of litter and duff can amount to as much as 24.5 metric tons per hectare, and this can reduce soil temperature 12–15°C in May,[444] as compared with areas from which litter is removed artificially. Under these conditions, as succession progresses dominance tends more and more to favor a single species.

Samples of litter, duff, and soil transplanted from beneath dense vegetation canopies to flats in glasshouses have been found to contain viable seeds in abundance that do not germinate under natural conditions.[314] This phenomenon may be partly explained as a consequence of temperatures unsuited to germination and may account for the rapid appearance of certain plants when a vegetation canopy is removed so that soil temperature is raised and made more variable.

In cool and cold climates soil temperatures under dense vegetation tend to be lower in spring and summer, but higher in autumn, as compared with bare and thinly populated habitats. By delaying the date of thawing and then the date of freezing of the soil, a forest canopy tends to shift the period of temperature favorable to plant growth to later in the annual precipitation and photoperiod cycles. This is one of the ways an overstory may exert some control over the relative abundance of different kinds of tree seedlings or low plants.

Where snowfall is scanty or comes late in winter, a dense evergreen canopy tends to intercept enough snow to allow the soil to freeze deeply before an insulating blanket of snow can accumulate. Thus soils in these regions may be expected to freeze more deeply as succession advances. Where this influence is extreme, it may start the accumulation of permafrost which then has a pronounced influence on the character of the equilibrium ultimately achieved.[369]

Dryness of air and soil surface.   The pioneers that initiate seres under water have no water-balance problem, but on land drought is a common hazard to seedling existence, and in nearly all xero- and mesoseres dryness of the air near the ground diminishes as succession advances (Table 15). The increasing mass of shoots retards air movement, trans-

Table 15   **Relation of evaporative power of the air to plant succession following fire**

Type of Vegetation	Relative Evaporation
Postfire stage of herbs and low shrubs	100.0
Seral forest of *Pinus contorta*	70.4
Climax forest of *Abies lasiocarpa* and *Picea engelmanni*	35.5

NOTE: Standardized Livingston atmometers were mounted a meter above the ground and maintained in contiguous communities for several weeks in summer.

fers more and more water from soil to the lower layers of air through transpiration, and elevates relative humidity by keeping temperatures lowered.

Germinating plants are very vulnerable to dryness between the time the testa splits and the radicle has made good contact with a fairly constant supply of growth water. However, once this critical period is passed, atmospheric dryness is of little direct importance to either seedlings or mature plants, so long as soil moisture remains above the wilting coefficient.[121] In fact, as pointed out earlier, the seedlings of certain pioneers seem to require a degree of atmospheric dryness as a protection against parasitic fungi. Thus the decreased evaporative rate as succession advances seems most significant in a positive way by aiding the establishment of contact between the radicle and permanently moist soil, and important negatively in relation to disease hazard.

Allogenic forces. In fen and bog seres, autogenic influences seem to provide the sole motivation of succession, at least in the later stages. Also, the readjustments in a community when herbivores are removed following a period of severe overgrazing are entirely autogenic.

On the other hand, in undrained depressions of arid regions, allogenic forces seem to be the sole cause of vegetation change, in that successive belts of halophytic vegetation spread centrifugally from the basin, encroaching on less halophytic communities, as a result of gradual accumulation of salts. The purely allogenic type of factor is also exemplified by the changes in vegetation that occur when livestock are confined to an area previously subject to negligible grazing influence.

Although the forces motivating a sere may be purely autogenic or purely allogenic, frequently both processes are at work. In this event the effects of one may be additive to the effects of the other, as where marl accumulation in a pond and down-cutting of the lip both reduce water depth and hence promote succession. In other situations allogenic and autogenic factors may be opposed, as on talus slopes where the stabilizing influence of pioneers may be offset by cliff exfoliation.

Some ecologists have objected to the inclusion of seres motivated by allogenic factors under the term succession, but little purpose is served by drawing such a distinction.[413] All seres, regardless of the proportion of autogenic and allogenic influences, involve invasion, environmental change, competition, and changes in taxonomic composition culminating in a final stage of relative permanence. And regardless of which class of forces prevails, prediction is possible only after the community sequences have been studied. Certainly a discussion of vegetation dynamics would be needlessly complicated if allogenic forces were not considered along with autogenic.

Consequences of changes in environment. Just as the creation of a bare area initiates the sere, changing environment normally keeps it active. Since all species differ in their environmental requirements and tolerances, during the course of succession there is a constant natural selection, the standard for which changes progressively.

During most seres environmental changes wrought by one stage favor invaders of the next, directly or indirectly, but by definition at climax the vegetation influences prevent further successful invasion by plants which could induce still different conditions, yet the conditions attained permit the regeneration of those organisms maintaining them. Explanations of successional phenomena call for a determination of those factors which permit each new species to become established at a particular point in the environmental evolution, and those factors which become so critical as to interfere with the continued completion of the life cycle of a previously established species.[135] Thus, although succession is basically a synecologic topic, its understanding hinges entirely on individual autecologies as worked out under field conditions.

Competition[84, 141, 297]

The scattered plants that first invade a bare area exert no influences on each other—they must cope only with physical conditions as determined directly by climate and soil (and sometimes herbivory as well). In severe environments this situation may persist indefinitely, but elsewhere more and more individuals get established and the crowded conditions bring about interrelationships that have a powerful influence on the establishment and development of late arrivals. These interrelationships may be helpful, neutral (rarely), or detrimental. Frequently helpfulness (anthropomorphism not implied) takes the form of previously established plants providing shelter, moisture, or some essential component of the substrate of another species. Our attention below will be directed mainly to the detrimental interrelationships.

Whenever the quantity of useful matter or energy falls below the level needed for the maximal growth of two or more organisms which must draw on the same supply, a contest arises. Despite its anthropomorphic connotation, the term competition is widely used for this phenomenon in which one organism is indirectly detrimental to another by making similar demands on environmental resources. Since Charles Darwin called attention to the point, it has been recognized that the more similar the needs of two organisms the more intense the contest, therefore intraspecific competition is keener than interspecific.

Competition among plants may be for: (1) water, wherever soil moisture is suboptimal for even part of the year, (2) nutrients, wherever the concentration of one or more nutrients is suboptimal, (3) light, wherever luminous energy is suboptimal for one plant as a result of shading by another, (4) heat, wherever in cold environments radiant energy is intercepted by the canopy of one plant to the detriment of another, providing light wavelengths alone are not involved, (5) carbon dioxide, at times in dense vegetation when photosynthesis is vigorous,

(6) oxygen, as with organisms in the hypolimnion of ponds, or roots in soil, and (7) space, as with algae requiring surfaces to attach holdfasts.

Species differ widely in their genetic capacities to cope with these consequences of crowded conditions, and the competitive capacity of a given kind of plant is subject to environmental modification so that it varies from one habitat type to another. Furthermore, the severity of competition commonly varies with the season, e.g., the foliage of a deciduous tree or shrub may intercept most of the light energy at a time when seedlings of another species need high intensities to survive.

Etymologically, the word competition means "seek together," and the usage followed above is consistent with the implied condition. However, some prefer to include any detrimental influence of one organism on another (short of parasitism), including not only competition in the strict sense but toxic influences, leaf smothering, aggravation of the spread of disease, etc. And others would define it as including all symbiotic phenomena relevant to natural selection. Although these broader usages are not followed here, they can be justified in the sense that any activity of one species that interferes with another's efficiency in the use of environmental resources has the same net advantage as superior competitive ability in the strict sense.

Changes in environment due to vegetation development have already been discussed, including changes involving competition as well as other types of mutual interference, but there remain to be considered certain aspects of crowding as they affect individuals and populations, together with some indication of the methods used in this phase of synecology.

Methods of studying competition. *Manipulation of established vegetation.* Because the roots of trees in a forest commonly exceed the lateral extent of the crown, and the crowns themselves may overlap, the root systems of trees form a complex interlacing network which enmeshes the subterranean organs of seedlings, shrubs, and herbs. The intensity of root competition in such closed communities has often been studied using a technique that originated in Germany more than half a century ago: A plot so restricted in area that it surrounds stems of only small plants is marked off and a narrow trench is excavated about the periphery, deep enough to sever all roots of the larger trees which extend into the plot. The trench is immediately filled in and the soil compacted to approximately original bulk density. This procedure is aimed entirely at freeing the small plants inside the plot from any competition that might have been afforded by the roots of large trees.

If competition for water or nutrients was a significant force before trenching, the seedlings and other small plants within such experimental plots should show accelerated growth when compared with a series of untrenched plots that serves as a control. On the other hand, if shade is the chief limitation, trenching should in theory result in negligible benefit to the enclosed plants.

In grassland or other low vegetation root competition can be evaluated by making careful measurements of selected experimental and control plants, then keeping all the surrounding individuals cut back to the ground for a few years. In a dense stand of young evergreen trees the significance of canopy competition has been evaluated by tying back the tips of trees surrounding experimental individuals, and the significance of root competition by poisoning (but leaving standing in place) those trees surrounding other experimental individuals. The validity of the last two techniques depends on an assumption that bending a live tree does not reduce its water uptake, and that poisons are not secreted by the tissues of individuals so treated.

If stimulation is observed after root competition is reduced by any of the above-mentioned techniques, further tests must be made to evaluate the relative intensities of competition for water and for nutrients. New series of experimental and control plants may be fertilized or watered for this purpose.

A complication in the interpretation of simple trenching experiments is that the act of severing roots which extend into trenched plots, or poisoning plants whose roots intermingle with those of experimental plants, may improve fertility through the decay of dead roots. For this reason some of the watered or fertilized plots should be trenched for comparison with trenched plots not otherwise treated.

If trenching produces no acceleration of growth, inadequate light or heat are suggested as limiting. But in the interpretation of experimental results it must be remembered that shading may be a primary factor that dwarfs the root system of one species until it can no longer take up water and nutrients in competition with plants with a more extensive root system.[262]

Another question may be raised if the results of trenching are positive: Is the change only a consequence of killing roots that formerly were actively secreting toxins within the plot? Still another complicating factor is the matter of root interconnections. The majority of trees in a dense stand of one species may be root-grafted.[50] Finally, it has been demonstrated that an herb and a tree may exchange solutes by way of the hyphae of a common mycorrhizal fungus.[37] Isotope techniques provide excellent means of attacking such problems.

Experimental plantings.   Many studies of competition have been made using plants rooted in containers since this permits a much more rigorous assessment of the factors involved. As an example, an experimenter[13] grew one plant of *Hordeum* surrounded by eight plants of

Persicaria under the following conditions: (1) no competition—shoots and roots of the two species separated by partitions, (2) competition for nutrients—shoots separated but roots intermingled, (3) competition for light—shoots intermingled but roots separated, and (4) full competition—both shoots and roots intermingled. A comparable series with *Persicaria* in the center and *Hordeum* outside was studied at the same time. Such an experiment allowed an assessment of the relative importance of root and shoot competition, which was found to change as the cultures developed.

A variant of this technique is to grow plants in pure stands and in mixtures to see if a certain number of individuals do better or worse when grown with an equal number of their own versus another species.[402]

When it is desirable to grow two species intimately intermingled, root competition can be eliminated from certain replicates by using a common culture solution that is replaced frequently. Such experiments have shown that intra- and interspecific competitive abilities may be unrelated.

Since the outcome of competition is strongly conditioned by environment, it is often desirable not only to vary density but to use replicates of a density series in which soil moisture, fertility, etc., are varied.

Usually competition in cultures is evaluated in terms of dry weight of individuals after an appropriate short period of growth, but in the field it is more common to use techniques less destructive and measure changes in dominance, sometimes over a period of years. The mechanisms of competition are more clearly portrayed by making successive quantitative assays of significant characters of populations during their development, for this may reveal a sequence of significant points. For example, changes in the LAI between two competing species may be very revealing in the interpretation of their competitive relations. Either in natural or artificial populations, the time when competition is most effective can be ascertained by eliminating, or introducing, competitors at successively later dates in a series of replicates, to note the influence on ultimate performance.

Exceedingly small differences among species, ecotypes, or biotypes may determine the outcome of competition. As an illustration, it has been observed that species A and B, which occur in nature on different soils, will grow quite well on reversed soils so long as they are grown in pure stands. But where A and B are grown together on soil which in the field is favorable only to A, the latter gains at the expense of B, and vice versa.[299]

Growing plants in containers has an advantage of permitting precise control over soil moisture, fertility, temperature, light, and herbivory, but there are serious disadvantages in that the artificial environments always differ significantly from conditions under which the plants usually operate. Also, differences in normal time of germination of associated species may have a powerful effect on their relative competitive strengths, and this consideration rarely enters into glasshouse studies. Thus the results are likely to have mainly theoretical interest and not necessarily contribute to an explanation of species interrelationships in the field. But this is not to deny that such experiments always yield useful information, and frequently suggest ways of planning more definitive tests under field conditions.

Soil fertility and natural thinning.[278] An abundant source of seed coupled with good weather for germination and survival often produce very dense populations of seedlings. For a time the crowded conditions may produce a microclimate highly favorable to seedling growth and development, but eventually some necessary requisite for normal rate of growth becomes deficient and this process stagnates.[340] Foresters have pointed out that subsequent events differ on fertile and on infertile soils.

On poor soils individuals are rather uniformly stunted despite potential differences in growth rates due to heterozygosity.[136] On the other hand, these genetic differences find expression in fertile habitats, with rapidly growing individuals progressively gaining at the expense of their less fortunate neighbors. Total density is accordingly reduced as the suppressed individuals die, with the remaining trees showing greater height and diameter than individuals of equal age on infertile soils where there has been limited natural thinning (Table 16). On poor soils

Table 16 **Some statistics referring to average conditions of 100-year-old stands of Pseudotsuga menziesii developing on burned areas west of the Cascades in Washington and Oregon**

Site-Quality Class[a]	Density of Trees per Acre	Average D.B.H. in Inches
80	403	9.4
120	239	14.2
160	182	19.7
200	75	27.6

[a] Expected average height in feet of the tallest individuals at 100 years age, when the trees have grown under fairly crowded conditions.
SOURCE: McArdle and Meyer, 1930.

where the growth of all individuals has stagnated, thinning eventually occurs too, but the process of breaking the deadlock is slow, for it must await isolated accidents such as animal injury, windthrow, lightning, etc., to reduce density locally and upset the equal balance of competition.

When seedlings of shade-tolerant species stagnate as a result of being overtopped by rapidly growing seral trees, their chances of eventual maturation depend on the length of time they can endure such conditions in relation to the time that will elapse before the death of taller trees provides release. Species differ greatly in their inherent capacity to endure such suppression, and in general fertile habitats appear to allow the suppressed seedlings to persist longer.

Adaptations significant in competition. Almost any adaptation that helps the plant cope with the total complex of environmental factors confers a measure of competitive advantage, at least indirectly. Thus, earliness of tap root penetration, ability to garner nutrients in short supply, and endurance of drought or poor soil aeration all make the plant more efficient in meeting the physical limitations of certain environments, and differences in the degree to which these characters are developed can determine the relative success of associated species. Longevity, abundant seed production, and efficient dissemination also have an obvious bearing on the relative success of different species. The discussion below will be limited to only a representative group of adaptations which have been considered crucial in determining the outcome of competition, but recognition should also be given to the fact that some species prove superior competitors without any specific adaptation being obvious.

Life-form. Several aspects of life-form seem to have an important bearing on the competitive abilities of plants. Because green plants are so dependent on light energy coming from above, tall plants have an inherent advantage over low ones. This is perhaps the most universally important morphologic feature that is critical in competition, yet height by itself is not decisive, for tall plants must have at least moderately dense canopies* to provide severe light competition, and if this is detrimental to short plants their own seedlings stand to suffer.

Other factors being equal, perennials have a theoretical advantage over annuals. Since only one season is available for the annual to complete its life cycle, the size of the plant body is limited and leaf area must expand slowly throughout most of the growing season unless light is very abundant. The perennial habit allows rapid expansion of foliage during the second and subsequent seasons, and there is less limitation in the ultimate height of shoot or depth of rooting.

---

* For low-growing vegetation point frequency can be used to estimate the total leaf surface above a unit of land; this is a valuable means of estimating light competition that can be used without damaging the community under study.[466]

Among perennials, woody plants have an advantage over herbs of equal stature in that the former have only to regenerate the leafy parts of their shoot systems each year. Thus, climate and soil permitting, woody plants tend to supersede herbaceous plants in succession.

By extension of the same logic, evergreens might seem to have an advantage over deciduous plants, for especially during the first week or so of the main growing season, deciduous plants can use only a small fraction of the available light as their leaves are expanding. But in the earth's vegetation there is no consistent tendency for evergreen plants to replace deciduous ones, and the apparent explanation is that an ever-green leaf must usually be equipped to endure cold or drought, and such a leaf is less efficient than one whose evolution has been directed primarily by pressure for maximum photosynthetic efficiency.

Whereas there is little basic difference among the canopies of an herb layer near the ground, of a shrub layer that is elevated a few meters, and of a tree layer that is still higher, there is a considerable difference in the amount of supporting tissue required to lift these canopies. The ratio of nonproductive to productive (i.e., photosyn-thetic) cells is at least doubled with increase in stature from herb to low tree.[186] This means that the taller the plant the greater the propor-tion of unproductive cells—cells that are produced and maintained at considerable expense to the energy-capturing mechanism. While the elevation of a plant's canopy above the ground provides it with a powerful advantage in competition, high annual productivity is essential. As the supply of moisture, nutrients, or heat declines, the proportion of unproductive cells must be reduced, and accordingly plant stature declines. This explains the persistence of shrub- or even herb-dominated vegetation in poor habitats of forest regions,[315] and the heat limitation reflected in the cold timberlines.[123] That the confinement of shorter species to poorer sites does not reflect an autecologic optimum there is demonstrated by a common tendency for them to invade adjacent better sites following disturbance, after which they are successionally elimi-nated there.

The general validity of most of the above concepts is attested by seres described earlier which frequently involve the replacement of annuals by perennial herbs, perennial herbs by low woody plants, with a final assumption of dominance by tall woody species where environment permits a high ratio of nonproductive to productive cells. On the other hand, such generalizations have many exceptions. The annual *Bromus tectorum*, for example, may supersede tall perennial grasses as a conse-quence of overgrazing in eastern Washington, then show no clear evidence of yielding even 50 years after the grazing factor is removed. Also in less xerophytic parts of this steppe region herbs can keep shrubs permanently dwarfed far below their potential size.[120] In cool moist climates trees can be superseded by mosses if the latter develop so vigorously as to prevent the establishment of tree seedlings.[477]

Low compensation point. In all but low or very sparse vegetation, the first requirement of a good competitor is that its seedlings can endure shade. Thus low compensation points are of obvious advantage in competition. If the mature plant also has a low compensation point, this can offset the disadvantage of limited stature.

Food reserves available to the young plant. Within a lot of seeds representing the same ecotype, those which are larger and heavier have an advantage in that a greater food supply may give the seedling a better start with larger cotyledons, and hence put it in a favorable position with regard to intraspecific competition. For example, one experimenter found that individuals resulting from relatively large seeds had an initial advantage that compounded so rapidly as the seedlings grew that after 84 days these plants were intercepting 98 percent of the available light.[38]

The same principle applies to interspecific competition where variation in seed size is much greater. In forest habitats there is a marked tendency for communities to produce larger and heavier disseminules as succession advances from pioneer to climax. A seedling that can draw on a large endosperm can endure shade during a long period of development, whereas seedlings from lightweight seeds are much more likely to exhaust their food reserves before attaining sufficient height and foliar surface to make their own way. Seed weight is thus roughly proportional to the length of time the seedling can grow actively under lighting conditions below the compensation point. In the small-seeded species that are characteristic invaders of bare areas, food reserves seem to have been sacrificed for high mobility, which reduces competition in another way—by increasing the probability that disseminules will reach all relatively unoccupied habitats. Low food reserves are no handicap where good lighting is obtained immediately upon germination, hence small seeds are common even among climax plants in low, open types of climaxes.

Earliness of starting growth. Earliness to start growth after a season of general dormancy confers a large measure of competitive advantage in that moisture, light, and nutrient supplies are preempted, with shoot systems gaining the advantage of height and spread while root systems gain an advantage in either depth or spread.[231, 272, 298]

It has long been recognized that the "germinative energy" of a lot of seeds (i.e., the percentage germination in a standard number of days arbitrarily selected for comparison) is an important base for predicting the success of a planting.

Rapid rate of growth.   Growth rate becomes important immediately after the seed has germinated, for the slower the seedling grows the more protracted the period of high vulnerability to heat, drought, frost, damping-off, sand-blast, smothering by leaf cast or a thickening moss mat, etc. Differential growth rates must account for much of the interesting variation in the composition of pastures when the same mixture of seeds is planted at successively later dates, with different seasons favoring different species in the mixture.[42] Experiments with *Fagopyrum* and *Phaseolus* showed that the former had double the growth rate of the latter, being capable of overtopping and suppressing *Phaseolus* even if planted as many as 13 days after the latter.[239]

Seral trees may have such rapid growth rates that this characteristic almost compensates for their intolerance of shading. When a large tree dies in a closed forest, a rapidly growing shade-intolerant tree may be able to germinate and project its crown upward into the gap in the canopy before it closes over from the sides, or before a slow-growing sapling of the shade-tolerant dominants can preempt the space. Thus dense climax forests often contain widely scattered individuals of species that are primarily seral in the habitat.

Efficient uptake of nutrients.   If one species is quick to incorporate most of the supply of a nutrient into its tissues, associates which take up this nutrient more slowly may be critically weakened. As an example, *Agrostis* and *Poa pratensis* take up potassium so readily as to eliminate *Medicago*, *Dactylis glomerata*, and *Bromus inermis* from a mixed planting.[330]

Vegetative reproduction.   The frequency with which vegetative reproduction is encountered among plants as the denseness of vegetation increases suggests that this character has positive survival value where competition is intense. Apparently the intensified intraspecific competition becomes less important than the advantage of having a propagule remain attached to its parent until well established. Also, vegetative reproduction may offer compensation for a species which can germinate successfully on only a narrow range of microsites.

Genetic variability.   Genetic variability that provides a rich assortment of biotypes brings more microsites into the ecologic amplitude of a species and thus is beneficial in the maintenance of high population densities.

Plasticity.   The ability of a plant to accommodate a severe condition, such as by becoming prostrate when subject to heavy grazing or severe winds, confers an advantage in competition similar to genetic variability. Also, the ability of an annual to reduce size until there is enough surplus metabolite for at least one seed is of value in preserving genetic diversity.

Root grafting. Natural intraspecific root grafts are fairly common in forests, giving up to 80 percent of the individuals effective physiologic continuity with one or more neighboring individuals.[50] Observations that disease or poisons affecting one tree may be transmitted to another individual as much as 13 m distant confirm the biologic importance of this phenomenon. In one species it was found that materials move primarily from a dominant to a suppressed individual when they are connected, which suggests that the survival of the latter may be enhanced, and thus the ability of a species to remain self-perpetuating may be increased by a genetic propensity for root grafting.[267] In other species superior growth of grafted individuals has been demonstrated, pointing to some advantage being gained by a pooling of resources.

Effects on the development of the individual. Competition frequently results in the death of weaker individuals, and so limits population size, but short of this it exerts strong influence over the developmental processes of those individuals which survive. Many aspects of structure and function differ when a plant is grown in crowded conditions, in comparison with wide spacing. Only some of the more important aspects will be considered here.

Form of plant. Competition alters the relative development of different organs. Thus, from the configuration of a tree standing alone one can easily tell whether it is the lone remnant of a forest, or whether it developed under open conditions from the time it germinated. A tree developing in the open tends to be exceptionally thick at the base, with the trunk having marked taper and bearing branches throughout most of its length. Lacking a special stimulus for rapid height growth, it is usually shorter than average for its age. But when crowding starts to reduce the side-lighting of a young tree that is surrounded by others, the cambium is put at a disadvantage in competition with the apical meristem for metabolites, so that height growth is stimulated at the expense of diameter growth. Thus trees in moderately dense stands have maximal height for their age, slender boles with minimal taper, and foliage tending to form an umbrella-shaped canopy. It is probably due to the meristem competition mentioned above that in the range of moderate to high tree densities, variation in the degree of crowding usually has negligible influence on the rate of apical growth, despite marked influence on diameter growth (Table 17). As shown in Table 17, differences in height are negligible, but trees at the widest spacing have 48 percent larger diameters in comparison with the closest spacing.

It is to the forester's advantage to promote stands sufficiently crowded

Table 17   **Diameter and height of Pinus banksiana stands 25 years after planting at different densities**

Spacing in Feet	Height in Feet	Diameter in Inches
5 × 5	25.7	3.1
7 × 8	25.6	4.1
10 × 11	25.2	4.6

SOURCE: Ralston, 1953.

to ensure a maximum rate of height growth, minimum taper, and early loss of lower limbs so that the size of knots in the lumber will be small. But he must be alert enough to thin the stand before crowding intensifies competition to the point of drastically reducing diameter growth, for once diameter growth stagnates, the benefits of thinning are slow to show up, with species differing markedly in their abilities to recover after release.[261]

Vigor: size of plant.   Stunting is a common consequence of intense competition among plants, so that some form of dominance analysis can be effectively employed to evaluate competition among species in a mixture. Among perennials dwarfing is cumulative with the passing of the seasons, the ratio of a poor competitor to other species, as well as its influence on the ecosystem as a whole, declining progressively to death.

Each habitat has a relatively fixed potential for dry-matter production that depends on the ecologic sum of all edaphic and aerial factors. In pure stands of one species, as population density increases from zero, productivity increases until light interception by the foliage is rather complete, then levels off and becomes constant regardless of the increasing numbers of ever smaller individuals.[19] But when some component of total productivity is singled out for study, e.g., seeds, fruits, tubers within a particular size range, leaves, etc., the production curve is typically parabolic, with a peak defining optimal population density for the character.[222, 223] Thus at plant densities necessary for maximal seed production, the individual may be less than 1/50 the size it can attain when free of competition.[140]

When dense stands of the seedlings of several species start growth at about the same time, the poor competitors begin to decline quickly, but in thin stands competition develops with time so that their reduction in size becomes noticeable only late in the life cycle. On the other hand, if one of two competitors matures early, the other may expand as competition lessens, resulting in a confinement of the dwarfing influence to early stages of ontogeny.

The effect of competition on roots can be easily overlooked. As the roots of a less successful competitor become restricted, they have access only to soil already partly exhausted of nutrients and moisture by the more successful individuals, and this is reflected in their lower nutrient content.

Since the size of a plant has so much to do with its influence on the remainder of the ecosystem, competition as it governs dominance is one of the most important of synecologic phenomena.

Vitality: reproductive potential. Agronomists have performed many experiments to determine the effects of increasing plant density on the seed yield of annuals. Plants spaced very widely generally produce the maximum numbers of seeds per individual, but seed production per hectare is very low simply as a result of the sparse population. As density increases and competition becomes effective, seed production per plant decreases, but seed production per hectare increases. Next there is reached a point beyond which seed production per hectare remains constant, with decreasing production per plant just offsetting further increases in density. Over a wide range of further increases in density, seed production per hectare remains constant, but eventually a point may be reached beyond which fewer seeds are produced per hectare.[159]

On abandoned cropland in southern Idaho where the annual *Bromus tectorum* is a dominant, its populations were observed to increase over a series of summers, then reach a point where seed production became drastically reduced. This resulted in a thin stand the next season, which started the cycle all over again.[339]

A tree growing isolated may produce its first seed at 25 years of age, whereas in moderately dense stands on the same habitat type, this event may require twice the age. Thus intense competition decreases the probability that a perennial will live to reproductive age. Not only is the sexual maturity of a perennial delayed, but as with annuals, the numbers of flowers per plant and the amount of seed that is set are reduced at very high densities, and under severe competition the plant may remain sterile.[449] In part, this reduction in seed yield, when it results from intraspecific competition, may sometimes reflect an increasing shortage of essential pollinators.

Whereas the numbers of seeds per plant are strongly reduced by competition, mean seed size is remarkably independent of such stress, unless competition involves shading from above.

Long-term consequences of competition. *Influence on stand composition.* In very extreme environments where seedling establishment is too rare a phenomenon for a closed plant cover to develop, each plant association seems to represent little more than a list of species that can immigrate and thereafter maintain a sparse population relative to their mortality rates under the rigorous physical conditions. Potential differences in competitive abilities find little chance for expression here.

Where there is more vegetation, as a sere progresses competition usually changes early dominants to subordinates, then eliminates them from the site. Through its continual tendency to narrow the species list down to a group with matched abilities to continue reproducing under a particular type and intensity of competition, competitive elimination is a major unifying force responsible for much of the similarity among stable vegetation units in similar habitats. The importance of chance survival of weak competitors declines to a very low level, and intrinsic factors now share importance with extrinsic in governing the character of the climax.

In layers where one taxon proves competitively superior to all others of similar stature, which is a common phenomenon in especially the dominant layer of rather cold or dry climates, pure or nearly pure stands may develop as climax is approached. These seem to reflect no more than the lack of ecologically equivalent species in the flora. The greater the diversity in a given stratum, the lower the probability that any one of the species can dominate the others, and the less the proportion of floristic variability that can be accounted for by extrinsic habitat factors.

It is common for trees to get established in such abundance early in a sere that excessive shade develops, choking off all further tree reproduction and even eliminating shade-tolerant shrubs and herbs. With the passing of time, the deadlock is broken by the occasional death of scattered trees, allowing seedlings of the most shade-tolerant species to succeed. At climax, tree density has become reduced to a point which allows the maintenance of complete replacement series of those species best adapted to intense competition.

Reduction of range and apparent ecologic amplitude. If plant species behaved individually, they would each show abundance gradients across environmental gradients that would reflect their optimal physical environment. But this is true only in disturbed landscapes where competition is weak. As succession advances and competition intensifies, a species finds itself eliminated from certain habitats where in early seral stages it grows well if not at its best, and the areas characterized by its success or failure become more sharply differentiated. As a specific example, in northern Idaho *Pinus ponderosa* is common or abundant in nine habitat types, but in four of these it is strictly a seral tree mingling with either *Pseudotsuga menziesii* or *Abies grandis* whenever fire sweeps the area and allows the pine to invade.[127] Thus the apparent ecologic amplitude of this pine is drastically reduced by competition alone, and what is more, the greatest vigor of the tree is shown in habitats from which it is completely eliminated in the course of secondary succession.

Crop plants, which can be grown over a wide spectrum of habitat types because man keeps competition under control, and the entry of weeds into an area only after native vegetation has been disturbed, provide illustrations of range limitation through competition.

Control over ecotypic specialization.   Since the time of Charles Darwin competition has been recognized as playing an important role in the process of natural selection, and consequently a guiding force in evolution. With survival restricted to the fittest, and individuals in a population varying slightly among themselves as to their fitness for a particular habitat, only the genetically superior live to produce subsequent generations. Each habitat type is a distinctive combination of environmental factors, so the different selection pressures in contiguous habitats tend to develop special ecotypes that are homozygous for at least the adaptive characters.[199, 288, 403, 407]

Since ecotypes are more distinctive physiologically than morphologically, the extent of a habitat type serves as a guide to the extent of possible small genetic differences which would otherwise pass unnoticed. Especially where a plant appears to grow well in a community devoid of its usual associates, one might suspect that it is represented there by a special ecotype. Some workers have suggested that different ecotypes may be involved where the same species is represented both early and late in stages of the same sere. These may be selected anew from the same gene pool each time a sere is repeated.[126]

Species that are annual and produce great numbers of seedlings probably tend to improve their adaptation to the habitat at a maximum rate, for each year a great many genetic combinations are produced for selection to operate on.[4] For other species competition may favor evolution through restriction of population size, for it is well established that the smaller the population the greater the opportunity for retention of advantageous innovations that appear. Where the struggle for existence favors longevity, genetic variability is better preserved since the plant can withstand environmental extremes even though each extreme destroys a generation of seeds.

Among crop plants artificial selection has tended to heighten the intraspecific competitive abilities of each species, since the physical hazards of environment are minimized to the best of man's abilities. Among wild plants, in contrast, selection is guided in large measure by adversity that is not necessarily related to competition. This may explain the high competitive rating of most crop plants when tested against a number of noncrop species. Abundant weeds in a field do not indicate low competitive abilities of the crop plant so much as they represent a consequence of economics dictating that the density of the crop be kept as low as possible without sacrificing productivity, leaving unused resources that are an invitation to weeds.

As a group, pioneer species have high reproductive capacities that enable them to avoid competition, and here adaptation may be but weakly guided by competition.

Stability: Homeostasis at the Community Level

Succession consists of a unidirectional metamorphosis of a bio-coenosis and its ecotope which allows different species to become established, or at least to assert their dominance, in a sequence that has many predictable features. By a process of natural selection certain plants are replaced by others which are better adapted to complete their life cycles under newly acquired conditions of the habitat. Seral species may be defined critically as those which enter the habitat during a period when environmental factors temporarily favor their establishment, then subsequently find conditions intolerable for their reproduction. Ultimately, the shifting population becomes restricted to those components of the local flora that are capable of completing their life cycles in the face of intense competition, the homeostasis thus attained reflecting a universal tendency for every process to work toward a condition of equilibrium.

Climaxes may be defined practically and conservatively as those communities for which there is no evidence of replacement. But climax is definitely not a permanent condition even though in common language we may use the words *permanent* and *stable* when referring to it. The death of a dominant alters the amount of resources available for each of its nearby associates with second-order changes affecting the abundance of other species, etc., and the significance of succeeding readjustments diminishes progressively. Since these population renewal sequences overlap in time and space, no part of the climax ecosystem is static, yet its average character over a span of time may remain remarkably constant. Superimposed on this wavering balance resulting from internal regenerative processes are the effects of short-term climatic fluctuations which favor first one species then another in the phytocoenosis. Taking a still broader view, floras, faunas, and environments change progressively with the passing of centuries, so that the midpoint of oscillations of several magnitudes can be expected to drift. Despite this complexity and continuity of change, it is possible and highly desirable to draw the line between seral and climax communities where the rate of change declines sharply—where the vegetation ceases to exhibit clear evidence of unidirectional change, so that the nature of future alterations is unpredictable.[421]

The progress of a sere commonly involves (1) change in dominance from small plants low on the phylogenetic scale to large plants high on this scale, (2) increasing longevity of the dominants, (3) conformity to a prevailing type of physiognomy that is characteristic of the region, (4) diversification of life form, (5) replacement of species with similar and broad ecologic amplitudes by groups having narrower and complementary requirements, (6) increasing numbers of interspecific dependencies, (7) increase in the bulk of living tissue and dead organic matter per unit land area, (8) increasing regularity of floristic composition and structure among stands representing one association, (9) increase in the number of possible pathways along which matter circulates and energy flows, but a general slowing of circulation and flow, (10) a higher proportion of nutrients tied up in living cells and organic debris, (11) an amelioration of microenvironmental extremes, (12) maturation of the soil profile, and (13) greater resistance of the ecosystem as a whole to disturbing forces. Finally, growth rates and the general health of the dominants decline. Thus in a seral forest defective individuals are more common among late recruits than among those plants which became established when environmental resources were more plentiful.[90] And in steppes too, the dominant grasses suffer loss of vigor and vitality in the absence of disturbance. Commonly, productivity increases during most of a sere, but it may decline somewhat as stability is approached.

While all of the above trends are demonstrable, individually or collectively they provide no definite criteria for recognizing the point at which stability has been maximized. The most certain evidence of stability would result from continued observation of the community over a long period, but obviously such evidence is all but nonexistent, and we must instead rely on inference based on population structure as our next most reliable criterion.

Positive evidence that a perennial species has achieved the self-perpetuating state is often clear from its population structure, i.e., age-class distribution. Earlier it was pointed out that a common attribute of a stable population is the abundance of very young individuals, with successively older groups rapidly diminishing in representation. The rate of decline is typically geometric (Fig. 32), but there are many age-class distributions that depart from this pattern and the species still seem to have indefinite tenure of their habitats. A few examples are in order.

Sometimes seedling establishment is possible only at intervals of several years, particularly at the cold or dry limits of a perennial's range, or where light fires run through the vegetation frequently, allowing only an occasional crop of seedlings to succeed. Reproduction is then episodic rather than continuing, and age-class distribution shows conspicuous steps when plotted against time, but in its gross configuration

FIG. 88. Successful establishment of seedlings comes at intervals of several to many years in most habitats where *Pinus ponderosa* maintains itself in pure stands, creating steplike discontinuities in age-class structure.

the curve may still conform to the geometric shape. Stands of *Pinus ponderosa* provide good examples, for they are often composed of small patches of individuals of the same age, but with the ages of the patches differing widely (Fig. 88). Light surface fires and frequent drought devastation of seedlings are responsible in varying proportions. The same steplike age-class distribution characterizes *Pinus sylvestris* at Arctic timberline, where the trees produce seeds only after unusually warm summers that occur at intervals of 60–100 years.[235] A period when a single disturbance interferes with seedling establishment that is otherwise essentially continuing typically results in a depression or gap in the curve which slowly shifts its position along the time axis until it disappears.[337, 436]

Rapid growth rate when a tree is young can also offset near-failure of seedling reproduction, providing the rare individuals that survive reach great age and maintain reproductive pressure over wide area so as to exploit limited opportunities for survival as they appear. Thus if a tree lives to be 500 years old, but seedlings grow so rapidly that only 30 years are required for a new plant to reach a break in the forest canopy when an old tree dies, then the species might be represented by a preponderance of individuals in the main canopy and still retain its position in the association. This seems to account for the small number of young trees representing a considerable number of dominants in tropical rain forest. In temperate and cold climates there are species which are mainly seral (e.g., *Betula papyrifera* in places where *Picea glauca* is the climax dominant, and *Abies grandis* in habitats where *Thuja plicata* is the climax dominant) but seem to persist indefinitely as rare individuals in an apparently stable forest. These trees set seed abundantly and are in a position to exploit any favorable microsite that appears in otherwise inimical environment, so balancing the rare demise of old individuals.

These few examples above show that the perpetuation of species in climax communities presents many intriguing problems, the solution of which demands a complete fusion of autecology with synecology.

The concept expressed earlier that climax represents the attainment of approximately maximum thermodynamic efficiency needs further amplification with regard to stability. Green vegetation serves as an energy trap, converting some of the solar radiation into potential chemical energy stored in organic compounds. The latter are then used successively by other organisms, with degradation through loss of some of the energy at each transformation, until finally all of a given unit of energy has been returned to space. Thus energy may be said to flow through an ecosystem along branching pathways, and the more complex the biocoenosis the greater the number of possible routes, the greater the likelihood of numerous stages, and the greater the possible delay between the capture of a unit of energy and its ultimate release. Collectively, the first plants to invade a bare area are relatively inefficient, yet they play an important role in initiating the accumulation of matter and energy. Formerly, nearly all solar radiation was quickly lost back into space, and as solutes weathered from soil minerals they were leached or blown away, but early immigrants are able to curtail these losses in part. Their inefficiency is a consequence of their fewness and their lack of diversification as to phenology and growth-form. But as colonization proceeds, not only is there an increase in number of plant individuals, but different types are added which occupy different niches and thus utilize the supply of matter and energy in complementary fashion. Living and dead organic matter accumulate progressively, for although the decay rate increases too, production continues to exceed decay in early stages of succession. At each step in the decay process compounds accumulate until the sheer quantity of material overcomes the bottleneck and a quantitative balance is struck between growth and decay—between uptake and release of environmental resources. Since the competitive relations among plants are not directly related to efficiency in accumulating dry matter, the general trend of increasing efficiency during a sere may be subject to small reversals from time to time, and in closed vegetation the point of maximum efficiency may be achieved before stability is reached. Still, the climax may be said to impound the maximum energy and retain it the longest, on a sustained basis.

Once equilibrium is achieved, any change in the constellation of environmental factors or in the biota, if maintained for a time, will be followed by readjustments in the remainder of the ecosystem until a new balance is reached. Communities of annuals are notoriously sensitive to changes in climate or biotic pressure and rapidly become attuned to an altered environment. Long-lived perennials, in contrast, are somewhat buffered against minor annual changes, but their longevity also results in a lagging response to progressive environmental change. This introduces an element of elusiveness to the concept of climax where seres are of long duration and climate changes rather rapidly. In New Zealand especially it is thought that the inability of apparently long-established climax types to regenerate is a consequence of rather recent climatic change that brought about physiologic maladjustment in individuals genetically equipped to regenerate only under climates which no longer exist.[224] This interpretation seems to apply in the Great Lakes region too, for conifer-dominated climaxes or near-climaxes on peat often do not redevelop following logging, but a new type of forest develops, apparently climax in status, that is dominated by *Acer rubrum*, *Ulmus*, and *Fraxinus*.[417]

The idea is often expressed that the more varied the taxonomy (i.e., the greater the "species diversity") and life-forms in a community, the more stable it is. In theory any change in climate or biotic conditions is likely to damage only certain species of the biocoenosis, with the remainder serving to dampen the influence on the ecosystem as a whole, and the richer the biocoenosis the smaller the percentage that would be directly damaged. Artificial monocultures, in contrast, are notoriously vulnerable, for an untimely frost or the irruption of a parasite can be devastating. The argument against the blanket use of weedicides and insecticides also rests on this principle, since lethal sprays nearly always kill organisms other than those we wish to destroy, and thus have the effect of producing a simplified and unbalanced biota. Ecologists are generally agreed that "biological control" is far more sound than chemical poisons for plants or animals, in both terrestrial and aquatic ecosystems.[328, 377]

The principle that relative stability varies directly with biotic complexity seems to apply mainly to climaxes, for seral communities can be far richer in both species and life-forms than the climaxes which replace them.

Several zoologists, basing their conclusions on experiments with simple, artificial ecosystems, have postulated that two species with

FIG. 89. *Sequoiadendron wellingtoniana,* a seral tree living to an age of over 3000 years, emphasizes the important role played by the life span of seral species in determining time for succession to reach stability. *Abies concolor, Libocedrus decurrens,* and other climax species surround the non-reproducing seral dominant.

closely similar ecologic amplitudes cannot continue to occupy the same niche jointly.[89] This idea finds little support as a principle of wide application in natural plant communities. Two or more dominants may exist together without any indication that one is progressively increasing at the expense of the others, and forest undergrowth is commonly a rich mixture of species that persist indefinitely. There is little doubt that what seem trifling differences between species may allow one to overcome the other, and little doubt that any two species have identical requirements and tolerances. Still, with light intensity varying so widely from place to place over the forest floor, two species with only *similar* degrees of shade tolerance can share climax status. Such variability in most natural habitat factors may explain the inapplicability of the zoologists' conclusions to plant communities.

Most forests have been disturbed so recently that areas where the long-lived tree stratum has become stable are difficult to find (Fig. 89). (Undergrowth usually approximates stability long before trees, at least in cold and cool climates.) The concept of climax here becomes an expression of the most probable nature of the stable condition that would result if the present climatic and biotic conditions continued, and there were no further disturbances by fire, grazing, etc. Its factual basis would rest on demonstrable differences among the tree species as to their abilities to reproduce under present conditions, and the absence of evidence of invasion (Table 18). From the population structure of seral stands

Table 18 **Prediction of succession from seral stands in northern Idaho**

Status	Tree Flora	D.B.H. in Decimeters								
		0–0.5	0.5–1.0	1–2	2–3	3–4	4–5	5–6	6–7	7–8
Seral	*Abies grandis*	37	4	12	7	2	2			
	Pseudotsuga menziesii				1	1				
	Pinus contorta			2	2	1				
	Pinus ponderosa					1				
Climax	*Abies grandis*	50	2	6	5	6	2	1	1	1
Seral	*Pseudotsuga menziesii*	2	11	29	20	1	4	1		1
	Larix occidentalis						4	1		
	Pinus ponderosa								1	
Climax	*Pseudotsuga menziesii*	107	4	8	2	8	9	2		

predictions can often be made as to the probable outcome of succession. Such predictions at one location may be supported by finding self-reproducing stands elsewhere that bear out predictions. The four sets of data in Table 18 show the total individuals found on 375 m^2 in each of four localities in northern Idaho. They exemplify two kinds of climaxes and two seral stands which seem to be progressing toward one climax or the other. The value of the climax concept is by no means dependent on the actual achievement of an equilibrium.

Changes in climax vegetation.   The nature of the plant community that is climax for a particular habitat is determined by the sum of physical factors operating there, interacting with the genetic characters of the plants, as the latter govern capacities to assert and maintain dominance. In theory any alteration of either intrinsic environmental factors or biota should alter the character of the climax. Although a climax community has demonstrable ecologic amplitude, enough is known of the earth's history to be certain that this amplitude is severely taxed from time to time, with a result that climaxes do not persist indefinitely. Three causes are involved.

Climate.   Climate drifts slowly through geologic time, for elevation, submergence, orogeny, and peneplanation change the distribution of heat and water. The simplest consequence of a *quantitative* change in climate is a shift in the geographic positions of a series of altitudinal or latitudinal vegetation belts, so that an association which is climax at one point moves away and the appropriate contiguous one takes its place. Thus in consequence of slowly rising temperature in extra-tropical regions, Arctic timberline has been shifting northward[197] and zones of xerophytic vegetation in the southern Rockies have been shifting to higher altitudes in the past century.[211] If such enforced migration is slow and uncomplicated by new edaphic or other factors that affect species very differently, there may be very little modification of the structure of each element of the migrating series.

But changes in climate may be *qualitative* rather than mainly quantitative, so that migration offers little or no opportunity to compensate for it. In this way balances between environment and genetic constitutions that had evolved over a long period become disrupted. Relative dominance changes, and species perish for lack of reproduction not only within their ranges but also on immediately adjacent territory. In New Zealand certain dominants of both forest[309] and grassland[425] seem incapable of reproduction, and at the same time there is no evidence of active migration. This suggests that recent qualitative changes in climate are bringing about extinctions.

Immigration. Each climax becomes saturated with all the qualified species within the native flora, and owing to competitive elimination, the constituent ecotypes become ever more closely adjusted to the biophysical peculiarities of their ecosystem. New immigrants lack this adjustment and are commonly successful only on disturbed areas where environmental resources are less completely used and competition from the natives is less decisive. Immigration is therefore far more likely to alter seral stages than climaxes.

Before human populations became so large and so mobile, floristic changes resulting from plant migration were constantly under way, but operating at a slow pace. Within the past few centuries man has accidentally or intentionally introduced thousands of plants into new regions where they are successful, although rarely as climax species. When they can enter established vegetation, aliens usually find a minor place in synusiae of similar life form, as did *Bromus tectorum* in eastern Washington. Some immigrants have become outright dominants, as *Tamarix pentandra* on floodplains in Arizona, *Aleurites moluccana* in Hawaiian rain forest, and *Opuntia inermis* in arid Australia. Disturbance may well have been essential for some or all of these species to claim the land, but they seem capable of holding the area indefinitely against competition from indigenes. Still other immigrants are parasites that have a tremendous indirect impact on climax structure, as did the fungus *Endothia parasitica* which virtually eliminated *Castanea dentata*, once a major dominant of forests in the Appalachian region.

Evolution. A third phenomenon which may alter the structure of climaxes is the evolution of new ecotypes or species which are able to assert a greater degree of dominance, or as more virulent parasites reduce the importance of a former dominant. The spread of the hybrid *Spartina townsendii* in western Europe, which is displacing the native parent in coastal salt marshes, shows clearly that new gene combinations (and new ecotypes may be no more than that) can have a potent influence on the outcome of competition.

In recent years biologists have been impressed by temporary increases in the activity of insect or fungus pests that bring about drastic reduction in the populations of dominant trees. These may represent some genetic change in the pest, or possibly just a rare combination of climatic conditions that is favorable to the pest, but in any event they must have the effect of depleting the most susceptible biotypes, and in this way bringing about modifications of the ecologic amplitudes of the trees by eliminating genes linked with those governing susceptibility.

Since all species in the community would not be expected to evolve at the same rate, slow shifts in relative dominance must frequently be in progress. Associations are thus evolutionary phenomena, and at any one point in geologic time there must be every kind of transition from newly divergent, to well established, to disappearing or merging units. But this remodeling of vegetation through time has been so slow that the evolution of major units can be traced through millions of years of the geologic record. An analogy has been drawn in which seres are comparable to the ontogeny of an individual, with the slow alteration of climaxes corresponding to phylogeny. Species change through time in reticulate patterns effected by introgression, biotype depletion, accumulations of rich pools of alleles during long periods when free of stress, etc. One can see many points of analogy between these phenomena and the evolution of associations.

Serules.   When a climax stand is subject to quantitative analysis and the data are summarized, our concept of the community takes on the character of an average, and fosters an assumption of perfect homogeneity. But in the course of making the analysis, an investigator usually finds definite evidence that such an assumption is not valid, for almost any stand consists of a mosaic of small areas, each representing different phases of regeneration, and having time relations like those of seres discussed earlier. Certain small patches are young, other parts are older, others mature, and still others senescent. Thus there is a minimal area for demonstrating that the stand as a whole is self-perpetuating—structural homogeneity is a matter of scale. The terms *serule* or *microsere* are appropriate for these orderly sequences of dynamically related patches that comprise a climax. They are equally conspicuous in nonclimax vegetation where succession is moving slowly, in which connection they are analogous to eddies in a river.

It is largely a consequence of this patchiness of regeneration patterns nearly everywhere that the subsamples used in studying one stand are most efficient if elongate and scattered.

Serules can be fairly easily divided into two major categories. One involves the immediate environment of a single plant, beginning with its germination and ending when the life cycle has run its course and the plant body has become an indistinguishable component of humus. The second is a result of very limited disturbance by an animal or a physical force. The terms autogenic and allogenic seem useful for these two categories.

When a seed comes to rest, it begins to release soluble substances, and these, together with the products of decomposition of surface tissues, begin at once to have an influence on other plants, especially microbes. As the radicle elongates into the substrate, it stimulates the activity of other microbes with which it comes into contact and these form an ensheathing microbiota. Interrelationships among these organisms at a given level along the young root change gradually as it thickens, presumably because of chemical differences in the surface tissues and their products.[79] As the root dies, the rhizosphere microbiota undergoes its last metamorphosis during tissue decay, then dwindles away.[435] The soil is thus an extremely complex reticulum of microbial serules that develop and decline in harmony with the longevity of the individual root, and of course differ according to the species of higher plant.[169]

Other serules are associated with the development and demise of the shoot aboveground.[167] First let us consider the effect on subordinates that depend directly upon a tree. Epiphytic communities evolve at different levels along the stem as it elongates, somewhat similar to the rhizosphere sequence. When the tree dies and topples over, the epiphytes degenerate, and successive waves of arthropods, fungi, and other organisms reduce the trunk to litter, duff, then humus. As this conversion approaches completion, macroscopic autotrophes characteristic of the forest floor take over.[284] Zoologists meanwhile may have traced a sequence in the animal life that starts when a branch dies and rot produces a small cavity that serves as a shelter. A succession of animals takes over the cavity as it enlarges, often with help from the inmates. Where the forest is dominated by more than one species of tree, the vacancy arising where one tree dies may happen to be preempted by the offspring of another, with a result that the dependent epiphytes, saprophytes, parasites, tree-cavity animals, etc., that formerly lived there may be replaced by others favored by the second tree species.

Organisms not directly dependent on the tree are also strongly influenced by its death. Much more solar energy and precipitation now come through the break in the canopy, and if thick layers of litter and duff had accumulated, these decompose quickly. At this time such animals as moles and angleworms often make their appearance and start the soil profile evolving in a new direction, yet this microcosm remains limited to the space dominated by the dead tree, being walled in by surrounding vegetation which antedated its origin. Within the island of more abundant resources, a luxurious florule of heliophytic herbs, shrubs, and mosses may become established simultaneously with a number of tree seedlings. Before many years these tree seedlings overtop other plants and the closing of their canopies changes insolation at the ground level from above-average to below-average intensities. With this swing of the pendulum, the heliophytic elements are eliminated and if any vascular plants persist they tend to be highly mycotrophic, remaining only because their dependence on insolation is less direct. Competition among the even-aged group of young trees results in near stalemate, but eventually some individuals die, the remaining one(s) develop, and the foliage cover opens enough that a more nearly average ground flora reappears beneath. Thus it is common for patches of heliophytes and of sciophytes to alternate in both time and space throughout the same stand, and if the stand is climax, its stability as a whole is of an oscillating type controlled by a feedback mechanism. The forces which promote such a serule set in motion the forces that return it by overcorrection to the initial state.

An interesting example of serules involving strictly herbaceous vegetation has been described in England.[438] *Pteridium aquilinum*, spreading by rhizomes, is an aggressive dominant, but a short-lived one. As a clone of this fern advances along one margin, the rhizome reticulum atrophies and vigor declines along the opposite side. *Festuca* and *Agrostis*, which are overwhelmed by advancing *Pteridium*, readily invade areas relinquished on the rear edge of the fern clones. But before the replacement by grasses is complete, the vanguard of another *Pteridium* clone appears, eventually to infilter, overtop, and replace the grasses.

If one records density or dominance in permanent plots each year, he can usually detect changes in the average density or dominance, but this is only a fraction of the dynamism that can be revealed by following the precise positions of individuals within the plots. In climax *Artemisia* vegetation of southeastern Idaho, marked changes were observed from year to year in perennials that lack taproots, yet the composition of the vegetation showed no trend during a number of years' study.[40] Among plants lacking a taproot an individual clump may fragment, the parts then uniting with neighboring clumps of the same species. Added to this were the plant "movements" resulting from the death of old individuals and establishment of new ones. Studies of this type are particularly useful in providing information on the competitive abilities of different species growing together.

Allogenic serules are equally diversified and widespread. A climax

FIG. 90. *Artemisia tridentata* dominating spots of heavy soil in otherwise coarse-textured till that supports *Stipa comata* and *Bouteloua gracilis*. Two ecosystems are clearly represented. Near Dillon, Montana.

Picea-Abies forest on Isle Royale, Lake Superior, was shown to be a mosaic of small groups of trees, each group dating back to a time when wind and/or snow breakage created a small opening in which a group of seedlings got started.[96] In Arctic regions where frost boils interrupt the continuity of a relatively stable tundra matrix (which may comprise but a small fraction of the total area), all stages of development from active frost boils to senescent and stabilized ones may be found in a limited area.[306]

Sociability analyses become meaningful chiefly when related to serules, otherwise they remain mere mathematical descriptions of distribution patterns treated as though they were static. An understanding of vegetation cannot have depth without a study of the multitude of such processes that are constantly at work within it. Serules must be distinguished from vegetation patterns that are a consequence of microclimatic or edaphic heterogeneity and are permanently differentiated (Fig. 90).

Serules usually differ from seres in one or more of these ways: (1) even an undisturbed tract of intrinsically homogeneous vegetation continues to foster serules indefinitely, (2) the average composition of the stand may remain essentially constant with the passing of time, despite turmoil within, (3) the serule often has a duration dependent on the length of the life span of a dominant plant, or its resistance to decay, and (4) saprophytes are often important pioneers in serules. Despite these criteria, there is little question that seres and some types of serules intergrade. For example, it is a matter of opinion as to how many contiguous trees must blow down at once to initiate a sere rather than a serule.

The microseral phenomenon throws into relief the remarkable capacity of an ecosystem to repair damage, whether due to natural causes or to selective use by man. Our civilization has not yet appreciated the importance of such self-restoring equilibria, for by wise limitation of use our ecosystemic resources could be renewed indefinitely, whereas our burgeoning population is courting disaster by overexploitation until, one by one, the earth's ecosystems are being degraded until they are no longer capable of repairing themselves.

Kinds of vegetation change. Although plant succession is sometimes defined tersely as "vegetation change," several distinctive kinds of vegetation change have been treated in the foregoing discussions, and there are still others. Not all of these are usually considered within the scope of the term succession, so it is desirable to clarify the synecologist's use of the term.

The following might all be referred to as kinds of "vegetation change": (1) Changes during the course of the year, repeated annually, that involve the appearance and disappearance of different components of a phytocoenosis,[394] a phenomenon that might appropriately be referred to as community phenology. (2) Erratic year-to-year fluctuations in the composition or abundance of annuals in a community,[214] which are related to weather variation (Table 2). (3) Small-scale cyclic changes in the structure of a biocoenosis that have been discussed as serules. (4) Community sequences initiated on bare or partly depopulated areas of considerable size. (5) Modification of the composition of an established community that is initiated when it is first subjected to some new but persistent disturbance such as grazing, burning, or mowing. (6) Extremely slow and cumulative drift in the composition of vegetation resulting from climatic change, immigration, or evolution.

Ordinarily the first three of the above are not embraced by the term plant succession; they are recognized as features common to both climax and seral communities. The fourth and fifth categories are accepted as successional here because both involve cumulative change in composition or structure that progresses in a predictable direction toward a predictable and apparently stable end point. The sixth involves forces that are unpredictable in character or timing, and results in a rather continuous evolution of the ecosystem through geologic time, at a pace that is too slow to measure. It is not here included within the scope of the term succession.

Ecologic classification of climaxes. The climax is a multicondi-
tioned product of succession, its character reflecting the influences of all
edaphic, aerial, and biotic factors that comprise the environmental complex. Since the climax is in close adjustment with all these aspects of its
habitat, it might be hypothesized that there are as many different types
of climaxes as there are different combinations of environmental factors.
This is patently not the case, however, for one can find amazingly similar stands of climax vegetation scattered over wide areas, many of them
in habitats demonstrably different in that they represent varying combinations of soil, topography, and climate interacting somewhat compensa-
tively so far as the vegetation is concerned. Thus an association exhibits
a degree of ecologic amplitude. It is able to absorb a certain amount of
environmental variation without showing an equal degree of variation
in its composition or structure. As a result, an undisturbed landscape
consists of a mosaic of a few rather well-defined climaxes, each normally
represented by stands that reappear wherever habitats are similar, rather
than consisting of endless gradients of vegetation running in all directions, which would make classification arbitrary if indeed possible.[114]
  Many ways of classifying and designating these types of climaxes
have been proposed, and none has gained universal acceptance, but the
scheme suggested by A. G. Tansley[413] is at least as good as any and will
be outlined below. In this system climaxes are classified into five categories, depending on the key forces most conspicuous in molding their
character.

The climatic climax. The concept of climatic climax hinges on an understanding of what constitutes normal conditions of the earth's surface.
Gently undulating topography, mantled with a fairly deep loamy soil
having neither excess nor deficiency of solutes with respect to the average plant, is the norm for terrestrial environment. Furthermore, it is
not normal to find herbivores or fire so important as to maintain vegetation in a clearly specialized condition. Any climax that characterizes
normal topography and soils, and shows no dependency for its character
upon the maintenance of recurrent disturbance, such as by animals or
fire, might be appropriately called a "normal climax" or a "zonal
climax," but the term *climatic climax* is usually used. The extent of its
ecologic amplitude must be determined by starting with conditions defined conservatively, then progressing outward along gradients in all
the climatic and edaphic factors to discover just how far one may go
along these gradients before an ecotone is encountered.
  All communities, seral and climax, that may be found in the vegetation matrix of a region are subject to the present limitations of (1) the
flora from which their populations may be drawn, and (2) the character
of the macroclimate. In the absence of strong limitations imposed by

microclimate, abnormal soil, fire, or other disturbance, climax vegetation reflects the character of macroclimate with a degree of faithfulness
which is conditioned only by the flora. The truth of this generalization
is shown by the fact that the more nearly alike the macroclimates of
remote areas, the more similar the structure and phenology of their
climax vegetation, no matter how different their floras, *so long as attention is restricted to normal soils and topography and vegetation free
from disturbance*. It is hazardous to predict the character of vegetation
on abnormal sites (or seral vegetation) from only a knowledge of
climate. Wet lands, for example, support divergent climaxes ranging
through marsh, swamp, fen, and bog even within one climatic province
of small extent, whereas they may support closely similar vegetation in
regions with very different climates. It is true that macroclimate influences all types of communities in a given landscape, but in the climatic
climax this influence makes its greatest proportionate contribution to
the sum of forces governing the expression of dominance.

The opinion has been expressed that the climatic climax occupies
the "most favorable" habitat type in the vegetation matrix. But this is
an anthropocentric value judgment. If the lichens on an outcrop could
express an opinion, it is doubtful if they would comment very favorably
on the growing conditions offered by adjacent loams.

The climatic climax has elsewhere been characterized as the "prevailing climax." But there exist extensive areas without normal soil or
topography (e.g., Sable Island, the Everglades, the Mississippi delta, the
glacier-scoured area east of Hudson's Bay), and other areas which have
been brought under the dominating influence of fire (eastern Africa,
southeastern North America), or animals (central valley of California),
or frost-churning of the soil, and in such areas the theoretical climatic
climax can be ascertained, if at all, only by finding small areas accidentally lacking these abnormal influences. This situation finds its
counterpart in pedology, for in the same areas referred to above,
pedologists are hard pressed to find zonal profiles that show much relation to the macroclimate. The climatic climax obviously correlates with
the pedologist's zonal soil, but there is no exact spatial coincidence, at
least with vegetation units and soil units defined as they have been.

The edaphic climax. Soils are commonly encountered which deviate
from the normal characters indicated above to the extent that the vegetation they support is specialized through sere and climax. Examples are
provided by bogs, by salt marshes along seacoasts, by serpentine outcrops, and by sand plains. In all situations where substratal peculiarities
are sufficiently pronounced to produce a self-perpetuating vegetation
that differs from the climatic climax of the area, this ultimate vegetation is appropriately designated as an *edaphic climax* (Fig. 91). These

FIG. 91. Geologically very old outcropping of limestone that is so free of insoluble minerals that it has never developed a soil. *Juniperus virginiana* and other plants rooted in the fractures illustrate an edaphic climax. Knox County, Tennessee.

are correlated with the pedologist's categories of regosols, lithosols, bog soils, solonchak, etc.

A shallow stony soil might in the course of many thousands of years be converted to a deep loam through the weathering of the stones and subjacent bedrock, and in this sense the vegetation it supports has sometimes been viewed as a long-enduring seral stage rather than an edaphic climax (Fig. 92). But after each disturbance vegetation in such habitats recovers and reaches a demonstrably self-perpetuating state in only a few centuries at most. Furthermore, in the many thousands of years required to eliminate the ecologic effectivity of the stones and shallowness of the rooting medium by means of rock weathering, there is a high probability of marked change in the climate or flora, so that if the presently self-perpetuating vegetation of the stony soil were considered as seral in the long view, we could make no predictions about the nature of the hypothetical climax for the site. Such a view is therefore impractical and pointless.

Owing to low fertility,[26] dryness, or solute imbalance, edaphic climaxes are often characterized by low productivity. On the other hand, they also embrace the world's most productive vegetation. Since maximum productivity requires a constantly high input of light in conjunc-

FIG. 92. No soil has formed on this granitic surface that was smoothed off by ice action in Wisconsin time. Forest has developed only in depressions containing a thin film of drift. The mosaic of lichen, herb, and forest communities that seems to be perpetuating itself here at present is probably different from the mosaics that were here in hypsithermal time or in the still earlier period of cold climate. Grand Marais, Minnesota.

tion with moderate but not excessive heat, water, and nutrient supplies, the most productive habitats are warm-climate marshes (edaphic climaxes) where flowing water constantly replenishes nutrient supplies.

The topographic climax. In extratropical regions, slopes facing the equator and those facing the poles usually have microclimates that are very contrasted, one receiving much less radiant energy than normal topography, the other receiving much more. Where such slopes are steep enough, their microclimates foster distinctive seres and climaxes.

Other special microclimates may be correlated with topography where strong winds carry a large share of precipitation just across a ridge to create a pair of microclimatic islands, one drier and the other wetter than average for the area (Fig. 93). Elsewhere hilltops and ridge summits may support relatively xerophytic climaxes owing to their excessive drainage, exposure to drying winds, and location in a thermal belt. In the tropics ridges that rise in the path of violent wind tracts may support only scrub owing to the frequency of severe damage.[445] Basins in cool climates may collect cold air so efficiently that the growing season is shortened, with severe frosts occurring even in summer, and only highly specialized vegetation can develop there. On steep mountain

FIG. 93. Extreme exposure to wind fosters transfer of most of the precipitation (which falls as snow) to lee slopes, producing a local area too dry for forest. A topographic climax is exemplified.

slopes there are frequently snow chutes where the annual cascading of snow permits only supple-stemmed shrubs to persist (Fig. 94).

Wherever local topography, usually operating through microclimate, produces a distinctive vegetation, the climax of these places has been classed as a *topographic climax*. While topography operates through either edaphic or microclimatic factors, the most obvious and most predictable correlation is with topography.

Frequently special topographic features favor special edaphic conditions that always accompany the effects of a special microclimate, with both being important in determining the nature of the special climax. For example, the occurrence of *Populus tremuloides* groves in the bottoms of morainic kettles in north central Montana is probably as much related to the accumulation there of fine sediments as to snow drifting and protection from desiccating winds.[281] The hybrid term *topo-edaphic climax* is meaningful in such connections.

The value of the concepts of climatic, edaphic, and topographic climaxes does not rest on their permitting unequivocable distinctions and so providing a perfect system in classification. For example, the "salt spray climax" that may form a narrow strip along a coastline does not fit easily into any of the above categories, and they do not accommodate

FIG. 94. Snow, frequently cascading down this mountain in winter, keeps stiff-stemmed conifers out of the chutes and allows the supple-stemmed *Alnus* to maintain dominance as a topographic climax. British Columbia.

the apparently permanent communities composed almost wholly of exotic species that are found in the Hawaiian Islands and New Zealand. The chief value of the system resides in directing interest toward understanding the role which environmental elements play in determining vegetation mosaics. The concept is thus ecosystem oriented.

The fire climax. The recurrent burning of vegetation eliminates fire-sensitive species, whose places are then taken by fire-tolerant members of the flora. Thus, as described earlier, over large areas in southeastern North America repeated burning has allowed fire-tolerant pines and perennial herbs to gain and retain dominance at the expense of dicot

FIG. 95. *Pinus palustris* in central Georgia that has been maintained as a pure stand by repeated burning in a habitat that would undoubtedly revert to a dicot forest if burning were stopped. Note charring between bark plates. Knapsack is 25 cm broad.

trees and shrubs (Fig. 95). Different equilibria are possible here, depending on the frequency of burning, for if fire sweeps an area annually even the pines cannot regenerate, so that purely herbaceous vegetation results. Any association that maintains its composition and structure only as a consequence of periodic burning may be referred to as a *fire climax.*

Other examples of areas where fire climaxes are extensive are worth mention. Forests on the midslopes of the Sierra Nevada Mountains of California have been subject to surface fires at intervals of 2–21 years over at least the past 2 centuries, and since this has affected forest composition by greatly reducing the abundance of *Libocedrus decurrens* in relation to some of its associates, these forests may be considered as weakly differentiated fire climaxes.[434] Over wide areas in eastern Africa annual firing of the vegetation by man for thousands of years has produced fire-resistant savannas where the physical environment has the potentiality of producing forest.[362] Locally in Ceylon where frequent burning has maintained grassland in what is intrinsically rain forest environment, the soils have been so altered by long domination of grasses that native trees cannot reinvade when burning ceases. It is of

FIG. 96. Fine wire netting, not readily visible in photo, forms an exclosure which protects the low shrub *Eurotia lanata* from jackrabbits. Outside the exclosure, the *Eurotia*, dominant of an edaphic climax, has been replaced by *Halogeton glomeratus* which maintains itself under heavy grazing pressure as a zootic climax. Wells, Nevada.

considerable ecologic interest that native trees will invade these areas, however, provided a cover of exotic *Eucalyptus* is first planted and left to modify the environment for a time.[226]

The zootic climax. It is normal for any ecosystem to include a modest population of pollinators, defoliators, borers, grazers, sapsuckers, and other animals which directly or indirectly depend on plants for food and shelter. In places, however, the structure and composition of a plant community are in large measure controlled by the constant and vigorous destructive activity of one kind of animal. Familiar examples are provided by communities which arise in response to grazing by domesticated animals, by carp in a pond, or by the nesting, trampling, and manuring influences of colonial birds (Figs. 81, 96).

When many cattle are turned into a pasture containing very lightly grazed vegetation in a relatively stable condition, their heavy selective feeding on certain species initiates a change away from the original climax (a phenomenon aptly called *retrogressive succession*) toward a community which eventually attains a balance with the herbivore pressure. The community so derived, in which the dominant herbivore and the modified vegetation form a dynamic and interlocking system, is appropriately called a *zootic climax*. If after such an equilibrium is established with a few animals, more are turned into the pasture, the heavier grazing pressure will cause the vegetation to retrogress still further until another balance is struck. Thus, until the point is reached where the depauperate vegetation will no longer support the herbivores, a series of zootic climaxes representing increasing proportions of less and less palatable plants may be maintained, these depending directly on the population densities of the herbivores.

The repeated burning that is required to produce fire climaxes is always a consequence of man's activity. Therefore all fire climaxes are actually *pyro-zootic climaxes,* and the use of the term fire climax is justified chiefly by the common understanding of man's role.

In a very real sense the earth's surface is progressively being converted to a mosaic of zootic climaxes in which man's influence varies from weak to strong. Even wilderness areas must be managed in some degree to preserve an approximation of their natural state as it was at the time white man first saw them.

• • •

It should be pointed out, perhaps, that the five types of climaxes discussed above have been defined differently elsewhere in the literature of ecology.

Primary climaxes versus disclimaxes. The term *disclimax* is appropriate when referring to fire and zootic climaxes which depend for their maintenance on continuing disturbance. Climatic, edaphic, and topographic climaxes are *primary climaxes* from which disclimaxes are derived. A disclimax may represent a modification or a replacement of a primary climax (Fig. 97), or the deflection of a sere that has been progressing toward a primary climax. Changes leading toward the establishment of a disclimax, then away from it in the event the disturbance ceases, do not involve the same series of successional stages, even though there may be some superficial resemblances. Furthermore, the disclimax may or may not be physiognomically similar to the primary climax it replaces (Table 19).

A landscape uninfluenced by fire or animal disturbance usually exhibits a mosaic of rather well-defined climaxes that are relatively simple in their floristic composition. As disturbance begins, the distinctiveness

Table 19   Successional relations resulting from grazing which reduce the distinctiveness of vegetation types in a mosaic

Soil Types	Primary Climaxes	Disclimaxes
Sandy loam	*Eucalyptus woolsiana–Callitris glauca* savanna	*Stipa falcata*
Clay loam	*Acacia pendula–Atriplex nummularia* scrub	*Stipa falcata–Danthonia caespitosa*
Light clay	*Atriplex nummularia* scrub	*Danthonia caespitosa*

SOURCE: After Williams, 1956.

of floras among the ecosystems declines and floristic complexity increases because much the same group of invaders penetrates all the habitat types. As disturbance intensifies, most species that characterized the primary climaxes disappear and one or a few disclimaxes take over all the habitat types, with a resultant simplification in flora as well as phytosociology.[33, 82, 460] As an example, low dense swards dominated by *Poa pratensis,* with variable amounts of *Trifolium repens, Taraxacum officinale,* etc., develop on a wide variety of habitat types in moist temperate climates, where cattle graze heavily. In northern Idaho such a sward develops where primary climaxes were steppe, *Crataegus* scrub, *Pinus ponderosa* forest, and *Tsuga heterophylla* forest. It reappears in totally different kinds of steppe communities in the upper Mississippi Valley, and continues eastward into the deciduous forest region of the Ohio Valley. While in theory an infinite number of disclimaxes could be derived from each of the three kinds of primary climaxes, owing to the limitations of any particular flora and to the ecologic amplitudes of plant communities, in reality only a few distinctive disclimaxes are found in any one region.

Usually any disclimax has the potential of reverting to the original primary climax from which it was derived—a fact which has been documented in very many areas. But if the disturbed area is extensive, reversion may be accomplished very slowly, owing to the time required for relatively immobile species of the primary climax to immigrate from distant relic stands. Also, if the disturbed ecosystem deteriorates through soil erosion or some more subtle changes, its reconstruction may involve centuries. Finally, in areas which have long supported dense human populations, disturbance by man or his livestock becomes so severe that the original climaxes appear unable to redevelop, presumably owing to a depletion of those ecotypes adapted to climax conditions.[437] In island floras, such as those of the Hawaiian Islands and New Zealand, the competitive abilities of the indigenes are so low that as aliens are introduced, new climaxes arise with only negligible disturbance by man. Perhaps a new term such as *neoclimax* would be useful for these nonreverting types resulting from man's activity. At the present state of man's influence they are still the exception rather than the rule over most of the earth's surface, therefore habitat types are usually best defined on the basis of their primary climaxes.

Significance of climax classification. Recognition of the different ecologic categories of climaxes as outlined above is useful in several connections.

The synecologist can use them as a means of grouping seral vegetation and disclimaxes into sequences with similar end points, i.e., associations, each of which defines the extent of a habitat type (Table 18). In the process of distinguishing these habitat types the observations required to relate seral communities to their proper categories of climax types demands study of the environmental complexes that produce the differentiation. Thus the classification of climaxes is of great value in directing attention to the environmental controls of vegetation mosaics.

In applied aspects of synecology it is sometimes essential to distinguish the role played by one climax association, which may exist as a topographic climax confined to poleward slopes in a warm macroclimate, then play the role of the climatic climax in a cooler area, and in a still colder macroclimate occur again as a topographic climax but here confined to warm slopes. Although the vegetative potential may be essentially the same throughout the geographic range of the habitat type, different management problems (involving movement of machinery, comfort factors of grazers, etc.) arise as a consequence of change in soil, microclimate, or simply steepness of slope.

The climatologist has still a different interest in climax types. Climates are continua and none but arbitrary boundaries can be recognized unless one uses the distribution of living organisms to show critical points along climatic gradients where physiologic limits of tolerance are reached. Ecotones provided by vegetation are definitely superior to zoogeographic limits since plants show far more regular relationships to climatic types than do animals. Among vegetation types, climaxes are more closely related to climatic patterns than are the vegetation types of disturbed areas, since the delicate balances in the former are achieved through competition, the nature of which is strongly conditioned by climate. But climate cannot be equated with all climaxes in a vegetation mosaic, for each of these tends to have a distinctive geographic range, with a result that one mosaic merges with another through the shifting frequencies and sizes of the different kinds of habitat types. With the climatic climax reflecting climatic influence most directly, it becomes the best criterion of the extent of biologically equivalent macroclimates. It is therefore feasible to divide the land surface into mutually exclusive areas characterized by climatic climaxes, for only one such type of vegetation is found in any one area.* This principle has long been recognized in a loose fashion, for every major proposal for a system of climatic classification has had as its aim the delimitation of areas on the basis of climatic statistics employed in such a fashion as to show the best correlation between climate and vegetation. There seems to be much doubt, however, that a universal quantitative classification of climates which correlates closely with vegetation is a possibility. Except for major physiognomic discontinuities which involve deep-seated biologic principles (e.g., the cold or dry limits of forest), the ecologic amplitudes of plants differ so much from region to region that a point along a climatic gradient that determines the position of an ecotone in one flora may not have an equivalent degree of phytogeographic importance on another continent.[124] Phytoclimatic zones, each distinguished by one climatic climax, would seem to permit the most useful climatic mapping from a biologic standpoint. But the positions of the boundaries must be worked out independently for each region, using climatic climaxes as the criteria.

Polyclimax versus monoclimax. In the early part of this century F. E. Clements developed an hypothesis that within a given area all differences among habitats due to soil and topography are eliminated with the passing of time, so that all the area is ultimately taken over by the same climax association, the nature of which reflects primarily the climate. His *monoclimax hypothesis*, as it later came to be known, therefore demanded that every piece of vegetation in a landscape be fitted into one or more seres, all of which converge in a common climax.[83]

Although earlier workers had concluded that contiguous but widely different soils and types of topography can produce different communities of equal stability, Clements' vigorous exposition of his philosophy quickly captivated North American workers who for the most part knew little about the earlier European literature on synecology, or the rate and limitations of soil evolution, or the rate of peneplanation. Much research since the heyday of the monoclimax hypothesis has shown that it is not merely objectionable for minimizing the significance of the time and soil factors, but environmental convergence to the point of approximate identity has not been convincingly demonstrated anywhere.[145,190,355] In reality, the present viewpoint represents a return to the pre-Clementsian concept. For example, in 1885 R. Hult concluded that in a part of Finland which he studied intensively, there are seven habitat types, each with a distinctive climax. It is significant that in

---

* Where every vestige of natural vegetation has been destroyed or seriously altered, or where topography or soil conditions do not provide suitable conditions for climatic climaxes, this procedure is of course not applicable. Bioclimatic zones of reasonable utility might then be based on the most stable types of vegetation available, or even on the relative success of important crop plants.

Clements' later expressions of his philosophy[85] he made an effort to accommodate reality by recognizing "lociations," "faciations," etc., these being different types of stable vegetation within a "single" very broadly defined climax. Nevertheless, during the period when Clements dominated the field of plant ecology in North America, his hypothesis became accepted as orthodoxy, and many workers still passively accept the terminology, with indeed some still accepting the major premise. It may help clarify the difficulties with the monoclimax interpretation to discuss a specific situation in detail.

In the Lake states many investigators have studied succession on peat, but none has been able to present acceptable evidence that the last stage in the sere on peat gives way to the same association that is climax on adjacent mineral soil. There are peat deposits old enough to bear dense self-reproducing forests of considerable age, but these are always distinct from upland communities.[172] It may be argued that base-leveling of the region will ultimately remove every vestige of these peat deposits, after which the upland forest can invade the sites. But such a process involves many thousands of years, during which climates are almost certain to change in a direction now unpredictable, and by the time the peat disappears some other associations, the nature of which we cannot foretell, will terminate seres on the mineral soils. Nor is it a satisfactory solution to look on the vegetation of such specialized soils as "subclimax,"* "preclimax," or "postclimax," for such terms imply either circumstances of "arrested succession," or the continuation of development beyond the usual climax, neither of which is borne out by facts. Seres on contiguous areas of mineral soil and peat differ from beginning to end. There is no more evidence that a climatic climax supersedes an edaphic climax than there is of the reverse. Since there is no known way for peat, siliceous sand, and other rooting media to acquire the same ecologic potentialities as normal loams, much more than semantics is involved. It is interesting to note that pedology, like synecology, has only recently emerged from a period when a theory prevailed that climate is paramount and profile convergence is inevitable.[108]

It is the task of the synecologist to go beyond the mere description of vegetation and evaluate the influences of environmental variation in bringing about vegetation differentiation. The monoclimax hypothesis, holding that vegetation differences in a limited area are all transitory, leads to an underestimation of the importance of environment in controlling the pattern and at the same time encourages tenuous extrapolations.

In commenting on the dynamic status of vegetation it is just as im-

---

* Clements, who originated this term, sometimes used it in connection with any seral community, and sometimes to designate edaphic, topographic, or disclimaxes.[413]

portant here as elsewhere in science to maintain a sharp distinction between facts and their interpretation. Evidence of succession, such as is described under methods of studying the phenomenon, should be presented wherever a writer wishes to establish that one community is seral to another.

Concepts of the degree of organization of the plant association.
Organismal concept.[20] Frequently in his writings, F. E. Clements referred to the plant community as an "organism." This use of the term seems entirely justified, for it has been applied even to whole galaxies. But Clements, and others inclined toward his views, developed the organismal concept by drawing many analogies between the plant association and an organism in the sense of the product of one zygote.[156] For example, it was pointed out that both the organism and the association have a birth, development, maturity, and death; both reproduce themselves through repetition of developmental stages; both consist of interdependent parts exhibiting organization; the community gains its character through the concerted influences of species in a manner similar to the way in which an assemblage of genes governs the appearance of an individual, and environment influences the degree of expression in both cases. Like the individual, the association varies continuously through time, with ontogeny being comparable to the sere and phylogeny comparable to the slow changes in climax structure through millennia. Variation related to environment demonstrates adaptability on the part of both individual and association. And the community as well as the individual organism inherits a legacy of special environmental influences resulting from the activities of its predecessors.

Difficulty arose in that these points of comparison were treated more as homologies than analogies, and negligible effort was made to point out the significant *differences* between the association and an adult individual. For example, one association may have diverse origins as through a mesosere or a hydrosere, whereas individuals of a species have essentially identical zygotic origins. Only in the sere may developmental stages be morphologically dissimilar to the mature entity, and only here may stages be skipped on occasion. The morphologic parts of an association are interrelated, but they are not united physiologically, with each performing all of one function for the whole association, as with the individual. The relation of the parts to the whole is vastly more complex in the latter.

Analogy plays a useful role in science, for it can lead to new and useful lines of thinking and testing, so it was rather unfortunate that this organismal concept aroused antagonism through its overenthusiastic and unbalanced exposition. In an effort to quell the storm, some writers suggested using the expression "quasiorganism," or "superorganism" for the community. These would certainly seem appropriate when applied to a lichen, but species aggregations show every conceivable degree of organization from this highly integrated community to groupings with negligible integration, as in extreme deserts or tundras.

Since most biotic communities possess characters that could not be predicted from the properties of the constituent species, they must be recognized as a distinct and higher level of organization than the individual. Thus associated organisms are all linked by numerous simultaneous interactions, they are all involved in the same anastomose system of cycling of matter and flow of energy, and the group tends to evolve in the direction of a stable system. These are further manifestations of organization. However, to consider the community homologous with an organism seems an overstatement of the integrity of the community. In the living world the degree of organization decreases from cell to organism to population to biocoenosis.

Individualistic concept.   Botanists had been describing *types* of vegetation for many decades before 1926 when H. A. Gleason challenged the validity of the practice.[180] He contended that no two species have the same spatial distribution, therefore vegetation varies continuously, so that recognition of types is strictly an arbitrary practice. Apparently no other substantial evidence in support of this "individualistic concept" was available in 1926. It was not until 1951 when J. T. Curtis and his students developed special techniques for analyzing vegetation and for processing the data, that quantitative evidence purporting to substantiate the independent distribution of species was offered. Others developed still different techniques that seem to show the same phenomenon.

The contention of this group is that the abundance of each species across an environmental gradient can be described by bell-shaped curves, with the curves for different species being offset so that no two coincide. These workers therefore uphold Gleason's contention that vegetation lacks objective discontinuities (other than the limits of species ranges, which are legion) and is therefore unclassifiable except by wholly arbitrary means.

To accept the hypothesis of complete independence of species with respect to their distribution over the landscape is to repudiate the thoroughly documented principle of competitive exclusion, for many species can invade a habitat following disturbance only to be completely eliminated by competitive pressures as equilibrium is restored. Continuum methodology throws together vegetation samples in different successional stages. Since species which are climax in one habitat type occur in seral roles on contiguous habitats, and since each sere in itself is a continuum in time, seral stands provide the bridges that link all stands into a single web of variation in space. *Floras** are clearly continua as Gleason pointed out, so that any method of sampling that is oriented toward flora, rather than toward taking population dynamics and ecologic considerations into account, can't fail to produce data amenable to an interpretation that species are distributed independently. On the other hand, if population data are used to evaluate successional status, and stand data are obtained from homogeneous areas and stratified ecologically, this reveals significant discontinuities across environmental gradients and shows few, if any, bell-shaped curves of relative abundance along these gradients.[128]

An abundance of association tables has been published showing in detail that at many places over the landscape competition results in the attainment of a remarkable degree of similarity in community composition and structure, these similarities being of such a high order as to have evoked comparisons between the association and the species for a long time. This phenomenon embarrasses the individualistic concept. That individual stands in an association table do not represent carefully located points on a continuum is proved by environmental variation among stands showing that associations have ecologic amplitude, and by data such as those in Fig. 28 showing that individual stands of a given type exhibit homogeneity rather than an ecotonal character.

The aircraft design that proves a failure (as many do) points up the hazard of predicting performance of something much simpler than an ecosystem even when detailed knowledge of the properties of all components is available from the start. In a similar sense, the biotic community is much more than a group of independent species. No organism lives in a biologic vacuum, as implied by the "individualistic" concept.

Ecosystem concept. The ecosystem concept developed at length earlier in this book and needing no further elaboration at this point, stands somewhere between the "organismal" and the "individualistic" concepts. One cannot use the term ecosystem without implying a certain amount of functional interrelatedness, yet the idea does not involve an overemphasis of the degree of organization.

Plant succession and vegetation mapping.[265] Vegetation maps have proved useful in theoretical ecology for demonstrating degrees of spatial relationships between vegetation and climate or soil. In applied ecology they are indispensable tools in the management of nonarable lands, and the utmost care in their preparation is needed since intensive management requires accurate information about vegetation mosaics.

Several bases for mapping have been used. Maps may reflect existing

---

* The basic unit of *flora* is the species; the basic unit of *vegetation* is the community. *Floristics* therefore deals with plants as elements of a flora, whereas *synecology* deals with communities as elements of a vegetation.

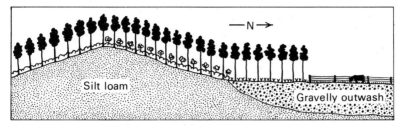

FIG. 97. Assuming stability in the ecosystems shown, this diagram illustrates two (dominants only) or four (entire phytocoenoses) cover types,
four stands, three habitat types, and five layers (or synusiae or unions).

communities (cover types) considering either just the present dominants
or the present phytocoenoses regardless of successional status, or they
may be based on habitat types, which are an expression of the potentialities as determined by intensive field study of vegetation dynamics
(Fig. 97).

The cover type basis has had wide appeal because it provides an
accurate inventory of existing plant resources. Also, it can be prepared
by persons with very minimal botanical training and no understanding
of the synecology of the area to be mapped. But as land management
has intensified, there has been a growing awareness that the cover type
is not the most useful basis of mapping. It is merely *descriptive*,
whereas an *interpretive* treatment is much more informative. Each
habitat type in the landscape is represented in the field by innumerable
stands exhibiting different stages of succession. Therefore cover types
must be divided arbitrarily and defined broadly to avoid overwhelming
complexity. Often it happens that similar stages of different seres fit
into the same cover type category, and often the climax of one habitat
type resembles a seral stage of another. Either of these two common
difficulties makes a map prepared on the cover type basis unreliable for
any interpretive use. Aside from this, a cover type map soon becomes
outdated, as when the trees depicted mature or are logged or burned,
or a grassland is subject to a different grazing regime, so that expensive
inventories must be repeatedly made on the same land. These important
limitations on their utility jeopardize the economic justification of a
cover type map, especially since another viewpoint incorporates the
same data, is of permanent value, and provides a reliable basis for
different types of land management. The oft-repeated comment that
different bases of mapping are needed for different purposes would
have little truth if mapping were done on a fundamental basis portray-
ing habitat types plus successional stages.

This alternative to cover type mapping involves interpretation of the
existing mosaic of communities, laying primary emphasis on the potentialities of the land as indicated by the primary climaxes actually or

potentially occupying it.[294] Such a map has value as enduring as the present topography, climate, soil, and flora. Within the area representing each habitat type, suitable symbols can be used to designate seral stages or disclimaxes that now occupy various parts of the unit, recognizing that these subdivisions (cover types) are subject to change with time. Past history, present conditions, and expected trends are easily read from this type of map, for the seres must be understood before it can be constructed. It is expensive, since highly trained personnel and years of work are required before its preparation, but having once been made, it has broad application in planning forest, game, livestock, and watershed management, and when cover types change revision of the map is simple. With a map of this type the forester knows what species to plant to get the greatest return on investment, the rates of tree growth to expect, and the disease hazards, while the game manager can evaluate the worth of the existing cover to game animals of different types and predict its direction and rate of change.

4 vegetation and ecosystem classification

All classifications have as their objective the orderly arrangement of a vast array of objects so that their differences and similarities can be better understood. Individual units that have been studied (single plants, stands of vegetation, soil profiles, etc.) are grouped into categories, each represented by one name. Unknowns are later identified in terms of the category which they most closely resemble.

In the history of any science the first classifications proposed are superficial ones based on a single manifest character and are of value chiefly where this character is important. Later, as the subject matter becomes better understood, correlations among characters are discovered and this eventually allows all properties of the units to be considered simultaneously so that through a series of successive approximations a more sophisticated classification is evolved that serves many purposes at once.* These are *natural* classifications (in contrast with their fore-runners the *artificial* classifications) and may be considered as developed to the maximum extent that the nature of the subject matter permits when the mere mention of an object's position in the scheme allows the maximum number of predictions about it. In addition to its value for showing degrees of similarity and difference, a classification is indispensable for the storage and retrieval of information. Since any classification is a product of man's brain, it is artificial, but classification has proved essential in all branches of science.

• THE PROBLEM[290, 344, 346, 411]

For centuries botanists have grappled with the problem of classifying plants into species, and, using the tremendous advantage of the unifying thread of lineal descent that binds individuals into natural series, much progress has been made. But lineal descent is lacking in plant communities (at least in the above sense), and even the stands themselves are usually more difficult to circumscribe than is the individual plant. Thus the precision of vegetation classification can be of no higher order than is possible in pedology or petrology, or in such difficult genera as *Crataegus, Crepis, Lupinus, Poa, Rosa,* and *Rubus.*[70] The basic problems and the necessity of classification are common to all branches of science, regardless of differences in levels of possible achievement. Vegetation specialists from tundra[179, 204] to tropical rain forest[67, 363] have indeed

---

* This is not to say that artificial classifications do not serve narrow purposes better. Thus all forest stands containing merchantable quantities of a timber species such as *Quercus alba* may be drawn together for purposes of timber inventory as a *Q. alba* "forest type," regardless of many other and wide differences in the ecosystems involved. Such a classification would serve no purpose other than inventory, however.

demonstrated the practicability of classification. Furthermore, it is highly significant that classifications at the association level as made by synecologists with diverse philosophies and using different methods of study show close correlation.[290]

In floristically poor areas there are categories of great homogeneity over wide areas, whereas in floristically rich areas some stands may differ considerably from norms of the basic units, therefore different standards for the association concept must be used in different parts of the world, with plant associations being equivalent only in the sense that they indicate distinguishable groups of stands. This problem has its counterpart in the species concept, which differs considerably between *Carex* and *Poa*, or between bacteria and molds. Inasmuch as it was not until the nineteenth century that serious interest developed in vegetation classification, it is not surprising that the field is still in a fluid and immature condition, with no standard system as yet in sight.

• SOME VIEWPOINTS

Since the need for classification begins to be felt as the first facts start to accumulate in a new science, it might be suspected that even in the relatively young discipline of synecology there has been appreciable activity in this area. Many classification schemes have indeed been proposed in the past century and a half, but none has gained universal acceptance. Even if the term association is accepted as a collective term for basic categories of vegetation, there still is no unanimity of opinion as to the scope of the association, or the best method of grouping associations into higher categories of a system. Some of the principal concepts will be considered briefly.

Physiognomy

In 1806 Alexander von Humboldt published the first formal classification of the growth-forms of plants. This classification was based entirely on outward appearance, with taxonomic and ecologic relations being ignored except that most of the 15 morphologic types he recognized were named after a suggestive genus or family (e.g., cactus, casuarina, liana, palm, grass, moss, lichen, needle-tree, etc., forms). A few years later he published a physiognomic classification of the earth's vegetation, i.e., one which reflected only the growth-forms of the dominant plants, and showed that 16 major units (called "associations" in this first synecologic use of the term) tend to be arranged in latitudinal and altitudinal belts that are related to climatic types. It is not surprising that emphasis on physiognomy should have characterized this first vegetation classification, for the basic terms and concepts are present in most languages. For example, the words *forest* and *meadow* were in common use in the English language long before synecology got its start. From time to time the physiognomic concept of classification has been modified and expanded* by botanists such as August Grisebach, Anton Kerner, Oscar Drude, and Eduard Rübel,[376] and special symbolism has been proposed for recording physiognomic details.[80, 117, 265]

The most fundamental fact supporting the validity of the physiognomic concept is that in any one region seres of very different character often lead to a swarm of climaxes with the same physiognomy, so

---

* The principal types of vegetation physiognomy, according to concepts that have been, for the most part, rather widely adopted in recent decades, are:

Forest trees 8 m or taller (meso- and megaphanerophytes) growing rather closely spaced

   Evergreen forest
     Needle-leaved
     Broad-leaved
   Deciduous ("seasonal") forest
     Needle-leaved
     Broad-leaved

Woodland woody plants 2–8 m tall (microphanerophytes) growing rather closely spaced (subdivided as forest)

Scrub woody plants less than 2 m tall (nanophanerophytes or chamaephytes) growing rather closely spaced (subdivided as forest)

Grassland herbs (usually grasses or sedges) dominant; woody plants either lacking or dwarfed and inconspicuous

Savanna microphanerophytes or taller woody plants scattered individually over a rather dense lower stratum of herbs or lichens

Shrub savanna nanophanerophytes scattered individually over a dense cover of herbs or lichens

Groveland similar to savanna except that the plants of the tallest stratum are aggregated into small *groves*

Parkland the reciprocal of groveland, with patches of lower vegetation (*parks*) abundantly distributed over a continuous phase of forest or woodland

   There are also some related categories in which an environmental character is an essential part of the definition:

Meadow dense grassland, usually rich in forbs, with the grasses having relatively broad and soft blades, and occurring in a relatively moist habitat

Steppe grassland in regions too dry for natural forest on the uplands

   Meadow-steppe: meadowlike vegetation characteristic of the less arid margin of steppe regions; dwarf shrubs may be common but not dominant

   True steppe: floristically poor and relatively xerophytic steppe, with the grasses having narrow blades, and forbs and shrubs poorly represented

   Shrub-steppe: steppe in which scattered shrubs form a layer rising above the grasses

Marsh grassland on wet, or periodically wet, mineral soil

Swamp woody vegetation of wet or periodically wet mineral soil

Fellfield discontinuous low plant cover in tundra regions in which chamaephytes are conspicuous and the soil is excessively stony

that there is a prevailing physiognomy for each region. Then wherever else over the earth's surface the climate is similar, the same physiognomy characterizes most climaxes.

Some consider it a distinct advantage of the approach that it can be applied without knowing the name of a single organism, or understanding any ecology, but therein lies its obvious limitation. For example, a "needle-leaved coniferous forest" category would embrace the *Pinus elliottii* forests of Cuba, the *Pinus ponderosa* forests of Colorado, the *Sequoia sempervirens* forests of California, the *Picea glauca* forests of Yukon Territory, etc. Collectively these share nothing in common from the synecologic standpoint. Furthermore, a *Picea mariana-Chamaedaphne bog* in Quebec, a *Pinus clausa-Quercus chapmani* woodland on Florida sands, and a *Pinus cembroides-Arctostaphylos pungens* woodland at the desert's edge in Arizona would be very difficult to separate on a physiognomic basis. Thus it is clear that physiognomy by itself lumps vegetation types that are vastly different in their ecologic relations, and so results in an artificial classification. Then the opposite difficulty with physiognomy is illustrated by Warming's placement of salt marshes dominated by shrubby *Salicornia* in a different category from salt marshes dominated by herbaceous species of the same genus.

All this is not to deny that physiognomy can serve a useful purpose in defining major plant groupings, but it is useful only when ecologic and other considerations are allowed to govern its application.[446]

One way to develop a comprehensive classification is to start with the largest units of the earth's vegetation, successively dividing these into smaller and smaller units. Physiognomic systems are the epitome of this ("subdivisive") approach, but since there are relatively few types of vegetation physiognomy, its utility ceases almost as soon as a score or so major units are distinguished.

Complexity of Layered Structure

A concept somewhat related to physiognomy is the grouping of communities according to whether they are one-layered, two-layered, three-layered, etc. This character has implications for degree of integration and capacity to use environmental resources efficiently, but again it provides very few vegetation categories in the face of tremendous vegetational diversity, and certainly the ecology of communities with similar numbers of layers can be extremely different. Furthermore, some types of obviously complex and efficient vegetation, including rain forest, have the height of the different species so staggered that strata cannot be distinguished.

In the hierarchy espoused by J. Braun-Blanquet, "classes" are defined on this basis.[345]

Floristics[29, 345]

The most popular method of vegetation classification in southern Europe is based primarily on floristics. Lists of plants are prepared for many restricted homogeneous stands (usually 1 to 10 m square), and the stands are then grouped on the basis of degrees of resemblance (constancy and fidelity) among the lists, with little attention being accorded quantitative differences and successional status of the stands. This reliance on species lists sometimes brings herb-dominated and tree-dominated communities together in the same association, and frequently brings vegetation types of clearly different ecologies into one association, which must then be subdivided into subassociations on the basis of differential species. Difficulty results from heavy emphasis on fidelity too, for a species with restricted ecologic amplitude in one area, hence useful in defining an association there, may exhibit wider or different ecologic amplitude elsewhere, so that the fidelity rating must be given geographic limitation.

The theoretical basis for the floristic method is an argument that since each species has a distinctive ecologic amplitude, a particular group found together indicates a restricted range of environment in which the ecologic amplitudes of all overlap. Nearly identical species lists in different areas are interpreted to mean that the ecologic sums of the habitat factors there are nearly equal.

It is significant that this concept was launched in 1921, before it was generally known that the species is not an ecologic unit—that even in contiguous habitats a species is commonly represented by ecotypes that have mutually exclusive ecologic amplitudes.[126, 199, 288, 403] Thus two areas drawn together in classification because they share certain species may be very different ecologically if the shared species are represented by different ecotypes, and evidence of this phenomenon is accumulating steadily.

Another type of difficulty with the method is that although the vegetation physiognomy and ecology, the soils, and the climates are strikingly similar between northern Chile and southwestern California, the floras are entirely different. In a floristically based classification the vegetation of southern California would show more relationship to New Jersey than to Chile.

Again, communities consisting chiefly of *Poa pratensis, Plantago major, Trifolium pratense,* and *Taraxacum officinale* may be produced by grazing in regions where soils range from chernozem to brown podsolic, but these are all lumped together in a floristic system, even though the potentialities of the regions are very different.

It cannot be denied that floristics are indispensable in vegetation classification, but the above points show clearly that floristics must not be allowed to overshadow such considerations as dynamism, environment, and historic factors. Floristics seem to be most useful in differentiating the finest subdivisions in classification.

As pointed out earlier, several workers interested primarily in the floristic list have devised statistical criteria for evaluating degrees of similarity and difference among stands and have offered these as mechanical devices for grouping them into associations.[115] But these methods give all species equal weight, despite the fact that some are ubiquists that have negligible value in defining units whereas others are closely restricted to a limited range of environmental variation and are therefore very useful. The method is indeed objective, but it rules out the use of any ecologic information.

Before leaving this topic, it should be noted that Braun-Blanquet's floristic system exemplifies an approach which starts with very small categories of vegetation, then combines these into successively larger and more heterogeneous units leading toward a worldwide classification. This, the "agglomerative" approach, is the exact opposite of the physiognomic method which starts with the large and heterogeneous units and works downward.

Dominance

Among the several bases which can be used to recognize and distinguish among plant communities, the kinds and relative proportions of the dominants have usually played an important part. It can be argued that the ecologic character of a particular habitat is reflected not only by the total list of species, but also by which of those species has been able to achieve dominance through competition. Three ways of emphasizing dominance have been tried.

In North America attention has usually been confined to the dominants of the tallest layer. This might be defended by pointing out that, owing simply to their height, these plants are most directly influenced by climate, and in fact they usually do exhibit more predictable relationship to the earth's pattern of climates than do lower layers. Also, these plants normally have strong influence on other components of an ecosystem.

The major limitation of this concept is that the dominants of a phytocoenosis are commonly wide-ranging species that extend across patently different habitats, as shown by sharp differences in subordinates. As an example, climax stands of *Pinus ponderosa* that occur in South Dakota, central British Columbia, central California, and Arizona dominate ecosystems that differ in practically every other detail of flora, and in most characters of climate, soil, and animal life as well. Even between contiguous stands of this pine there are often pronounced differences in soil or microclimate that are correlated with pronounced differences in subordinates. If attention is confined to the tallest stratum, classification remains too crude to be ecologically satisfactory.

A second application of the dominance concept is the reciprocal of the above—the tallest stratum is ignored, and classification is based on dominance among shrubs, herbs, and terrestrial bryophytes and lichens. This is the "forest site type" of Finnish foresters,[68] and its merits in Finland have been proved by testing for more than half a century. However, only in a limited area where the tree layer is floristically as simple as in Finland can such a system be satisfactory. With the overstory showing little variation at climax, important differences in soil or microclimate are clearly reflected by a series of undergrowth types. In other regions, however, ecologic differences among certain habitat types may be reflected more clearly in the overstory than in the undergrowth.[122, 224]

A third application of the dominance concept is to consider dominance throughout all vegetation layers without emphasizing one layer at the expense of the others. Each kind of phytocoenosis is defined in terms of a combination of dominants divided among the layers. A strong argument can be made that the similarity of dominants in the different layers arising anew at different places through competitive elimination is the most perfect evidence of a high degree of ecologic equivalence through a series of stands. Not only do all these habitats lie within the environmental ranges of the component species, they lie within that part of such areas where certain species of each life-form type can assert dominance concurrently. Where a mosaic of ecotypes permits an overstory dominant to extend over a wide array of habitat types, discontinuities in subordinate layers can be relied on to reveal this ecologic pattern. Thus the method meets the objections raised to the other two applications of dominance as discussed above.

Environment

If the value of some of the preceding proposals is weak from ecologic considerations, why not base classification primarily on environment? This should produce major groupings that are ecologically homogeneous throughout the world. Especially, it should help overcome difficulties due to migrational barriers and accidents of distribution which result in areas closely similar in ecology sharing few, if any, species.

Such a classification was attempted in the midnineteenth century by A. de Candolle who grouped plants according to their climatic requirements into megistotherms, xerophiles, mesotherms, microtherms and hekistotherms, and later by E. Warming who grouped plants according to their characteristic substrates into psammophytes, chasmophytes, oxylophytes, halophytes, etc. But the inability of this approach to account for more than a small fraction of the earth's tremendous vegetal diversity soon became so apparent that no major attempt has since been made to base a comprehensive classification on environmental factors. The basic difficulty is this: No two points over the land surface are alike in all their factor complements, and without taking vegetation structure and composition into account, man can never judge when one factor sufficiently compensates for deficiencies in others to result in ecologic equivalence. For example, *Picea mariana-Ledum groenlandicum-Sphagnum* bog in southeastern Canada occupies basins with very poor drainage and wholly lacking in permafrost. Under a very different climate in Alaska, essentially the same community occurs on steep north-facing slopes where permafrost remains very near the surface. Ecotypes and minor floristic details differ, but even so, the two communities must be placed very close together in classification in view of the striking similarities in dominance among the three major layers. This degree of equivalence would scarcely be guessed without primary dependence on vegetation to demonstrate it.

Clearly, we must depend heavily on the character of vegetation, at least its morphologic and physiologic character, if not its taxonomic character as well, to indicate environmental equivalence, and a classification that accommodates the ecosystem concept must reflect degrees of environmental equivalence. But at the same time environmental features themselves are often useful in deciding what is a homogeneous stand, and how much variation among stands is allowable in grouping them into associations, and these in turn into still larger categories. Attending closely to environment serves as a check against viewing floristic accidents as phenomena of high significance, and allows inclusion in an association of occasional stands which, through accidents of dissemination, happen to lack one or more of the usual dominants.

Succession

In some areas, as in the mountains of southern Norway,[115] successional considerations are no problem in vegetation classification since the entire mosaic is in essentially climax condition. In other areas the vegetation has been so strongly disturbed by man that the pre-*Homo* climax pattern is unknown, is incapable of reconstituting itself, and disclimaxes are all that are available for study. Intermediate between these are far more extensive areas in which fragments of primary climaxes are available as reference points for aligning a variety of disturbed stands in seres according to climax potentialities.

The importance of succession in vegetation classification was a matter of special concern to F. E. Clements, although Anton Kerner and others had clearly shown its importance earlier. Clements held that the dynamic relations among communities must be taken into account at the outset, for they are developmentally related to each other somewhat as the larva, pupa, and adult of an insect. Just as the taxonomist recognizes such a series as one taxonomic unit, gives it a single binomial, and in description emphasizes the mature stages of the life cycle, so in the interpretation of vegetation there would seem to be justification for emphasizing direct developmental relationships. Then too, since seral stages often pass from one to the other only gradually, emphasis on the relatively discrete climaxes minimizes subjectivity in classification.

The rarity of climax stands is not such a drawback as the uninitiated might imagine, for much of the disturbed vegetation can show in its population structure the nature of the climax type from which it was derived and to which it can revert. Even if the nature of the climax can only be approximated, this still provides a basis for an alignment of seral stands.

There is no really valid argument against giving succession the consideration in classification indicated above, but Clements' application of the principle to his monoclimax hypothesis jeopardized its acceptance. However, successional status by itself does not provide an adequate basis for vegetation classification. It must be looked upon as one of the characters of vegetation that must be taken into account regardless of which other characters are emphasized, if the classification is to rest on a sound basis.

Ordination[56, 277]

Floras are continua. Traveling in any direction new species are added to a floristic list one after another, while all along others are dropping out, with the total geographic ranges of many species seldom showing more than regional correlation. Where each species is first encountered, it is usually scarce and restricted to a single habitat type, but nearer the center of its range it ordinarily becomes quite abundant, with representation on diverse habitats at least as a seral species. Therefore, any method of analyzing vegetation that is intended to reflect relative abundance over the landscape as a whole can hardly fail to lead to a conclusion that vegetation, like flora, is a continuum.

Gaps between related but distinctive climaxes can be bridged in tabulation by setting seral stands between, for the distinguishing species of both types temporarily grow mixed in areas where competitive balances have been upset.[128] Since widespread disturbance in a landscape promotes convergence of formerly distinctive types, continua are most easily demonstrated in such places. That unstable communities are a major factor in demonstrating continua is shown by studies of marine plankton where there seems to be no successional phenomena comparable to those of terrestrial communities. Computer analysis of zooplankton populations sampled at 201 stations scattered over the North Pacific have demonstrated the existence of multispecific groups which characterize particular segments of environmental gradients.[164] Even if one confined his attention to stable vegetation, the acceptance of plots that fall astride ecotones would provide apparent bridges between distinctive associations.

Those who prefer to look upon plant life as a continuum claim that an objective classification of vegetation is not possible, and that stands should instead be aligned in unbroken series according to degrees of resemblance—an ordination.

Since all ordinations thus far proposed ignore population structure, they fail to reflect habitat potentialities. An area undergoing secondary succession has a different position on the continuum scale as time passes and communities replace each other, and some of the stages involved in one sere fall closer to the climax of another habitat type than to the climax that will eventually replace them. Thus in a continuum index proposed for Wisconsin, a pure stand of *Quercus macrocarpa* occurring as a topo-edaphic climax on the thin soil of a slope facing steeply to the south has an identical position in the ordination with a seral stand of the same tree that may have invaded a deep loam on gentle topography where an *Acer-Tilia* forest has been temporarily eliminated by fire.

As others would strive to interpret a vegetation mosaic in terms of tolerance limits at the ecotones of each association, those who practice ordination attempt to define the environmental conditions that seem to determine one or more floristic gradients. The latter has proved a formidable task even where only two factor gradients are studied.[56]

There is no denying that the stand data representing a series of related associations can often be aligned to demonstrate a continuous series of species with overlapping ranges, but a few dominants in such a series will show striking discontinuities at rather well-defined points. These points where dominance passes from one species to another (whether in the tallest or some lower stratum) when correlated with a specific point on an environmental gradient, represent objective discontinuities in ecosystems, even where most subordinates do not exhibit the same pattern. One has the choice of emphasizing either the element of discontinuity, or the element of continuity, whichever seems the more significant and useful.

Ecosystem

In the history of species taxonomy, workers for several centuries sought single attributes which, with little or no consideration of others, would serve as the basis for a comprehensive classification. This perspective led to stalemate until the evolution concept as strengthened by genetics revealed that physiology, morphology, chemical composition, cytology, anatomy, geographic distribution, etc., are *all* significant for classification, and this has allowed modern taxonomy to move onto a broader base.

Vegetation classification has had a somewhat parallel history, with the ecosystem concept now promising to play the critical role of broadening perspectives and reducing divergence of opinion. If attention is restricted to only a portion of each ecosystem (e.g., to forest undergrowth, or to the dominants, or to the soil), this leads to different but equally defensible treatments of the same landscape mosaic. But if the ecosystem is accepted as the basic unit, the classification must accommodate all its components and show their interrelationships. Most of the previously considered viewpoints have both merits and limitations, but since the ecosystem principle permits a judicious combination of just the favorable features of each of them, it should lead to the closest approach to a natural system.

• A LANDSCAPE HIERARCHY

In the section that follows, a classification scheme will be developed which is based on the ecosystem concept and takes organisms, their environment, and time into consideration. It is an attempt to take advantage of the most favorable features of the various viewpoints on classification that have been reviewed, and at the same time avoid most of the pitfalls. Structurally it allows all terrestrial vegetation to be considered in one system.

Early in this book attention was directed to the smallest unit of vegetation classification, the association, and this was defined as a climax. Later it was pointed out that most landscapes are not covered with climax vegetation; they support instead innumerable successional stages representing several seres, these leading to still fewer climaxes. Bringing succession into consideration at once directs attention toward *potentialities* of landscape components, rather than dividing attention over a wide variety of merging vegetation types of differing successional status. Thus one might argue that vegetation should not be the center of attention in ecosystem classification, but rather the intrinsic pattern of environmental variation. In our classification scheme emphasis will be laid on units of environment having similar biotic potentialities, using vegetation as an indicator of degrees of similarity.

The Habitat Type

At this, the lowest level in an ecosystem classification that aims to reflect potentialities, attention is divided among layered structure, floristics, dominance, edaphic factors, microclimate, and succession.

All parts of the landscape that support, or are capable of supporting, what seems desirable to consider as the same kind of relatively stable phytocoenosis (homogeneous as to dominants in all layers) in the absence of disturbance, comprise one habitat type. Each of these has different kinds of potential vegetation, depending on whether it is free of disturbance or is regularly burned or grazed, etc.

Ordinarily one habitat type is highly discontinuous, with intervening areas occupied by other habitat types differentiated by either soil or microclimate. The communities occupying the scattered units of one habitat type usually embrace a wide variety of seral stages as a result of disturbances at varied times in the past. In different places climax vegetation in this habitat type may play the role of climatic, edaphic, or topographic climax, but it may be restricted to only one or two of these roles. Although each habitat type is conveniently identified using vegetation, and appropriately named after a distinctive combination of plants in the climax, other biotic and some physical characters of the habitats are often useful in their definition.

Since each piece of demonstrably seral vegetation, as well as each disclimax, can be related dynamically to some one primary climax, a system based on habitat types is infinitely simpler than one giving equal weight to all describable types of plant cover. This emphasis on potentialities regardless of the current status of the vegetation permits the closest possible correlation among vegetation, microclimate, and soil.

Since the field ecologist must deal more with an extensive array of seral vegetation than with climaxes, and since site potential varies according to treatment, the term habitat type is more realistic than potential vegetation, which is sometimes used for the same unit.

If we accept the well-documented principle that different combinations of dominant and subordinate layers in climax stands indicate distinctive ecotopes, one might start classification by recognizing as major groupings those stands sharing the same dominant layer, then subdividing according to differences in dominants of the subordinate layers. Or, with equal justification, he might proceed in the reverse, establishing major units on the basis of subordinates, with these subdivided to reflect variations in the overstory. The first of these alternatives is distinctly superior from the standpoint of constructing higher levels in the classification hierarchy. For example, pure stands of *Pinus ponderosa* that are climax always occur in environments that are slightly drier than those in which *Pseudotsuga menziesii* is a climax dominant, from Canada to Mexico, and Wyoming to California. Throughout this range there are many complete changes in undergrowth species. The question arises: Should the *P. ponderosa* stands in British Columbia be grouped with the wetter *Pseudotsuga* forests there on the basis of close similarity of undergrowth, rather than with *P. ponderosa* stands in remote places where there are no undergrowth species in common? If the former practice were followed, each unit (as in British Columbia) would embrace a broad spectrum of variation in climate, soil, and overstory dominants, whereas in different geographic locations equivalent units would embrace a similar broad range of variation. On the other hand, recognition of all climax stands of *P. ponderosa* as a basic group permits emphasis on climate as a master factor, with soil, microclimate, and vegetation all under its control, and sets all *P. ponderosa* climaxes in an ecologically meaningful relation to all climax forests of *Pseudotsuga menziesii*.

The Vegetation Zone

For over a century the principle has been recognized that in a local landscape edaphic and microclimatic conditions are the primary factors bringing about the differentiation of undisturbed vegetation, but on a larger geographic scale these factor complexes dwindle in importance, with macroclimate becoming decisive. While macroclimate was of no immediate concern in defining habitat types above, it becomes the pivotal consideration at the next higher level of an hierarchy.

All the area over which one association is climatic climax represents a vegetation zone of essentially uniform macroclimate insofar as vegetation is concerned. The concept of zone is of special value in connection with climatic classification, since vegetation is widely recognized as the best indicator of biologically significant nodes along climatic gradients, and climatic climaxes alone are legitimate for use in this connection. In rugged topography where climatic climaxes may not be distinguishable, zones may not be delimited, but all other bases for delimiting climatic units also fail here.

The zone is based on only part of the total area of one habitat type, that part in which the association plays the role of climatic climax. Within the boundaries of one zone there occur a number of other habitat types, some of which may be intrazonal stands of associations that characterize adjacent zones.

As a concrete illustration of the application of the zonal concept, the steppes of eastern Washington have been shown to be divisible into nine zones, these fitting together as a mosaic, each element of which is characterized by a single type of stable vegetation occupying undisturbed sites on deep upland loams. Each zone has climatic individuality, with the difference between the climates of contiguous zones being related to requirements and tolerances of major species. Enmeshed in each zone are habitat types representing a variety of edaphic and topographic climaxes, almost none of which is confined to any one zone.

The Vegetation Province

The geologic histories of floras are clearly imprinted in vegetation patterns. This historic aspect of vegetation can be conveniently emphasized in the next higher category in classification—the vegetation province.

Swarms of plant species have had somewhat parallel histories of migration in recent geologic time, owing to common limitations in the configuration of land masses, and climatic pressures that have induced migrations within each land mass. This is a significant point, since similar migratory patterns are evidence of a degree of similarity in the ecologies of the species. The vegetation province includes those zones which have had a somewhat common and distinctive geologic history, which form a distinctive geographic unit at present, and which exhibit strong threads of taxonomic homogeneity, sometimes even at the species level. Paleobotany is not very useful in classification below the level of province because associations often represent superimposed elements with diverse geographic affinities, and different associations within a zone often show diverse affinities. In fact, even at the level of the province attention must be centered on the major dominants to demonstrate a common historic background for a group of climatic climaxes.

As a specific illustration, the group of nine steppe zones recognized in eastern Washington belong to a different province than the steppe zones east of the Rockies in the same latitude. The chief dominants of the former (*Agropyron spicatum, Festuca idahoensis, Poa secunda, Artemisia tridentata, A. tripartita*) are derivatives of a boreal flora (arctotertiary geoflora) and are adapted to grow in cool spring weather and endure a dry summer, while most of the characteristic dominants of the latter (*Bouteloua gracilis, Buchloe dactyloides, Aristida, Sporobolus, Stipa*) are derived from an ancient subtropical xerophytic flora (madrotertiary geoflora) and stay dormant until high temperatures arrive and so require summer rainfall to prosper.

The Vegetation Region

Taking the broadest view of the earth's vegetation, there is a pattern that tends to be repeated on different continents. The elements of this pattern have a characteristic physiognomy, at least in the climatic climaxes, that is associated with a distinctive climatic regime. At this, the highest level of ecosystem classification, there is no necessity for any taxonomic homogeneity, or similarity in geologic history, and the climatic limitations are broader and less specific than those which distinguish zones. In contrast with the habitat type at the lowest level of the hierarchy, where many statements are applicable to all parts of the collective unit, relatively few characters can be used to define a vegetation region at the highest level of classification.

A region may be continuous within a continent, or it may be discontinuous if the alternation of mountains and plains interrupt major climatic trends. Usually it reappears on different continents. For example, this level of classification draws together the five chaparral provinces that are widely scattered over the world. They comprise a unit that can be characterized by mostly broad-leaved evergreen scrub, woodland or savanna, occurring where winters are cool and wet, summers hot and dry. Since such a climate favors the spread of vegetation fires, there are conspicuous adaptations (serotinous germination, lignotubers, root-sprouting) that have evolved independently in each province due to the long-standing importance of fire as an ecosystem component.

Again, the *Agropyron spicatum* province between the Cascades and the Rockies, along with the *Bouteloua gracilis* province just east of the Rockies, would be grouped with all other areas in temperate climates where the climatic climaxes are treeless because of climatic dryness, into a steppe region.

The vegetation region as defined above differs from the "plant formation" of Clements and certain others chiefly in that a geographic *area* is emphasized, rather than a kind of vegetation. As with the other three elements of this classification, the region retains its boundaries, its climatic characters, and its biotic potentialities even where most of the land may be in cultivated fields.

5 vegetation as an objective of study

• OPERATIONAL PROCEDURES

The study of vegetation involves a logical sequence of steps, if it is to be done efficiently.

Reconnaissance and classification

Reconnaissance, the first field work, is done with maps, compass, shovel, plant press, and cards or printed forms for taking notes. It aims at a characterization of the major communities, and a tentative interpretation of environmental controls from simple inspection of topography and soil. Using a separate card or form at each site, species lists are made with rough notations of coverage class, and unknown plants are collected for later herbarium identification. Attention should be concentrated on stands that are least disturbed and most nearly climax, but with any observations on successional relations as inferred from fence lines, etc., being recorded. This ground reconnaissance is more effective if it follows aerial reconnaissance so that a photo mosaic can be used to ensure coverage of all physiognomically different elements of the landscape. At this step, the level of detail in describing each stand is minimized so that a great many stands can be covered, and all the area chosen for study can be covered.

Owing to the integrative capacity of the human mind, continued contact with a vegetation matrix inevitably leads to a mental grouping of the stands into categories, and to hypotheses regarding environmental controls. As the work progresses these hypotheses are repeatedly checked against fact, and the provisional classification is emended successively until there is a maximum fit for all the facts, at which time association tables can be put into final form and the classification considered at least the first approximation of a natural system.

A classification can be satisfactory without including all the vegetation in the landscape. There is little reward in greatly increasing the complexity of a classification in an attempt to make it include a motley array of one-of-a-kind ecosystem scraps associated with unusual combinations of environmental conditions which commonly occur but occupy little area even in the aggregate. As a final check on the adequacy of a classification one should visit at least 100 objectively located points in a landscape and see what percentage of these is accounted for by the classification.

Although the grouping of stands into associations should be based on a broad consideration of all vegetation, soil, and climatic data, it is usually possible to construct a useful key to ecosystems or habitat types based on a few readily observable features of vegetation and environment which have proved reliable.

Correlation Synecology

Reconnaissance data by themselves are adequate to construct a sound classification of ecosystems,[205] but a higher level of accuracy in both vegetal and environmental analysis is desirable to establish quantitatively the degrees of correlation between the two.

From reconnaissance notes one can select a series of stands to revisit for intensive quantitative analysis, aiming to encompass most botanical variations exhibited by each association, and sufficient environmental variation to demonstrate the ecologic amplitude of the association. Although hybrid stands may be very abundant, the best use of time is to replicate analyses of the pure types (rather than spreading the same effort thinly along connecting gradients) so as to demonstrate the degree to which associations recur in approximately the same form wherever equivalent environmental conditions are encountered.

This is the procedure that furnishes the most basic synecologic data: quantitative analyses of all layers of vegetation in small homogeneous areas, which are related to a specific set of environmental records. Although one may encounter extensive and continuous areas that represent the same association, within such areas it is desirable to select for analysis areas of maximum homogeneity, so that if there are small intraassociational variations in community structure that are related to small variations within the habitat type, these can be discovered and evaluated quantitatively. Useful autecologic information can be obtained by such rigorous stratification, for if the stand is homogeneous, then the entire suite of environmental records is relatable to the quantities of each species present.

So many relevant historic and environmental factors may possibly prove decisive individually or in combination that the task of deciding what kinds of data to collect is formidable, with the training, experience and alertness of the investigator all being important in determining success. It is important to keep the level of precision in both environmental and vegetational analyses in balance.

Detailed analyses of this type may take less time to bring to a useful degree of completeness than did the reconnaissance, for the investigator knows precisely where he wants to go and what information is needed, with no time being lost in exploring areas that had to be covered as a matter of routine in reconnaissance, but which yielded few useful sites.

Correlations that are established by summarizing these relatively accurate environmental records in relation to both communities and individual species narrow the range of working hypotheses as to the factors most directly involved in determining community and species limits. Mapping community distributions establishes their degree of correlation with macroclimate, if the necessary records are available from a standard weather network, with aspect, percent slope, and position on slope suggesting the range of microclimates.

Experimental Synecology

The vegetation survey always brings to light significant correlations and problems that would otherwise pass unnoticed. These phenomena involve functional interpretation and demand field experiments for satisfactory solution, although the sheer weight of abundant correlation data by themselves make a substantial contribution. Much use can be made of experimental modification of environment and the planting of disseminules and small plants beyond the natural range of established individuals. The immediate environment of the seedling is a particularly important focus of study, and one must always be careful to discriminate as much as possible between intrinsic and extrinsic factors, for these differ in their interpretive value.

Many factors militate against complete success in solving synecologic problems. (1) Complex relations among different factors sometimes create situations that are very difficult to evaluate. For example, a dilute solution moving horizontally through the soil can provide nutrients equal to that of a more concentrated solution that is nearly static, yet there seems to be no satisfactory means for equating these two situations. Also, the well-known limitations on the use of even the most complete chemical assays of soil fertility emphasize the great gap between the complexity of environment and our ability to interpret it. (2) The conditions which allow a particular vegetation mosaic to become established may cease to exist, yet the established pattern then persists relatively unmodified for a long time, since plants can often live out their life span under conditions that no longer permit more seedlings to become established. (3) Climatic change, or the cessation of regular burning, may allow a community to invade a habitat where the soil had slowly come into equilibrium with another kind of vegetation over a long period in the past. The new association can then approximate stability before the soil profile shows much evidence of readjustment, resulting in a low degree of correlation between profile development and vegetation types. (4) Inconsistent relationships between a dominant and physical or biotic factors at different places in its range may result from obscure ecotypic differentiation. (5) Owing to different types of competition, a species or community may be crowded into different kinds of habitats in different places. (6) The critical conditions that limit a plant's distribution or functions may be evanescent, obtaining only occasionally in the course of a season or annual cycles of weather and climate. Factor intensities varying through time at an ecotone tend to frustrate attempts to assign quantitative values to limiting factors.[342]

Using laboratory, glasshouse, garden, and controlled environment chambers, in conjunction with manipulations of natural environment and measurements of plant responses to factors in their natural habitats,[230, 245, 321, 454, 478] work can be directed toward an understanding of how each life cycle fits into each ecosystem of which it is a part, the tempo and mode of turnover of matter and energy flow, the aspects of environment that become most decisive at ecotones, the critical factors motivating succession, etc. In addition, experiments aimed at discovering feasible methods of bringing about desirable modifications of biota and ecotope can be planned efficiently after the ecosystem patterns have been worked out, knowing that the sites selected for experiments are highly representative of specific habitat types, so that the results can be extrapolated with confidence.

Ecosystems are so tremendously complex that much that goes on within them appears to be unknowable, but there are rich rewards to be won by gaining even a partial understanding.

• ORGANIZATION OF SYNECOLOGIC INFORMATION

The earth's vegetation is so vast and complicated an object of study that our knowledge of it as a whole must be based on a synthesis of bits of detailed work done by a multitude of individuals. The product of such a synthesis is dependent on the quality of the ingredients.

Most vegetation accounts which have been published to date are not only meager, but if quantitative data are presented, the lack of uniformity in methods used in obtaining them makes it difficult to draw close comparisons using the literature. Different investigators tend to stress different concepts, leaving so little common ground that comparisons are impractical. Facts that should be explicitly stated may be omitted because each writer is prone to neglect recording that which has been obvious to him from the start of the study. The more complete the documentation, the more easy it is to make reinterpretations in the face of new developments in synecology.

It is clearly desirable to strive for some standard plan of description so that, for example, an ecologist studying desert in one continent can make satisfactory comparisons of his work with, and gain inspiration from, studies of deserts in other continents. It is true that the character of the vegetation, the time available for study, and any limitation of objectives all have a bearing on the methods to be used, but unnecessary differences in methods stand as obstacles to progress. Standardization need not stifle new approaches, but widely used techniques should always be used, along with any that are being newly proposed, for it has generally proved true that most proposed innovations are no better than techniques already in use.

A well-rounded treatment of an ecosystem characterized by one plant association should contain detailed information in the following seven categories.

Floristic Composition

All species play some role in an ecosystem, so that a complete floristic list is a basic requirement. While the role of minor species may be obscure, each has a distinctive ecology and can contribute something to our understanding of its ecosystem, once we have determined its requirements and tolerances. Unfortunately, owing to limitations in the taxonomic competence one person can achieve, and the scarcity of areas where the taxonomy of all plant groups has been worked out, the floristic list is always incomplete. Studies of terrestrial ecosystems often consider only vasculares, sometimes lichens and bryophytes in addition, but algae, fungi, and bacteria never get the consideration they deserve.

Structural Characters

The gross aspect of vegetation structure can be indicated by a description of its physiognomy, including the mean height and degree of development of any layers that may be distinguishable, foliage persistence and color, etc. Finer details are provided by analyses of dominance, density, sociability, life-forms, and leaf sizes. All these characters are complementary, therefore as many as possible should be included. In tabulation the data may be grouped to show layers, life-forms, or other segregates that are of more ecologic significance than a mere alphabetic or stereotyped taxonomic arrangement.

Analytic data can be supplemented by photographs,* by detailed maps, and by diagrams representing vertical sections through the community drawn to scale in the field (Fig. 3). The last (sometimes called "bisects") are especially useful if the extent of subterranean organs is included, and the relationships to relief, water tables, soil horizons, etc., are brought out.

---

* Forest interiors can be photographed successfully with black-and-white film only when the sky is overcast, and since time exposures are often necessary, the low wind velocities at dawn and dusk make these periods especially suitable for photography. Low communities that are unshaded from above generally photograph best with the camera pointed somewhat in the direction of the sun, but with the lens shaded.

Functional Characters

Phenologic studies of all the constituent species permit an expression of the responses of the community as a whole to the cycle of the season (Fig. 4). Often the phenologies of the different strata or life-form groups are contrasted, and this should be shown. Vitality and vigor ratings reveal the degree to which each species is adapted to the sum of biologic and physical forces currently operative. Classification of dissemination and pollination agents, and an expression of the degree of prevalence of vegetative reproduction bring out other dependencies and limitations within the ecosystem. Productivity is still another important functional attribute to be assessed.

Environmental Relations

An evaluation of the most critical factors, biotic and abiotic, which permit the development and maintenance of an association, is an important part of any study purporting to be synecology. Owing to factor compensation, the same type of community can occur in a variety of climatic and edaphic conditions, and it is important to have its ecologic amplitude recorded in detail. Pathways and flow rates of matter and energy must be described.

Successional Status

Studies of dynamic relationships are needed to establish the modes of origin, course of development, and manner of self-maintenance of the plant association and its complement of animal life. Through a study of fossil floras, combined with interpretations of modern distribution patterns, it is often possible to determine at least some of the major features of the past history of a community through geologic time.

Geography

Usually a complete study of an association throughout its geographic range is beyond the facilities of a single worker, but within the limits of his opportunities all information on geographic limits should be assembled. Local and geographic aspects of etiology are mutually supporting in that facts established in one suggest critical points of attack in the other. The relative amount of the habitat type represented in different landscapes is also desirable information.

Classification

Each ecosystem shares at least a few characters with several others. It is a distinctive unit only to the extent that all stands share certain features which as a group are not found elsewhere, and it is therefore important for the investigator to state specifically these distinguishing characters. Constancy and fidelity figure most prominently in defining types of phytocoenoses, but since animal life, soils, and climate are all interrelated, distinctive characters of these are also useful additions to the list of attributes that distinguish the ecosystem.

references

1. *Adamson, R. S.* 1931. The plant communities of Table Mountain. II. Life-form dominance and succession. *J. Ecol.* 19:304–320.
2. *Adamson, R. S.* 1939. The classification of life-forms of plants. *Bot. Rev.* 5:546–561.
3. *Albertson, F. W., and G. W. Tomanek.* 1965. Vegetation changes during a 30-year period in grassland communities. *Ecol.* 46:714–720.
4. *Allen, P. H.* 1961. Natural selection in loblolly pine stands. *J. For.* 59:598–599.
5. *Anderson, C. H., and C. R. Elliott.* 1957. Studies of the establishment of cultivated grasses and legumes on burned-over land in northern Canada. *Can. J. Plant Sci.* 37:97–100.
6. *Anderson, J. M.* 1950. Some aquatic vegetation changes following fish removal. *J. Wildlife Man.* 14:206–209.
7. *Andresen, J. W., and J. McCormick.* 1962. An evaluation of devices for estimation of tree cover. *Broteria* 31:1–18.
8. *Anon.* n.d. *Bibliography on rate of nutrient cycling in ecosystems.* (1963–1956.) Commonw. Bur. Soils, Harpenden, England, 24 pp.
9. *Anon.* 1957. Black grama varies with rainfall. *Annual Report for 1956.* Rocky Mtn. For. & Range Exp. Sta. p. 61.
10. *Anon.* 1962. *Annual Report for 1961.* Pacific Northw. For. & Range Exp. Sta. 105 pp. *Anon.*
11. *Armour, C. J.* 1963. The use of repellents for preventing mammal and bird damage to trees and seed: A review. *For. Abstr.* 24:xxvii–xxxviii.
12. *Ashby, W. C.* 1961. Responses of American basswood seedlings to several light intensities. *For. Sci.* 7:273–281.
13. *Aspinall, D.* 1960. An analysis of competition between barley and white persicaria. II. Factors determining the course of competition. *Ann. Appl. Biol.* 48:637–654.
14. *Atkinson, I. A. E.* 1961. Conservation of New Zealand soils and vegetation for scientific and educational purposes. *Sci. Rev.* 19:65–73.
15. *Austin, R. C., and D. H. Baisinger.* 1955. Some effects of burning on forest soils of western Oregon and Washington. *J. For.* 53:275–280.
16. *Auten, J. T.* 1945. Relative influences of sassafras, black locust and pines upon old-field soils. *J. For.* 43:441–446.
17. *Backlund, H. O.* 1955. Red locusts and vegetation. *Oikos* 6:124–148.
18. *Bailey, E. W., and I. W. Sinnott.* 1916. Investigations on the phylogeny of Angiosperms. 6. The climatic distribution of certain types of Angiosperm leaves. *Am. J. Bot.* 3:24–39.
19. *Baker, F. S.* 1953. Stand density and growth. *J. For.* 51:94–97.
20. *Baker, H. G.* 1966. Reasoning about adaptations in ecosystems. *Bioscience* 16:35–37.
21. *Bank, T. B.,* II. 1953. Ecology of prehistoric Aleutian village sites. *Ecol.* 34:246–264.
22. *Barber, S. A.* 1959. The influence of alfalfa, bromegrass and corn on soil aggregation and crop yield. *Soil Sci. Soc. Am. Proc.* 23:258–259.
23. *Bard, G. E.* 1952. Secondary succession on the Piedmont of New Jersey. *Ecol. Mono.* 22:195–215.

24. *Barkman, J. J.* 1958. *Phytosociology and ecology of cryptogamic epiphytes.* Koninklyke Van Gorcum Co., Assen, Netherlands, 628 pp.
25. *Bartlett, H. H.* 1933. The nomenclature of plant associations. *Ecol.* 14:157–162.
26. *Beadle, N. C. W.* 1962. Soil phosphate and the delimitation of plant communities in eastern Australia. *Ecol.* 43:281–288.
27. *Beard, J. S.* 1945. The progress of plant succession on the Soufriere of St. Vincent. *J. Ecol.* 33:1–9.
28. *Beard, J. S.* 1953. The savanna vegetation of northern tropical America. *Ecol. Mono.* 23:149–215.
29. *Becking, R. W.* 1957. The Zurich-Montpellier school of phytosociology. *Bot. Rev.* 23:411–488.
30. *Becking, R. W.* 1963. Quantitative evaluation of plant communities and the IBM codification of phytosociological data. *Tropical Ecol.* 4:21–28.
31. *Beschel, R. E.* 1961. Dating rock surfaces by lichen growth and its application to glaciology and physiography (lichenometry). In G. O. Raasch (ed.) *Geology of the Arctic,* vol. 2, Univ. Toronto Press, Canada, pp. 1044–1062.
32. *Bharucha, F. R., and D. B. Ferreira.* 1941. The biological spectra of the Matheran and Mahabaleshwar flora. *J. Indian Bot. Soc.* 20:195–211.
33. *Biddiscombe, E. F.* 1953. A survey of the natural pastures of the Trangie district, New South Wales, with particular reference to the grazing factor. *Austral. J. Agr. Res.* 4:1–28.
34. *Billings, W. D.* 1938. The structure and development of old field shortleaf pine stands and certain associated physical factors of soil. *Ecol. Mono.* 8:437–499.
35. *Bird, E. C. F., and D. S. Ranwell.* 1964. *Spartina* salt marshes in southern England. IV. The physiography and Poole Harbour, Dorset. *J. Ecol.* 52:355–366.
36. *Birse, Evelyn M.* 1958. Ecological studies on growth-form in bryophytes. IV. Growth-form distribution in a deciduous woodland. *J. Ecol.* 46:29–42.
37. *Bjorkman, E.* 1960. *Monotropa hypopitys* L.—an epiparasite on tree roots. *Physiol. Plantarum* 13:308–327.
38. *Black, J. N.* 1958. Competition between plants of different initial seed sizes in swards of subterranean clover (*Trifolium subterraneum* L.) with particular reference to leaf area and the light microclimate. *Austral. J. Agr. Res.* 9:299–318.
39. *Black, J. N.* 1960. An assessment of the role of planting density in competition between red clover (*Trifolium pratense* L.) and lucerne (*Medicago sativa* L.) in the early vegetative state. *Oikos* 11:26–42.
40. *Blaisdell, J. P.* 1958. Seasonal development and yield of native plants on the upper Snake River Plains and their relation to certain climatic factors. U.S.D.A. *Tech. Bull.* 1190. 68 pp.
41. *Blaser, R. E., et al.* 1952. Ecological and physiological factors in compounding forage seed mixtures. *Adv. in Agron.* 4:179–219.
42. *Blaser, R. E., et al.* 1956. Seedling competition in compounding forage seed mixtures. *Agron. J.* 48:118–123.
43. *Bliss, L. C., and C. W. Cox.* 1964. Plant community and soil variation within a northern Indiana prairie. *Am. Midl. Nat.* 72:115–128.
44. *Bliss, L. C., and R. M. Linn.* 1955. Bryophyte communities associated with old field succession in the North Carolina Piedmont. *Bryol.* 58:120–131.
45. *Bloomfield, C.* 1954. A study of podsolization. V. The mobilization of iron and aluminum by aspen and ash leaves. *J. Soil Sci.* 5:50–56.
46. *Blum, B. M.* 1961. Age-size relationships in all-ages northern hardwoods. Northeastern For. Exp. Sta. Res. Note 125. 3 pp.

47. *Bonner, J., and A. W. Galston.* 1944. Toxic substances from the culture media of guayule which may inhibit growth. *Bot. Gaz.* 106:185–198.
48. *Booth, W. E.* 1941. Revegetation of abandoned fields in Kansas and Oklahoma. *Am. J. Bot.* 28:415–422.
49. *Booth, W. E.* 1943. Tripod method of making chart quadrats. *Ecol.* 24:262.
50. *Bormann, F. H., and B. F. Graham, Jr.* 1959. The occurrence of natural root grafting in eastern white pine, *Pinus strobus* L. *Ecol.* 40:677–691.
51. *Bourdo, E. A., Jr.* 1956. A review of the general land office survey and of its use in quantitative studies of former forests. *Ecol.* 37:754–768.
52. *Bradshaw, A. D., et al.* 1960. Experimental investigations into the mineral nutrition of several grass species. III. Phosphate level. *J. Ecol.* 48:631–637.
53. *Bray, J. R.* 1957. Climax forest herbs in prairie. *Am. Midl. Nat.* 58:434–440.
54. *Bray, J. R.* 1963. Root production and the estimation of net productivity. *Can. J. Bot.* 41:65–72.
55. *Bray, J. R.* 1964. Primary consumption in three forest canopies. *Ecol.* 45:165–167.
56. *Bray, J. R., and J. T. Curtis.* 1957. An ordination of the upland forest communities of southern Wisconsin. *Ecol. Mono.* 27:325–349.
57. *Brougham, R. W.* 1962. The leaf growth of *Trifolium repens* as influenced by seasonal changes in the light environment. *J. Ecol.* 50:449–459.
58. *Brown, Dorothy.* 1954. Methods of surveying and measuring vegetation. Commonw. Bur. Pastures & Field Crops Bull. 42. 223 pp.
59. *Budowski, G.* 1965. Distribution of tropical American rain forest species in the light of successional processes. *Turrialba* 15:40–42.
60. *Buell, J. H., et al.* 1952. Are natural areas essential? *J. For.* 50:237–239.
61. *Buell, M. F., and H. F. Buell.* 1941. Surface level fluctuation in Cedar Creek Bog, Minnesota. *Ecol.* 22:317–321.
62. *Buell, M. F., and W. E. Gordon.* 1945. Hardwood-conifer forest contact zone in Itasca Park, Minnesota. *Am. Midl. Nat.* 34:433–439.
63. *Buell, M. F., and W. E. Martin.* 1961. Competition between maple-basswood and fir-spruce communities in Itasca Park, Minnesota. *Ecol.* 42:428–429.
64. *Burges, A., and D. P. Drover.* 1953. The rate of podzol development in sands of the Woy Woy District, N. S. Wales. *Austral. J. Bot.* 1:83–94.
65. *Burgt, J. H. van der, and L. van Bendegom.* 1949. The use of vegetation to stabilize sand-dunes. *Inst. Civ. Engr., Conf. Biol. & Civ. Engineering, Proc.* 1948:158–180.
66. *Cain, S. A.* 1950. Life-forms and phytoclimate. *Bot. Rev.* 16:1–32.
67. *Cain, S. A., et al.* 1956. Application of some phytosociological techniques to Brazilian rainforest. *Am. J. Bot.* 43:911–941.
68. *Cajander, A. J.* 1926. The theory of forest types. *Acta Forestalia Fenn.* 29:108.
69. *Camp, J. C., van, Jr.* 1948. The nutrient element content of certain species of minor forest vegetation. *J. For.* 46:823–826.
70. *Camp, W. H.* 1951. Biosystematy. *Brittonia* 7:113–127.
71. *Campbell, R. S.* 1931. Plant succession and grazing capacity on clay soils in southern New Mexico. *J. Agr. Res.* 43:1027–1051.
72. *Cannon, W. A.* 1949. A tentative classification of root systems. *Ecol.* 30:542–549.
73. *Cannon, W. A.* 1954. A note on the grouping of lateral roots. *Ecol.* 35:293–295.
74. *Carlson, N. K.* 1961. Fog and lava rock, pines and pineapples. *Am. For.* 67:8–11.
75. *Carson, Rachel L.* 1962. *Silent Spring.* Houghton Mifflin, Boston, Mass. 368 pp.
76. *Catana, A. J., Jr.* 1963. The wandering quarter method of estimating population density. *Ecol.* 44:349–360.
77. *Chapman, V. C.* 1949. The stabilization of sand-dunes by vegetation. *Inst. Civ. Engineers, Conf. on Biol. & Civil Engineering, Proc.* 1948:142–157.

78. *Chapman, V. J., and J. W. Ronaldson.* 1958. The mangrove and salt-marsh flats of Auckland isthmus. Dept. Sci. Indus. Res., N.Z., Bull. 125. 79 pp.

79. *Chesters, C. G. C., and D. Parkinson.* 1959. On the distribution of fungi in the rhizospheres of oats. *Plant & Soil* 11:145–156.

80. *Christian, C. S., and R. A. Perry.* 1953. The systematic description of plant communities by the use of symbols. *J. Ecol.* 41:100–105.

81. *Clapham, A. R.* 1932. The form of the observational unit in quantitative ecology. *J. Ecol.* 20:192–197.

82. *Clayton, W. D.* 1963. The vegetation of Katsina Province, Nigeria. *J. Ecol.* 51:345–351.

83. *Clements, F. E.* 1916. Plant succession, an analysis of the development of vegetation. Carnegie Inst. Wash. Publ. 242. 512 pp.

84. *Clements, F. E., et al.* 1929. Plant competition. Carnegie Inst. Wash. Publ. 398. 340 pp.

85. *Clements, F. E.* 1936. Nature and structure of the climax. *J. Ecol.* 24:252–284.

86. *Cochran, W. G.* 1953. *Sampling Techniques.* Wiley, New York. 330 pp.

87. *Cochrane, G. R.* 1963. Vegetation studies in forest-fire areas of the Mount Lofty Ranges, south Australia. *Ecol.* 44:41–52.

88. *Coile, T. S.* 1939. Soil changes and loblolly pine succession. *Soil Sci. Soc. Am. Proc.* 4:353–354.

89. *Cole, L. C.* 1960. Competitive exclusion. *Sci.* 132:348–349.

90. *Collins, S.* 1962. Three decades of change in an unmanaged Connecticut woodland. Conn. Agr. Exp. Sta. Bull. 653. p. 32.

91. *Conard, H. S.* 1951. *The Background of Plant Ecology.* Iowa State College Press, Ames, Iowa. 238 pp.

92. *Conklin, H. C.* 1963. The study of shifting cultivation. Pan American Union, Dept. Soc. Affairs, Studies & Mono. 6. 185 pp.

93. *Cook, C. W.* 1942. Insects and weather as they influence growth of cactus on the central Great Plains. *Ecol.* 23:209–214.

94. *Cooper, C. F.* 1961. Pattern in ponderosa pine forests. *Ecol.* 42:493–499.

95. *Cooper, C. F.* 1963. An evaluation of variable plot sampling in shrub and herbaceous vegetation. *Ecol.* 44:565–569.

96. *Cooper, W. S.* 1913. The climax forest of Isle Royale, Lake Superior, and its development. *Bot. Gaz.* 55:1–44, 115–140, 189–235.

97. *Cooper, W. S.* 1924. An apparatus for photographic recording of quadrats. *J. Ecol.* 12:317.

98. *Cooper, W. S.* 1928. Seventeen years of successional change upon Isle Royale, Lake Superior. *Ecol.* 9:1–5.

99. *Cornelius, D. R.* 1946. Establishment of some true prairie species following reseeding. *Ecol.* 27:1–12.

100. *Costello, D. F., and Helen Foot.* 1932. Reconstruction of a late-Pleistocene biotic community in Minneapolis, Minn. *Ecol.* 13:63–72.

101. *Costello, D. F.* 1944. Natural revegetation of abandoned plowed land in the mixed prairie association of northeastern Colorado. *Ecol.* 25:312–326.

102. *Costello, D. F., and G. T. Turner.* 1941. Vegetation changes following exclusion of livestock from grazed ranges. *J. For.* 39:310–315.

103. *Cottam, G.* 1949. The phytosociology of an oak woods in southwestern Wisconsin. *Ecol.* 30:271–287.

104. *Coupland, R. T.* 1961. A reconsideration of grassland classification in the northern Great Plains of North America. *J. Ecol.* 49:135–167.

105. *Couppis, T. A.* 1956. Reclamation of sand dunes with particular reference to Ayia Erini sand drifts, Cyprus. *Emp. For. Rev.* 35:77–84.

106. *Cowles, H. C.* 1899. The ecological relations of the vegetation on the sand dunes of Lake Michigan. *Bot. Gaz.* 27:95–117, 167–202, 281–308, 361–391.

107. *Crampton, C. B.* 1963. Contrasting vegetational histories of certain soils in South Wales. An interpretation of their pollen content. *J. Ecol.* 51:453–459.

108. *Crocker, R. L.* 1952. Soil genesis and pedogenic factors. *Quart. Rev. Biol.* 27:139–168.

109. *Crocker, R. L., and J. Major.* 1955. Soil development in relation to vegetation and surface age at Glacier Bay, Alaska. *J. Ecol.* 43:427–448.

110. *Cummins, D. G., et al.* 1965. Chemical and physical properties of spoil banks in the eastern Kentucky coal fields. U.S.F.S. Res. Paper CS-17. 11 pp.

111. *Curtis, J. T.* 1959. *The Vegetation of Wisconsin.* Univ. Wis. Press, Madison, Wis. 657 pp.

112. *Curtis, J. T., and G. Cottam.* 1950. Antibiotic and autotoxic effects in prairie sunflower. *Torrey Bot. Club Bull.* 77:187–191.

113. *Curtis, J. T., and R. P. McIntosh.* 1950. The interrelations of certain analytic and synthetic phytosociological characters. *Ecol.* 31:434–455.

114. *Dahl, E.* 1956. Rondane Mountain vegetation in south Norway and its relation to the environment. Skrift. Utgitt av det Norske Videnskap-Adad. I Oslo, 1. Mat. Naturv. Klasse. 1956. 3. 373 pp.

115. *Dahl, E.* 1960. Some measures of uniformity in vegetation analysis. *Ecol.* 41:805–808.

116. *Dahlman, R. C., and C. L. Kucera.* 1965. Root productivity and turnover in native prairie. *Ecol.* 46:84–89.

117. *Dansereau, P.* 1951. Description and recording of vegetation upon a structural basis. *Ecol.* 32:172–229.

118. *Dansereau, P., and K. Lems.* 1957. The grading of dispersal types in plant communities and their ecological significance. Univ. Montreal, Contrib. Bot. Inst. 71. 52 pp.

119. *Daubenmire, R.* 1936. The "Big Woods" of Minnesota: its structure, and relation to climate, fire and soils. *Ecol. Mono.* 6:233–268.

120. *Daubenmire, R.* 1942. An ecological study of the vegetation of southeastern Washington and adjacent Idaho. *Ecol. Mono.* 12:53–79.

121. *Daubenmire, R.* 1943. Soil temperature versus drouth as a factor determining lower altitudinal limits of trees in the Rocky Mountains. *Bot. Gaz.* 105:1–13.

122. *Daubenmire, R.* 1952. Forest vegetation of northern Idaho and adjacent Washington, and its bearing on concepts of vegetation classification. *Ecol. Mono.* 22:301–330.

123. *Daubenmire, R.* 1954. Alpine timberlines in the Americas and their interpretation. *Butler Univ. Bot. Studies* 11:119–136.

124. *Daubenmire, R.* 1956. Climate as a determinant of vegetation distribution in eastern Washington and northern Idaho. *Ecol. Mono.* 26:131–154.

125. *Daubenmire, R.* 1959. A canopy-coverage method of vegetational analysis. *Northw. Sci.* 33:43–64.

126. *Daubenmire, R.* 1960. An experimental study of variation in the *Agropyron spicatum-A. inerme* complex. *Bot. Gaz.* 122:104–108.

127. *Daubenmire, R.* 1961. Vegetative indicators of height growth of ponderosa pine. *For. Sci.* 7:24–34.

128. *Daubenmire, R.* 1966. Vegetation: identification of typal communities. *Sci.* 151:291–298.

129. *Daubenmire, R., and W. E. Colwell.* 1942. Some edaphic changes due to overgrazing in the *Agropyron-Poa* prairie of southeastern Washington. *Ecol.* 23:32–40.

130. Daubenmire, R., and A. W. Slipp. 1943. Plant succession on talus slopes in northern Idaho as influenced by slope exposure. *Torrey Bot. Club Bull.* 70:473–480.

131. Davidson, R. L. 1943. Some observations on the relationships between vegetation and insect populations. *S. Afr. J. Sci.* 39:139–146.

132. Davidson, R. L. 1965. An experimental study of succession in the Transvaal highveld. In D. H. S. Davis (ed.) *Ecological Studies in Southern Africa.* W. Junk Publishers, Netherlands. Pp. 113–125.

133. Dawson, J. E. 1956. Organic soils. *Adv. in Agron.* 8:378–401.

134. Day, W. R. 1949. The relation between soil conditions, type of ground vegetation, and the growth of trees. *For.* 22:184–194.

135. Decker, J. P. 1959. A system for analysis of forest succession. *For. Sci.* 5:154–157.

136. Deen, J. L. 1933. Some aspects of an early expression of dominance in white pine. *Yale Univ. Sch. For. Bull.* 36.

137. Dickson, B. A., and R. L. Crocker. 1953. A chronosequence of soils and vegetation near Mt. Shasta, Cal. *J. Soil Sci.* 4:123–142, 143–154.

138. Dimbleby, G. W. 1952. Soil regeneration on the northeast Yorkshire moors. *J. Ecol.* 40:331–341.

139. Dimbleby, G. W. 1961. Transported material in the soil profile. *J. Soil Sci.* 12:12–22.

140. Dimbleby, G. W. 1961. Competition for light in crops and pastures. In F. L. Milthorpe (ed.) *Mechanisms in Biological Competition.* Soc. Exptl. Biol. Sympos. 15. Cambridge Univ. Press, England. Pp. 282–313.

141. Dimbleby, G. W. 1963. Competition among crop and pasture plants. *Adv. in Agron.* 15:1–118.

142. Drew, W. B. 1942. The revegetation of abandoned cropland in the Cedar Creek area, Boone and Callaway Counties, Missouri. *Mo. Agr. Exp. Sta. Bull.* 344.

143. Drew, W. B. 1944. Studies on the use of the point-quadrat method of botanical analysis of mixed pasture vegetation. *J. Agri. Res.* 69:289–297.

144. Du Rietz, G. E. 1936. Classification and nomenclature of vegetation units. *Sven. Bot. Tids.* 30:580–589.

145. Dyksterhuis, E. J. 1949. Condition and management of range land based on quantitative ecology. *J. Range Man.* 2:104–115.

146. Dyksterhuis, E. J. 1958. Ecological principles in range evaluation. *Bot. Rev.* 24:253–272.

147. Eden, T. 1924. The edaphic factors accompanying the succession after burning on Harpenden Common. *J. Ecol.* 12:267–286.

148. Edwards, R. W., and M. W. Brown. 1960. An aerial photographic method for studying the distribution of aquatic macrophytes in shallow waters. *J. Ecol.* 48:161–163.

149. Edwards, R. W., and M. Owens. 1960. The effects of plants on river conditions. I. Summer crops and estimates of net productivity of macrophytes in a chalk stream. *J. Ecol.* 48:161–163.

150. Eggler, W. A. 1963. Plant life of Paricutín Volcano, Mexico, eight years after activity ceased. *Am. Midl. Nat.* 69:38–68.

151. Ellenberg, H., and G. Cristofolini. 1964. (Visual punched cards as instruments for ordinating and evaluating vegetation releves.) Engl. summary. *Ber. Geobot. Inst. Techn. Hochschule Stiftung Rübel* 35:124–134.

152. Ellison, L. 1942. A comparison of methods of quadratting shortgrass vegetation. *J. Agr. Res.* 64:595–614.

153. *Ellison, L.* 1960. Influence of grazing on plant succession of rangelands. *Bot. Rev.* 26:1–78.

154. *Emerson, F. W.* 1935. An ecological reconnaissance in the White Sands, New Mexico. *Ecol.* 16:226–233.

155. *Endo, S.* 1939. Relation between the climatic condition and the morphology of dictoyledonous plant-leaf. *J. Geol. Soc. Tokyo* 46:334–335.

156. *Evans, F. C.* 1952. Individuals and communities—A biologist's view. *Mich. Alumnus Quart. Rev.* 58:297–299.

157. *Evans, F. C.* 1956. Ecosystem as the basic unit in ecology. *Sci.* 123:1127–1128.

158. *Evans, F. C., and E. Dahl.* 1955. The vegetational structure of an abandoned field in southeastern Michigan. *Ecol.* 36:685–706.

159. *Evans, G.* 1959. Establishment of herbage seed crops: Seed rates and population density—the experimental evidence. *J. Natl. Inst. Agr. Bot.* 8:495–500.

160. *Evans, L. T.* 1953. The ecology of the halophytic vegetation at Lake Ellesmere, New Zealand. *J. Ecol.* 41:106–122.

161. *Evans, R. A., and M. B. Jones.* 1958. Plant height times ground cover versus clipped samples for estimating forage production. *Agron. J.* 50:504–506.

162. *Evenari, M.* 1961. Chemical influences of other plants (allelopathy). In W. Ruhland (ed.) Encyclopedia of Plant Physiology. vol. 16, pp. 691–736.

163. *Faegri, K., et al.* 1964. *Textbook of Pollen Analysis.* 2nd ed. Blackwell Sci. Publ., Oxford, England. 240 pp.

164. *Fager, E. W., and J. A. McGowan.* 1963. Zooplankton species groups in the north Pacific. *Sci.* 140:453–460.

165. *Finch, R. H.* 1937. A tree-ring calendar for dating volcanic events at Cinder Cone, Lassen National Park, California. *Am. J. Sci.* 33:140–146.

166. *Florence, R. G., and R. L. Crocker.* 1962. Analysis of blackbutt (*Eucalyptus pilularis* SM) seedling growth in a blackbutt forest soil. *Ecol.* 43:670–679.

167. *Frankland, J. C.* 1966. Succession of fungi on decaying petioles of *Pteridium aquilinum. J. Ecol.* 54:41–63.

168. *Fry, E. J.* 1927. The mechanical action of crustaceous lichens on substrata of shale, schist, gneiss, limestone and obsidian. *Ann. Bot.* 41:437–460.

169. *Garrett, S. D.* 1955. Presidential address: Microbial ecology of the soil. *Brit. Mycol. Soc. Trans.* 38:1–9.

170. *Garrison, G. A.* 1949. Uses and modifications for the "moosehorn" crown closure estimator. *J. For.* 47:733–735.

171. *Garrison, G. A.* 1953. Annual fluctuation in production of some eastern Oregon and Washington shrubs. *J. Range Man.* 6:117–121.

172. *Gates, F. C.* 1942. Bogs of northern lower Michigan. *Ecol. Mono.* 12:213–254.

173. *Gates, F. C., and G. E. Nichols.* 1930. Relation between age and diameter in trees of the primeval northern hardwood forest. *J. For.* 28:395–398.

174. *Gatherum, G. E.* 1961. Variation in measurement of light intensities under forest canopies. *For. Sci.* 7:144–145.

175. *George-Barcley, Harriett.* 1924. The plant succession of the floodplain of the Mississippi River with special reference to the pioneer stage. Unpubl. thesis, Univ. Minnesota, Minneapolis.

176. *Gillham, Mary E.* 1960. Destruction of indigenous heath vegetation in Victorian sea-bird colonies. *Austral. J. Bot.* 8:277–317.

177. *Gilham, Mary E.* 1963. Some interactions of plants, rabbits and sea-birds on South African islands. *J. Ecol.* 51:275–294.

178. *Gimingham, C. H., and R. Boggie.* 1957. Stages in the recolonization of a Norwegian clay-slide. *Oikos* 8:38–64.

179. *Gjaerevoll, O.* 1956. The plant communities of the Scandinavian alpine snow-beds. *D. K. N. Vid. Selsk. Skrifter* 1956 (1):1–405.

180. *Gleason, H. A.* 1926. The individualistic concept of the plant association. *Torrey Bot. Club Bull.* 53:7–26.

181. *Gleason, H. A.* 1933. On concepts in phytosociology. *Sci.* 78:238–239.

182. *Gleason, H. A.* 1936. Is the synusia an association? *Ecol.* 17:444–451.

183. *Glew, D. R.* 1963. The results of stand treatment in the white spruce-alpine fir type of the northern interior, British Columbia. B.C. For. Serv. For. Man. Notes 1. 27 pp.

184. *Godwin, H.* 1960. The history of weeds in Britain. In J. L. Harper (ed.) *The Biology of Weeds.* Blackwell Sci. Publ., England. pp. 1–10.

185. *Golley, F. B.* 1961. Energy value of ecological materials. *Ecol.* 42:581.

186. *Golley, F. B.* 1965. Structure and function of an old-field broomsedge community. *Ecol. Mono.* 35:113–131.

187. *Good, R. E.* 1965. Salt marsh vegetation, Cape May, N.J. N.J. Acad. Sci. Bull. 10:1–11.

188. *Goodall, D. W.* 1952. Quantitative aspects of plant distribution. *Biol. Rev.* 27:194–245.

189. *Gorham, E.* 1953. Chemical studies on the soils and vegetation of waterlogged habitats in the English Lake District. *J. Ecol.* 41:345–360.

190. *Gorham, E.* 1955. Vegetation and the alignment of environmental forces. *Ecol.* 36:514–515.

191. *Gorham, E.* 1957. The development of peat lands. *Quart. Rev. Biol.* 32:145–166.

192. *Gorham, E., and W. H. Pearsall.* 1956. Acidity, specific conductivity and calcium content of some bog and fen waters in northern Britain. *J. Ecol.* 44:129–141.

193. *Gortner, R. A.* 1934. Lake vegetation as a possible source of forage. *Sci.* 80:531–533.

194. *Greenland, D. J., and Kowall, J. M. L.* 1960. Nutrient content of the moist tropical forest of Ghana. *Plant & Soil* 12:154–174.

195. *Gregory, R. A.* 1960. The development of forest soil organic layers in relation to time in southeast Alaska. Alaska For. Res. Center Tech. Note 47. 3 pp.

196. *Greig-Smith, P.* 1964. *Quantitative Plant Ecology.* 2nd ed. Butterworth, Inc., Washington, D.C. 242 pp.

197. *Griggs, R. F.* 1934. The edge of the forest in Alaska and the reasons for its position. *Ecol.* 15:80–96.

198. *Grümmer, G., and H. Beyer.* 1960. The influence exerted by species of *Camelina* on flax by means of toxic substances. In J. L. Harper (ed.) *The Biology of Weeds.* Blackwell Sci. Publ., England. pp. 153–157.

199. *Habeck, J. R.* 1958. White cedar ecotypes in Wisconsin. *Ecol.* 39:457–463.

200. *Hack, J. T.* 1941. Dunes of the western Navajo country. *Geogr. Rev.* 31:240–263.

201. *Hamilton, E. S.* 1953. Bryophyte life forms on slopes of contrasting exposures in central New Jersey. *Torrey Bot. Club Bull.* 80:264–272.

202. *Hannon, Nola J.* 1958. The status of nitrogen in the Hawksbury sandstone soils and their plant communities in the Sydney district. II. The distribution and circulation. *Linn. Soc. N. S. Wales Proc.* 23:65–85.

203. *Hannon, Nola J.* 1961. The status of nitrogen in the Hawksbury sandstone soils and their plant communities in the Sydney district. III. The source of loss of nitrogen. *Linn. Soc. N. S. Wales Proc.* 86:207–216.

204. *Hanson, H. C.* 1953. Vegetation types in northwestern Alaska and comparisons with communities in other Arctic regions. *Ecol.* 34:111–140.

205. *Hanson, H. C., and E. Dahl.* 1957. Some grassland communities in the mountain-front zone of northern Colorado. *Vegetatio* 7:249–270.
206. *Hanson, H. C., and D. Love.* 1930. Comparison of methods of quadratting. *Ecol.* 11:734–748.
207. *Harper, J. L.* (ed.). 1960. *The Biology of Weeds.* Blackwell Sci. Publ., Oxford, England. 256 pp.
208. *Harper, J. L.* 1960. Factors controlling plant numbers. In J. L. Harper (ed.) *The Biology of Weeds.* Blackwell Sci. Publ., Oxford, England. pp. 119–132.
209. *Harris, S. W., and W. H. Marshall.* 1963. Ecology of water-level manipulations on a northern marsh. *Ecol.* 44:331–343.
210. *Hasel, A. A.* 1941. Estimation of vegetation-type areas by linear measurement. *J. For.* 39:34–40.
211. *Hastings, J. R., and R. M. Turner.* 1965. *The Changing Mile.* Univ. Ariz. Press, Tucson. 317 pp.
212. *Heady, H. F.* 1956. Changes in a California annual plant community induced by manipulation of natural mulch. *Ecol.* 37:798–812.
213. *Heady, H. F.* 1957. The measurement and value of plant height in the study of herbaceous vegetation. *Ecol.* 38:313–320.
214. *Heady, H. F.* 1958. Vegetational changes in the California annual type. *Ecol.* 39:402–416.
215. *Heinselman, M. L.* 1963. Forest sites, bog processes, and peatland types in the glacial Lake Agassiz region, Minnesota. *Ecol. Mono.* 33:327–374.
216. *Helmers, A. E.* 1947. Direct seedling experiments in the Inland Empire. *Northw. Sci.* 21:84–88.
217. *Hepher, B.* 1962. Primary production in fish ponds and its application to fertilization experiments. *Limnol. & Oceanogr.* 7:131–136.
218. *Heusser, C. J.* 1954. Additional pollen profiles from southeastern Alaska. *Am. J. Sci.* 252:106–119.
219. *Heyward, F.* 1939. The relation of fire to stand composition of longleaf pine forests. *Ecol.* 20:287–304.
220. *Hilder, E. J., and B. E. Mottershead.* 1963. The redistribution of plant nutrients through free-grazing sheep. *Austral. J. Sci.* 26:88–89.
221. *Hill, L. W.* 1960. Forest plantation development influences stream flow. *Soc. Am. For. Proc.* 1960:168–171.
222. *Hogetsu, K., et al.* 1960. Growth analytical studies on the artificial communities of *Helianthus tuberosus* with different densities. *Jap. J. Bot.* 17:278–305.
223. *Holliday, R.* 1960. Plant population and crop yield. *Nature* 186:22–24.
224. *Holloway, J. T.* 1947. Principles of primary forest ecological survey: Their application to forests of Otagi and Southland. *N. Z. J. For.* 5:285–294.
225. *Holmes, C. H.* 1954. Forests and climates in the South Island of New Zealand. N. Z. For. Serv. Tech. Paper 3. 82 pp.
226. *Holmes, C. H.* 1951. The grass, fern and savannah lands of Ceylon, their nature and ecological significance. Imperial For. Inst. Paper 28. 95 pp.
227. *Horikawa, Y., and A. Histsugu.* 1952. A short study on the growth-form of bryophytes and its ecological significance. Hikobia 1:119–128.
228. *Hormay, A. L.* 1949. Getting better records of vegetation changes with the line interception method. *J. Range Man.* 2:67–69.
229. *Hosokawa, T.* 1950. Epiphyte-quotient. *Bot. Mag.* (*Tokyo*) 63:18–20, also: *Formosa Nat. Hist. Soc. Trans.* 33:18–20.
230. *Houston, W. R.* 1960. Effects of water spreading on range vegetation in eastern Montana. *J. Range Man.* 13:289–293.

231. *Hulbert, L. C.* 1955. Ecological studies of *Bromus tectorum* and other annual bromegrasses. *Ecol. Mono.* 25:181–213.

232. *Hummel, S. C.* 1952. An experiment on the sampling of early thinning. *Forestry* 25:19–31.

233. *Humphrey, R. R.* 1953. The desert grassland, past and present. *J. Range Man.* 6:159–164.

234. *Hunt, K. W.* 1943. Floating mats on a southeastern coastal plain reservoir. *Torrey Bot. Club Bull.* 70:481–488.

235. *Hustich, I.* 1948. The Scotch pine in northernmost Finland and its dependence on the climate in the last decades. *Acta Bot. Fenn.* 42:1–75.

236. *Hutchings, S. S., and R. C. Holmgren.* 1959. Interpretation of loop-frequency data as a measure of plant cover. *Ecol.* 40:668–677.

237. *Hutnik, R. J.* 1952. Reproduction on windfalls in a northern hardwood stand. *J. For.* 50:693–694.

238. *Isaak, D., et al.* 1959. A record of reverse plant succession in a tamarack bog. *Ecol.* 40:317–320.

239. *Iwaki, H.* 1959. Ecological studies on interspecific competition in a plant community. I. An analysis of growth of competing plants in mixed stands of buckwheat and green grams. *Jap. J. Bot.* 17:120–138.

240. *Jameson, D. A.* 1963. Responses of individual plants to harvesting. *Bot. Rev.* 29:532–594.

241. *Jenny, H., et al.* 1949. Comparative study of decomposition rates of organic matter in temperate and tropical regions. *Soil Sci.* 68:419–432.

242. *Johnsgard, P. A., and W. H. Rickard.* 1957. The relation of spring bird distribution to a vegetation mosaic in southeastern Washington. *Ecol.* 38:171–174.

243. *Johnson, N. E., et al.* 1963. Mortality and damage to Pacific silver fir by the balsam wooly aphid in southwestern Washington. *J. For.* 61:854–860.

244. *Johnston, D. W., and E. P. Odum.* 1956. Breeding bird populations in relation to plant succession. *Ecol.* 37:50–62.

245. *Jones, H.* 1955. Studies on the ecology of the river Rheidol. I. Plant colonization and permanent quadrat records in the main stream of the lower Rheidol. *J. Ecol.* 43:462–476.

246. *Jones, M. B., and R. A. Evans.* 1959. Modification of the step-point method for evaluating species yield changes in fertilizer trials on annual grasslands. *Agron. J.* 51:467–470.

247. *Jones, M. G.* 1933. Grassland management and its influence on the sward. *Empire J. Exptl. Agr.* 1:43–58, 122–129, 223–234, 361–367.

248. *Jorgensen, E. G.* 1956. Growth-inhibiting substances formed by algae. *Physiol. Plant.* 9:712–726.

249. *Karsten, K. S.* 1939. Root activity and the oxygen requirement in relation to soil fertility. *Am. J. Bot.* 26:855–860.

250. *Keay, R. W. J.* 1957. Wind-dispersed species in a Nigerian forest. *J. Ecol.* 45:471–478.

251. *Keever, Catherine.* 1950. Causes of succession on old fields of the Piedmont, North Carolina. *Ecol. Mono.* 20:229–250.

252. *Keever, Catherine.* 1957. Establishment of *Grimmia leavigata* on bare granite. *Ecol.* 38:422–429.

253. *Kell, Lucille L.* 1938. The effect of the moisture-retaining capacity of soils on forest succession in Itasca Park, Minnesota. *Am. Midl. Nat.* 20:682–694.

254. *Kelting, R. W.* 1954. Effects of moderate grazing on the composition and plant production of a native tall-grass prairie in central Oklahoma. *Ecol.* 35:200–207.

255. Kemp, C. D., and A. W. Kemp. 1956. The analysis of point quadrat data. *Austral. J. Bot.* 4:167–174.
256. Kershaw, K. A. 1963. Pattern in vegetation and its causality. *Ecol.* 44:377–388.
257. King, C. A. M. 1961. *Beaches and Coasts.* Edward Arnold, Ltd., London. 403 pp.
258. Kittredge, J., Jr. 1938. The interrelations of habitat, growth rate, and associated vegetation in the aspen community of Minnesota and Wisconsin. *Ecol. Mono.* 8:151–246.
259. Kittredge, J., Jr. 1948. *Forest Influences.* McGraw-Hill, New York. 394 pp.
260. Klingman, D. L., et al. 1943. The cage method for determining consumption and yield of pasture herbage. *J. Am. Soc. Agron.* 35:739–746.
261. Krajicek, J. E., et al. 1961. Crown competition—a measure of density. *For. Sci.* 7:35–42.
262. Kramer, P. J., et al. 1952. Survival of pine and hardwood seedlings in forest and open. *Ecol.* 33:427–430.
263. Krause, H. A., et al. 1959. Soils and forest growth of different aspects of the Tanana watershed in interior Alaska. *Ecol.* 40:492–495.
264. Kucera, C. L., and J. M. Aikman. 1951. Secondary plant succession on an eroded Lindley soil as affected by variations in cultural treatment. *Iowa State Coll. J. Sci.* 25:581–597.
265. Küchler, A. W. 1949. A physiognomic classification of vegetation. *Assoc. Am. Geogr. Ann.* 39:201–210.
266. Küchler, A. W. 1961. Mapping the dynamic aspects of vegetation. Méthodes de la cartographie de la vegetation. *Colloq. Internat. du Centre Nat. Rech. Sci.* 97:187–201.
267. Kuntz, J. E., and A. J. Riker. 1956. The use of radioactive isotopes to ascertain the role of root grafting in the translocation of water, nutrients, and disease-producing organisms among forest trees. *Internat. Conf. Peaceful Uses Atomic Energy Proc.* 12:144–148.
268. Laing, C. C. 1958. Studies in the ecology of *Ammophila breviligulata.* I. Seedling survival and its relation to population increase and dispersal. *Bot. Gaz.* 119:208–216.
269. Lambert, J. M., and W. T. Williams. 1962. Multivariate methods in plant ecology. IV. Nodal analysis. *J. Ecol.* 50:775–803.
270. Lawrence, D. B. 1950. Estimating dates of recent glacier advances and recession rates by studying tree growth layers. *Am. Geophys. Union Trans.* 31:243–248.
271. Lawrence, W. H. 1952. Evidence of the age of beaver ponds. *J. Wildl. Man.* 16:69–79.
272. Lazenby, A. 1961. Studies on *Allium vineale* L. II. Establishment and growth in different intensities of competition. *J. Ecol.* 49:543–558.
273. Leisman, G. A. 1957. Further data on the rate of organic matter accumulation in bogs. *Ecol.* 38:361.
274. Leyton, L. 1955. The influence of artificial shading of the ground vegetation on the nutrition and growth of Sitka spruce (*Picea sitchensis* Carr.) in a heathland plantation. *Forestry* 28:1–6.
275. Lindeman, R. L. 1942. The trophic-dynamic aspect of ecology. *Ecol.* 23:399–418.
276. Lister, P. B., and F. X. Schumaker. 1937. The influence of rainfall upon tuft area and height growth of three semidesert range grasses in southern Arizona. *J. Agr. Res.* 54:109–121.
277. Loucks, O. L. 1962. Ordinating forest communities by means of environmental scalars and phytosociological indices. *Ecol. Mono.* 32:137–166.

278. *Lutz, H. J.* 1932. Relation of forest site quality to number of plant individuals per unit area. *J. For.* 30:34–38.

279. *Lutz, H. J.* 1963. Forest ecosystems: their maintenance, amelioration, and deterioration. *J. For.* 563–569.

280. *Lutz, H. J., and A. L. McComb.* 1935. Origin of white pine in virgin forest stands of northwestern Pennsylvania. *Ecol.* 16:252–256.

281. *Lynch, D.* 1955. Ecology of the aspen groveland in Glacier County, Montana. *Ecol. Mono.* 25:321–344.

282. *McArdle, R. E., and W. H. Meyer.* 1930. The yield of Douglas-fir in the Pacific Northwest. U.S.D.A. Tech. Bull. 201. 64 pp.

283. *McCormick, J., and J. W. Andresen.* 1960. Some effects of animals on the vegetation of the New Jersey pine barrens. *Torrey Bot. Club Bull.* 87:375–385.

284. *McCullough, H. A.* 1948. Plant succession on fallen logs in a virgin spruce-fir forest. *Ecol.* 29:508–513.

285. *McDermott, R. E.* 1954. Seedling tolerance as a factor in bottomland timber succession. Mo. Agr. Exp. Sta. Res. Bull. 557. 11 pp.

286. *McIntosh, R. P.* 1962. Raunkiaer's "law of frequency." *Ecol.* 43:533–534.

287. *McLaughlin, W. T., and R. L. Brown.* 1942. Controlling coastal sand dunes in the Pacific Northwest. U.S.D.A. Cir. 660. 46 pp.

288. *McMillan, C.* 1959. The role of ecotypic variation in the distribution of the central grassland of North America. *Ecol. Mono.* 29:285–308.

289. *Major, J.* 1951. A functional, factorial approach to plant ecology. *Ecol.* 32:392–412.

290. *Major, J.* 1959. A comparison of two different schemes for mapping vegetation. *Ecol.* 40:524.

291. *Malmer, N., and H. S. Sjörs.* 1955. Some determinations of elementary constituents in mire plants and peat. *Bot. Notiser* 108:46–80.

292. *Mansur, C. I.* (ed.). 1947. *Malaria Control on Impounded Water.* Fed. Security Agency, U.S. Publ. Health Serv., & Tenn. Valley Authority, Health & Safety Dept., Washington, D.C. 422 pp.

293. *Marshall, J. K.* 1965. *Corynephorus canescens* (L.) P. Beauv. as a model for the *Ammophila* problem. *J. Ecol.* 53:447–463.

294. *Medwecka-Kornas, A., and J. Kornas.* 1963. Potential natural vegetation of the Ojocow National Park (southern Poland). *Acad. Polon. Sci. Bull.* 11:357–359.

295. *Merz, R. W., and S. G. Boyce.* 1956. Age of oak "seedlings." *J. For.* 54:774–775.

296. *Miller, H. C. E., and M. F. Buell.* 1956. Life-form spectra of contrasting slopes in Itasca Park, Minnesota. *Bot. Gaz.* 117:259–263.

297. *Milthorpe, F. L.* (ed.). 1961. Mechanisms in biological competition. *Soc. Exptl. Biol. Symp.* 15. 365 pp.

298. *Moore, C. W. E.* 1959a. The competitive effect of *Danthonia* spp. on the establishment of *Bothriochloa ambigua*. *Ecol.* 40:141–143.

299. *Moore, E. J.* 1959b. Interaction of species and soil in relation to the distribution of eucalypts. *Ecol.* 40:734–735.

300. *Moore, E. J.* 1931. The ecology of Ayreland of Bride, Isle of Man. *J. Ecol.* 19:115–136.

301. *Moss, C. E.* 1910. The fundamental units of vegetation. *New Phytol.* 9:18–53.

302. *Moss, E. H.* 1936. The ecology of *Epilobium angustifolius* with particular reference to rings of periderm in the wood. *Am. J. Bot.* 23:114–120.

303. *Moss, E. H.* 1955. The vegetation of Alberta. *Bot. Rev.* 21:493–567.

304. *Moss, E. H., and J. A. Campbell.* 1947. The fescue grassland of Alberta. *Can. J. Res.* (C) 25:209–227.
305. *Muelder, D. W., et al.* 1962. Biotic factors in natural regeneration of *Sequoia sempervirens*. Internat. Union For. Res. Organ., Proc. 13th Congr., 1961, Teil 2, Band 1:21/4–1. 10 pp.
306. *Muller, C. H.* 1952. Plant succession in Arctic heath and tundra in northern Scandinavia. *Torrey Bot. Club Bull.* 79:296–309.
307. *Muller, C. H., et al.* 1964. Volatile growth inhibitors produced by aromatic shrubs. *Sci.* 143:471–473.
308. *Neyman, J.* 1952. *Lectures and Conferences on Mathematical Statistics and Probability.* 2nd ed. U.S.D.A. Grad. School, Washington, D.C.
309. *Nicholls, J. L.* 1956. The historical ecology of the indigenous forest of the Taranaki upland. *N.Z.J. For.* 7:17–34.
310. *Nielsen, E. S.* 1957. The chlorophyll content and the light utilization in communities of plankton algae and terrestrial higher plants. *Physiol. Plant.* 10:1009–1021.
311. *Northcraft, R. D.* 1948. Marine algal colonization on the Monterey Peninsula, California. *Am. J. Bot.* 35:396–404.
312. *Numata, M.* 1950. The investigation of vegetation by means of sampling method—studies on the structure of plant communities. V. *Bot. Mag.* (*Tokyo*) 63:149–154.
313. *Nye, P. H., and D. J. Greenland.* 1960. The soil under shifting cultivation. Commonw. Bur. Soils, Tech. Commun. 51. 156 pp.
314. *Olmsted, N. W., and J. D. Curtis.* 1947. Seeds of the forest floor. *Ecol.* 28:49–52.
315. *Olsen, C.* 1943. Natural glades in beech-wood on calcareous soil. *Bot. Tidsk.* 46:95–115.
316. *Olsen, C., et al.* 1959. Eastern hemlock seed and seedlings, response to photoperiod and temperature. Conn. Agr. Exp. Sta. Bull. 620. 70 pp.
317. *Olson, J. S.* 1958a. Rates of succession and soil changes on southern Lake Michigan sand dunes. *Bot. Gaz.* 119:125–170.
318. *Olson, J. S.* 1958b. Lake Michigan dune development. I. Wind-velocity profiles. *J. Geol.* 66:254–263.
319. *Omura, M.* 1950. Life-forms of epiphytic lichens. *Bot. Mag.* (*Tokyo*) 63:155–160.
320. *Oosting, H. J.* 1942. An ecological analysis of the plant communities of Piedmont, North Carolina. *Am. Midl. Nat.* 28:1–126.
321. *Oosting, H. J.* 1945. Tolerance to salt spray of plants of coastal dunes. *Ecol.* 26:85–89.
322. *Oosting, H. J.* 1954. Ecological processes and vegetation of the maritime strand in the southeastern United States. *Bot. Rev.* 20:226–262.
323. *Oosting, H. J., and L. E. Anderson.* 1939. Plant succession on granite rock in eastern North Carolina. *Bot. Gaz.* 100:750–768.
324. *Oppenheimer, H. R.* 1957. Further observations on roots penetrating into rocks. Res. Council Israel Bull. 6D(1):18–31.
325. *Osborne, J. G.* 1942. Sampling errors of systematic and random surveys of cover-type areas. *J. Am. Statis. Assoc.* 37:257–264.
326. *Osvald, H.* 1952. Notes on the vegetation of British and Irish mosses. *Acta Phytogeogr. Suecica 26.* 62 pp.
327. *Ovington, J. D.* 1958. Studies of the development of woodland conditions under different trees. VI. Soil sodium, potassium and phosphorus. *J. Ecol.* 46:127–142.

328. *Palmer, C. M.* 1964. Algae in water supplies of the United States. In D. F. Jackson (ed.) *Algae and Man.* Plenum Press, New York. Pp. 239–261.
329. *Palmer, W. H., and A. K. Miller.* 1961. Botanical evidence for the recession of a glacier. *Oikos* 12:75–86.
330. *Parsons, J. L., et al.* 1953. Yield and vegetative chemical composition of forage crops as affected by soil treatment. *Soil Sci. Soc. Am. Proc.* 17:42–46.
331. *Pearsall, W. H.* 1947. Water supply and biology. *Nature* 160:176–178.
332. *Pearse, K., et al.* 1935. An improved pantograph for mapping vegetation. *Ecol.* 16:529–530.
333. *Penfound, W. T.* 1948. A phytosociological analysis of a goldenrod community near Kenner, Louisiana. *Ecol.* 29:124–125.
334. *Penfound, W. T.* 1963. A modification of the point-centered quarter method for grassland analysis. *Ecol.* 44:175–176.
335. *Penfound, W. T., and J. D. Schneidau.* 1945. The relation of land reclamation to aquatic wildlife resources in southeastern Louisiana. *N. A. Wildl. Conf. Trans.* 10:308–318.
336. *Penfound, W. T., et al.* 1945. The spring phenology of plants in and around the reservoirs in north Alabama with particular reference to malaria control. *Ecol.* 26:332–352.
337. *Peterken, G. F., and C. R. Tubbs.* 1965. Woodland regeneration in the new forest, Hampshire, since 1650. *J. Appl. Ecol.* 2:158–170.
338. *Pickford, G. D., and G. Stewart.* 1935. Coordinate method of mapping low shrubs. *Ecol.* 16:257–261.
339. *Piemeisel, R. L.* 1951. Causes affecting change and rate of change in a vegetation of annuals in Idaho. *Ecol.* 32:53–72.
340. *Pimentel, D., et al.* 1962. Alteration of plant growth and microclimate by crowding. *Ecol.* 43:765–768.
341. *Platt, R. B., and F. P. Amsler.* 1955. A basic method for the immediate study of lichen growth rates and succession. *Tenn. Acad. Sci. J.* 30:177–183.
342. *Poel, L. W.* 1961. Soil aeration as a limiting factor in the growth of *Pteridium aquilinum* (L.) Kuhn. *J. Ecol.* 49:107–111.
343. *Pond, R. H.* 1905. The biological relation of aquatic plants to the substratum. U.S. Fish Comm. Rept. for 1903:483–526.
344. *Ponyatovskaya, V. M.* 1961. On two trends in phytoconeology. *Vegetatio* 10:373–385.
345. *Poore, M. E. D.* 1955–56. The use of phytosociological methods in ecological investigations. *J. Ecol.* 43:226–244, 245–269, 606–651; 44:28–50.
346. *Poore, M. E. D.* 1962. The method of successive approximation in descriptive ecology. *Adv. Ecol. Res.* 1:35–68.
347. *Poore, M. E. D.* 1964. Integration in the plant community. *J. Ecol.* 52:213–226.
348. *Potter, L. D.* 1962. Limitations of palynology to paleoecological reconstruction. Fort Burgwin Res. Center, Taos, N. Mex. Publ. 3:39–42.
349. *Proebsting, E. L., and A. E. Gilmore.* 1941. The relation of peach root toxicity to the reestablishment of peach orchards. *Am. Soc. Hort. Sci. Proc.* 38:21–26.
350. *Provost, M. W.* 1948. Marsh-blasting as a wildlife management technique. *J. Wildl. Man.* 12:350–387.
351. *Ralston, R. A.* 1953. Some effects of spacing on jackpine development in lower Michigan after twenty-five years. *Mich. Acad. Sci. Arts Lett. Papers* 38:137–143.

352. *Ramsay, D. M.* 1964. An analysis of Nigerian savanna. II. An alternative method of analysis and its application to the Gombe sandstone vegetation. *J. Ecol.* 52:457–466.
353. *Ranwell, D.* 1958. Movement of vegetated sand dunes at Newborough Warren, Anglesey. *J. Ecol.* 46:83–100.
354. *Raunkiaer, C.* 1934. *The Life Forms of Plants and Statistical Plant Geography; Being the Collected Papers of C. Raunkiaer.* Clarendon Press, Oxford, England. 632 pp.
355. *Rees, T. K.* 1940. The algal colonization at Mumbles Head. *J. Ecol.* 28:403–437.
356. *Rennie, R. J.* 1955. The uptake of nutrients by mature forest growth. *Plant & Soil* 7:49–95.
357. *Reppert, J. N., et al.* Herbage yield and its correlation with other plant measurements. U.S.D.A. Misc. Publ. 940:15–21.
358. *Reynolds, H. G.* 1962. Use of natural openings in a ponderosa pine forest of Arizona by deer, elk and cattle. Rocky Mtn. For. & Range Exp. Sta. Res. Note 78. 4 pp.
359. *Rhodes, R. R.* 1953. A device for determining boundaries of browse plots. *J. Range Man.* 6:318–319.
360. *Rice, E. L., and J. W. Bohning.* 1956. Effects of burning on a desert grass-shrub range in southern Arizona. *Ecol.* 37:679–777.
361. *Rice, E. L., et al.* 1960. Seed dispersal and mineral nutrition in succession in abandoned fields in central Oklahoma. *Ecol.* 41:224–228.
362. *Richards, P. W.* 1952. *The Tropical Rainforest.* Cambridge Univ. Press, New York. 423 pp.
363. *Richards, P. W.* 1956. Study of tropical vegetation with special reference to British Guiana and British West Africa. *Unasylva* 10:161–165.
364. *Richardson, J. A.* 1958. The effect of temperature on the growth of plants on pit heaps. *J. Ecol.* 46:537–546.
365. *Rickard, W. H.* 1960. The distribution of small mammals in relation to the climax vegetation mosaic in eastern Washington and northern Idaho. *Ecol.* 41:99–106.
366. *Rickard, W. H.* 1963. Cesium-137 in dried milk products in relation to phyto-climatic zones. *Nature* 197:197–198.
367. *Rigg, G. B., and H. R. Gould.* 1957. Age of Glacier Peak eruption and chronology of post-glacial peat deposits in Washington and surrounding areas. *Am. J. Sci.* 255:341–363.
368. *Rigg, G. B., and C. T. Richardson.* 1938. Profiles of some Sphagnum bogs of the Pacific coast of North America. *Ecol.* 19:408–434.
369. *Ritchie, J. C.* 1957. The vegetation of northern Manitoba. II. A prisere on the Hudson Bay lowlands. *Ecol.* 38:429–435.
370. *Robel, R. J.* 1962. Changes in submerged vegetation following a change in water level. *J. Wildl. Man.* 26:221–224.
371. *Roberts, H. A.* 1958. Studies on the weeds of vegetable crops, I. Initial effects of cropping on the weed seeds in the soil. *J. Ecol.* 46:759–768.
372. *Romell, L. G.* 1930. Comments on Raunkiaer's and similar methods of vegetation analysis and the "law of frequency." *Ecol.* 11:589–596.
373. *Rose, E. T.* 1954. Blue-green algae control at Storm Lake. *Iowa Acad. Sci. Proc.* 61:604–614.
374. *Rowe, J. S.* 1953. Forest sites—a discussion. *For. Chron.* 29:278–289.
375. *Rowland, J. W., and J. M. Hector.* 1934. A camera method for charting quadrats. *Nature* 133:179.

376. *Rübel, E.* 1936. Plant communities of the world. In T. H. Goodspeed *Essays in Geobotany.* Univ. California Press, Berkeley, Calif. pp. 263–290.

377. *Rudd, R. L.* 1964. *Pesticides and the Living Landscape.* Univ. Wisconsin Press, Madison, Wis. 320 pp.

378. *Russell, R. J.* 1942. Flotant. *Geogr. Rev.* 32:74–98.

379. *Ryder, Vera L.* 1954. On the morphology of leaves. *Bot. Rev.* 20:263–276.

380. *Salmon, S. C.* 1953. Random versus systematic arrangement of field plots. *Agron. J.* 45:459–462.

381. *Salmon, S. C.* 1955. Random versus systematic in non-Latin square field experiments. *Agron. J.* 47:289–294.

382. *Sarvas, R.* 1953. Measurement of the crown closure of a stand. *Inst. For. Fennica Commun.* 41:1–13.

383. *Schramm, J. R.* 1966. Plant colonization studies on black wastes from anthracite mining in Pennsylvania. *Am. Philos. Soc. Trans.* 56:1–194.

384. *Schultz, V.* (ed.). 1963. Offsite ecological research of the Division of Biology and Medicine—terrestrial and freshwater. U.S. Atomic Energy Comm. TID-13358 (1st rev.) Biol. & Med. (TID 4500, 2nd. ed.) 122 pp.

385. *Schulz, J. P.* 1960. Ecological studies on rain forest in northern Suriname. *Verh. der Konin. Nederl. Akad. Wetens., Afd. Naturkunde* 53:1–267.

386. *Scott, D. R. M.* 1955. Amount and chemical composition of the organic matter contributed by overstory and understory vegetation to forest soil. Yale Sch. For. Bull. 62. 73 pp.

387. *Scott, J. D.* 1956. Study of primoidial buds and the reaction of roots to defoliation as the basis of grassland management. *Internat. Grassl. Congr. Proc.* 7:479–487.

388. *Sears, P. B.* 1947. *Deserts on the March.* Univ. Okla. Press, Norman, Okla. 178 pp.

389. *Seely, H. E.* 1961. Some investigations of forest sampling methods. Dept. For. Can. Tech. Note 111. 17 pp.

390. *Seim, A. L., et al.* 1955. Bryophyte growth forms and cover in a jack pine stand, Itasca Park, Minnesota. *Bryol.* 58:326–330.

391. *Shanks, R. E.* 1953. Forest composition and species association in the beech-maple forest region of western Ohio. *Ecol.* 34:455–466.

392. *Shepherd, R. F.* 1959. Phytosociological and environmental characteristics of outbreak and non-outbreak areas of the two-year cycle spruce budworm, *Choristoneura fumiferana. Ecol.* 40:608–620.

393. *Silker, T. H.* 1948. Planting of water-tolerant trees along margins of fluctuating-level reservoirs. *Iowa State Coll. J. Sci.* 22:431–447.

394. *Silvey, J. K. G., and A. W. Roach.* 1964. Studies on microbiotic cycles in surface water. *Am. Water Works Assoc. J.* 56:60–72.

395. *Sjörs, H.* 1955. Remarks on ecosystems. *Svensk. Bot. Tids.* 49:155–169.

396. *Sjörs, H.* 1961. Surface patterns in boreal peatland. *Endeavour* 20:217–224.

397. *Smith, A. D.* 1944. A study of the reliability of range vegetation estimates. *Ecol.* 25:441–448.

398. *Smith, C. C.* 1940. Biotic and physiographic succession on abandoned eroded farmland. *Ecol. Mono.* 10:421–484.

399. *Smith, E. V., and H. S. Swingle.* 1941. The use of fertilizer for controlling the pond weed *Najas guadaloupensis. N.A. Wildl. Conf. Trans.* 6:245–250.

400. *Smith, H. T. U.* 1940. Geologic studies in southwestern Kansas. Sand dunes. Kans. State Geol. Surv. Bull. 34:153–168.

401. *Smith, J. G.* 1959. Additional modifications of the point frame. *J. Range Man.* 12:204–205.

402. *Snaydon, R. W.* 1962. The growth and competitive ability of contrasting natural populations of *Trifolium repens*. L. on calcareous and acid soils. *J. Ecol.* 50:439–447.

403. *Snaydon, R. W., and A. D. Bradshaw*. 1961. Differential response to calcium within the species *Festuca ovina* L. *New Phytol*. 60:219–234.

404. *Specht, R. L.* 1961. Flora conservation in south Australia. I. The preservation of plant formations and associations recorded in south Australia. *Roy. Soc. S. Austral. Trans.* 85:177–196.

405. *Specht, R. L., et al.* 1958. Dark Island heath (Ninety-mile Plain, south Australia) VI. Pyric succession: changes in composition, coverage, dry weight, and mineral status. *Austral. J. Bot.* 6:59–88.

406. *Spence, D. H. N.* 1959. Studies on the vegetation of Shetland. II. Records for the restriction of the exclusive pioneers to serpentine debris. *J. Ecol.* 47:641–649.

407. *Squillace, A. E., and R. T. Bingham*. 1958. Localized ecotypic variation in western white pine (*P. monticola*). *For. Sci.* 4:20–34.

408. *Stephenson, T. A., and A. Stephenson*. 1961. Life between tide-marks in North America. IV. Vancouver Island. *J. Ecol.* 49:1–29.

409. *Stewart, G., and W. Keller*. 1936. A correlation method for ecology as exemplified by studies of native desert vegetation. *Ecol.* 17:500–514.

410. *Stoesz, A. D., and R. L. Brown*. 1957. Stabilizing sand dunes. U.S.D.A. Yearbook 1957:321–326.

411. *Symposium*. 1960. Forest types and forest ecosystems. *Silva Fenn.* 105. 142 pp.

412. *Tamm, C. O.* 1951. Removal of plant nutrients from tree crowns by rain. *Physiol. Plant.* 4:184–188.

413. *Tansley, A. G.* 1935. The use and abuse of vegetation concepts and terms. *Ecol.* 16:284–307.

414. *Tevis, L., Jr.* 1956. Effect of a slash burn on forest mice. *J. Wildl. Man.* 20:405–409.

415. *Tezuka, Y.* 1961. Development of vegetation in relation to soil formation in the volcanic island of Oshima, Izu, Japan. *Jap. J. Bot.* 17:371–402.

416. *Thomas, G. P.* 1958. The occurrence of the Indian paint fungus, *Echinodontium tinctorium* E. and E., in British Columbia. Can. Dept. Agr. Div. For. Biol. Publ. 1041. 30 pp.

417. *Thornton, P. L.* 1957. Problems of managing upper Michigan's coniferous swamps. *J. For.* 55:192–197.

418. *Tiemeir, O. W.* 1951. Studies on Kanopolis Reservoir in 1950. *Kans. Acad. Sci. Trans.* 54:175–189.

419. *Tiwari, D. K. et al.* 1963. Statistical technique for correcting botanical or floristic estimates in pasture research. *Agron. J.* 55:226–228.

420. *Tomanek, G. W.* 1948. Pasture types of western Kansas in relation to the intensity of utilization in past years. *Kans. Acad. Sci. Trans.* 51:171–196.

421. *Tutin, T. G.* 1941. The hydrosere and current concepts of the climax. *J. Ecol.* 29:268–279.

422. *Udall, S. L.* 1963. *The Quiet Crisis*. Holt, Rinehart & Winston, New York. 209 pp.

423. *Uggla, E.* 1958. *Ecological Effects of Fire on North Swedish Forests*. Almquist & Wiksells, Uppsala. 18 pp.

424. *Vaartaja, O.* 1962. The relationship of fungi to survival of shade tree seedlings. *Ecol.* 43:547–548.

425. *Various authors*. 1954. The high-altitude snow-tussock grassland in South Island, New Zealand. *N.Z.J. Sci. & Technol.* (A) 36:335–364.

426. *Veatch, J. O.* 1933. Some relationships between water plants and water soils in Michigan. *Mich. Acad. Sci. Papers* 17:409–413.

427. *Vechten, G. W. van., and M. F. Buell.* 1959. The floodplain vegetation of the Millstone River, New Jersey. *Torrey Bot. Club Bull.* 86:219–227.

428. *Vestal, A. G.* 1943. Unequal scales for rating species in communities. *Am. J. Bot.* 30:305–310.

429. *Virtanen, A. I.* 1937. Associated growth of legumes and non-legumes. *Internat. Grassl. Congr. Rept.* 4:78–89.

430. *Voss, J.* 1934. Postglacial migration of forests in Illinois, Wisconsin and Minnesota. *Bot. Gaz.* 96:3–43. The University of Chicago Press.

431. *de Vries, D. M.* 1953. Objective combinations of species. *Acta Bot. Neerl.* 1:497–499.

432. *de Vries, D. M.* 1959. Methods used in botanical grassland research in the Netherlands and their application. *Herbage Abstr.* 29:1–7.

433. *de Vries, D. M., and G. C. Ennik.* 1953. Dominancy and dominance communities. *Acta Bot. Neerl.* 1:500–505.

434. *Wagener, W. W.* 1961. Past fire incidence in Sierra Nevada forests. *J. For.* 59:739–748.

435. *Waid, J. S.* 1957. Distribution of fungi within the decomposing tissues of ryegrass roots. *Brit. Mycol. Soc. Trans.* 40:391–406.

436. *Wardle, P.* 1963. The regeneration gap of New Zealand gymnosperms. *N.Z.J. Bot.* 1:301–315.

437. *Watt, A. S.* 1944. Ecological principles involved in the practice of forestry. *J. Ecol.* 32:96–104.

438. *Watt, A. S.* 1947. Pattern and process in the plant community. *J. Ecol.* 35: 1–22.

439. *Watt, A. S.* 1960. Population changes in acidophilous grass-heath in Breckland 1936–1957. *J. Ecol.* 48:605–629.

440. *Weatherell, J.* 1957. The use of nurse species in the afforestation of upland heaths. *Quart. J. For.* 51:298–304.

441. *Weaver, J. E.* 1917. A study of the vegetation of southeastern Washington and adjacent Idaho. *Univ. Neb. Studies* 17(1):1–133.

442. *Weaver, J. E.* 1958. Classification of root systems of forbs of grassland and a consideration of their significance. *Ecol.* 39:393–401.

443. *Weaver, J. E., and F. W. Albertson.* 1936. Effects of the great drought on the prairies of Iowa, Nebraska and Kansas. *Ecol.* 17:567–639.

444. *Weaver, J. E., and N. W. Rowland.* 1952. Effects of excessive natural mulch on development, yield and structure of native grassland. *Bot. Gaz.* 114:1–19.

445. *Webb, L. J.* 1958. Cyclones as an ecological factor in tropical lowland rainforest, north Queensland. *Austral. J. Bot.* 6:220–228.

446. *Webb, L. J.* 1959. A physiognomic classification of Australian rain forests. *J. Ecol.* 47:551–570.

447. *Weeraratna, W. G.* 1960. The ecology and biology of parasitism of Loranthaceae of Ceylon. In J. L. Harper (ed.) *The Biology of Weeds.* Blackwell Sci. Publ., Oxford, England. pp. 189–202.

448. *Weevers, T.* 1952. Flower colours and their frequency. *Acta Bot. Neerl.* 1:81–92.

449. *Weimarck, H.* 1945. Experimental taxonomy in *Aethusa cynapium. Bot. Notiser* 1945:351–380.

450. *Welch, P. S.* 1952. *Limnology.* McGraw-Hill, New York. 538 pp.

451. *Went, F.* 1942. The dependence of certain annual plants on shrubs in southern California deserts. *Torrey Bot. Club Bull.* 69:110–114.

452. *Westveld, M.* 1953. Ecology and silviculture of the spruce-fir forests of eastern North America. *J. For.* 51:422–430.

453. *Wheeting, L. C.* 1938. Some forest-soil relationships. *Northw. Sci.* 12:63–67.
454. *Whitehead, F. H.* 1959. Vegetational changes in response to alterations of surface roughness on Mt. Maiella, Italy. *J. Ecol.* 47:603–606.
455. *Whitford, L. A., and G. J. Schumacher.* 1964. Effect of a current on respiration and mineral uptake in *Spirogyra* and *Oedogonium*. *Ecol.* 45:168–170.
456. *Whitford, P. B.* 1949. Distribution of woodland plants in relation to succession and clonal growth. *Ecol.* 30:199–208.
457. *Whitman, W. C., and E. I. Siggeirsson.* 1954. Comparison of line interception and point contact methods in the analysis of mixed grass range vegetation. *Ecol.* 35:431–436.
458. *Whitman, W. C., et al.* 1943. Natural revegetation of abandoned fields in western North Dakota. N.D. Agr. Exp. Sta. Bull. 321. 18 pp.
459. *Wicht, C. L.* 1949. Forestry and water supplies in South Africa. Union S. Afr., Dept. For. Bull. 33. 58 pp.
460. *Williams, O. B.* 1956. Studies in the ecology of the riverine plain. II. Plant-soil relationships in three semi-arid grasslands. *Austral. J. Agr. Res.* 7:127–139.
461. *Willingham, J. W.* 1962. Error in wedge prism calibration. *J. For.* 60:123–127.
462. *Willis, A. J.* 1963. Braunton Burrows: The effects on the vegetation of the addition of mineral nutrients to the dune soils. *J. Ecol.* 51:353–374.
463. *Wilm, H. G., et al.* 1944. Estimating forage yield by the double-sampling method. *Am. Soc. Agron. J.* 36:194–203.
464. *Wilson, J. W.* 1960. Inclined point quadrats. *New Phytol.* 59:1–8.
465. *Wilson, J. W.* 1963a. Errors resulting from thickness of point quadrats. *Austral. J. Bot.* 11:178–188.
466. *Wilson, J. W.* 1963b. Estimation of foliage denseness and foliage angle by inclined point quadrats. *Austral. J. Bot.* 11:95–105.
467. *Wilson, L. R.* 1937. A quantitative and ecological study of the larger aquatic plants of Sweeney Lake, Oneida County, Wisconsin. *Torrey Bot. Club Bull.* 64:199–209.
468. *Winter, A. G.* 1961. New physiological and biological aspects of the interrelationships between higher plants. In F. L. Milthorpe (ed.) *Mechanisms in Biological Competition.* Soc. Exptl. Biol. Sympos. 15. pp. 228–244.
469. *Winterringer, G. S., and A. G. Vestal.* 1956. Rock-ledge vegetation in southern Illinois. *Ecol. Mono.* 26:105–130.
470. *Witherspoon, J. P., Jr.* 1962. Cycling of Cs[134] in white oak trees. U.S.A.E.C., Health Physics Div., Ann. Progr. Rept. 1962:65–66.
471. *Wood, R. D.* 1963. Adapting SCUBA to aquatic plant ecology. *Ecol.* 44:416–419.
472. *Woods, F. W., and K. Brock.* 1964. Interspecific transfer of Ca-45 and P-32 by root systems. *Ecol.* 45:886–889.
473. *Woodwell, G. M.* 1962. Effects of ionizing radiation on terrestrial ecosystems. *Sci.* 138:572–577.
474. *Wright, J. R., et al.* 1959. Chemical, morphological and mineralogical characteristics of a chronosequence of soils on alluvial deposits in the northwest territories. *Can. J. Soil Sci.* 39:32–43.
475. *Wright, J. R.* 1956. Profile development in the sand dunes of Culbin Forest, Morayshire. II. Chemical properties. *J. Soil Sci.* 7:33–42.
476. *Yeager, L. E., and L. E. Riordan.* 1953. Effects of beetle-killed timber on range and wildlife in Colorado. *N. Am. Wildl. Conf. Trans.* 18:596–616.
477. *Zach, L. W.* 1950. A northern climax, forest or bog? *Ecol.* 31:304–307.
478. *Zahner, R.* 1958. Controlled soil-moisture experiments in forest tree-water relations. In *First North American Forest Soils Conf., Sept. 8–11, 1958.* Mich. Agr. Exp. Sta., E. Lansing. pp. 12–19.

Index